ELEMENTARY CALCULUS

BY

FREDERICK S. WOODS

AND

FREDERICK H. BAILEY

PROFESSORS OF MATHEMATICS IN THE MASSACHUSETTS
INSTITUTE OF TECHNOLOGY

REVISED EDITION

GINN AND COMPANY
BOSTON · NEW YORK · CHICAGO · LONDON
ATLANTA · DALLAS · COLUMBUS · SAN FRANCISCO

The Athenæum Press

GINN AND COMPANY · PRO-
PRIETORS · BOSTON · U.S.A.

PREFACE

This book is adapted to the use of students in the first year in technical school or college, and is based upon the experience of the authors in teaching calculus to students in the Massachusetts Institute of Technology immediately upon entrance. It is accordingly assumed that the student has had college-entrance algebra, including graphs, and an elementary course in trigonometry, but that he has not studied analytic geometry.

The first three chapters form an introductory course in which the fundamental ideas of the calculus are introduced, including derivative, differential, and the definite integral, but the formal work is restricted to that involving only the polynomial. These chapters alone are well fitted for a short course of about a term.

The definition of the derivative is obtained through the concept of speed, using familiar illustrations, and the idea of a derivative as measuring the rate of change of related quantities is emphasized. The slope of a curve is introduced later. This is designed to prevent the student from acquiring the notion that the derivative is fundamentally a geometric concept. For the same reason, problems from mechanics are prominent throughout the book.

With Chapter IV a more formal development of the subject begins, and certain portions of analytic geometry are introduced as needed. These include, among other things, the straight line, the conic sections, the cycloid, and polar coördinates.

The book contains a large number of well-graded exercises for the student. Drill exercises are placed at the end of most sections, and a miscellaneous set of exercises, for review or further work, is found at the end of each chapter except the first.

Throughout the book, the authors believe, the matter is presented in a manner which is well within the capacity of a first-year student to understand. They have endeavored to teach

iii

the calculus from a common-sense standpoint as a very useful tool. They have used as much mathematical rigor as the student is able to understand, but have refrained from raising the more difficult questions which the student in his first course is able neither to appreciate nor to master.

Students who have completed this text and wish to continue their study of mathematics may next take a brief course in differential equations and then a course in advanced calculus, or they may take a course in advanced calculus which includes differential equations. It would also be desirable for such students to have a brief course in analytic geometry, which may either follow this text directly or come later.

This arrangement of work the authors consider preferable to the one — for a long time common in American colleges — by which courses in higher algebra and analytic geometry precede the calculus. However, the teacher who prefers to follow the older arrangement will find this text adapted to such a program.

F. S. WOODS
F. H. BAILEY

PREFACE TO THE REVISED EDITION

The text has been carefully revised as suggested by experience in the classroom, and the exercises for the use of the student have been largely changed. In addition there has been an extension of the work in analytic geometry, and the process of integration has been more closely interwoven with that of differentiation. Certain topics previously treated by double integration have been transferred to the chapter on simple integration, and new applications of integration have been added.

F. S. WOODS
F. H. BAILEY

CONTENTS

CHAPTER I. RATES

CHAPTER II. DIFFERENTIATION

CHAPTER III. SUMMATION

CONTENTS

CHAPTER IV. ALGEBRAIC FUNCTIONS

CHAPTER V. TRIGONOMETRIC FUNCTIONS

CHAPTER VI. EXPONENTIAL AND LOGARITHMIC FUNCTIONS

CHAPTER XI. APPLICATIONS

CHAPTER XII. REPEATED INTEGRATION

ELEMENTARY CALCULUS

CHAPTER I

RATES

1. Limits. Since the calculus is based upon the idea of a limit, it is necessary to have a clear understanding of the word. Two examples already familiar to the student will be sufficient.

In finding the area of a circle in plane geometry it is usual to begin by inscribing a regular polygon in the circle. The area of the polygon differs from that of the circle by a certain amount. As the number of sides of the polygon is increased, this difference becomes less and less. Moreover, if we take any small number e, we can find an inscribed polygon whose area differs from that of the circle by less than e; and if one such polygon has been found, any polygon with a larger number of sides will still differ in area from the circle by less than e. The area of the circle is said to be the *limit* of the area of the inscribed polygon.

As another example of a limit consider the geometric progression with an unlimited number of terms

$$1 + \tfrac{1}{2} + \tfrac{1}{4} + \tfrac{1}{8} + \cdots.$$

The sum of the first two terms of this series is $1\frac{1}{2}$, the sum of the first three terms is $1\frac{3}{4}$, the sum of the first four terms is $1\frac{7}{8}$, and so on. It may be found by trial and is proved in the algebras that the sum of the terms becomes more nearly equal to 2 as the number of terms which are taken becomes greater. Moreover, it may be shown that if any small number e is assumed, it is possible to take a number of terms n so that the sum of these terms differs from 2 by less than e. If a value of n has thus been found, then the sum of a number of terms greater than n will still differ from 2 by less than e. The number 2 is said to be the *limit* of the sum of the first n terms of the series.

1

In each of these two examples there is a certain variable — namely, the area of the inscribed polygon of n sides in one case and the sum of the first n terms of the series in the other case — and a certain constant, the area of the circle and the number 2 respectively. In each case the difference between the constant and the variable may be made less than any small number e by taking n sufficiently large, and this difference then continues to be less than e for any larger value of n.

This is the essential property of a limit, which may be defined as follows:

A constant A is said to be the limit of a variable X if, as the variable changes its value according to some law, the numerical difference between the variable and the constant becomes and remains less than any small positive quantity which may be assigned.

The definition does not say that the variable never reaches its limit. In most cases in this book, however, the variable fails to do so, as in the two examples already given. For the polygon is never exactly a circle, nor is the sum of the terms of the series exactly 2. Examples may be given, however, of a variable becoming equal to its limit, as in the case of a swinging pendulum finally coming to rest. But the fact that a variable may never reach its limit does not make the limit inexact. There is nothing inexact about the area of a circle or about the number 2.

The student should notice the significance of the word "remains" in the definition. If a railroad train approaches a station, the difference between the position of the train and a point on the track opposite the station becomes less than any number which may be named; but if the train keeps on by the station, that difference does not remain small. Hence there is no limit approached in this case.

If X is a variable and A a constant which X approaches as a limit, this fact is expressed by the notation

$$X \to A. \tag{1}$$

It follows from the definition that we may write

$$X = A + e, \tag{2}$$

where e is a quantity (not necessarily positive) which may be made, and then will remain, as small as we please.

Conversely, if as the result of any reasoning we arrive at a formula of the form (2), where X is a variable and A a constant, and if we see that we can make e as small as we please and that it will then remain just as small or smaller as X varies, we can say that A is the limit of X. It is in this way that we shall determine limits in the following pages.

2. Average speed. Let us suppose a body (for example, an automobile) moving from a point A to a point B (Fig. 1), a distance of 100 mi. If the automobile takes 5 hr. for the trip, we are accustomed to say that it has traveled at the rate of 20 mi. an hour. Everybody knows that this does not mean that the automobile went exactly 20 mi.

A   P   Q   B

FIG. 1

in each hour of the trip, exactly 10 mi. in each half hour, exactly 5 mi. in each quarter hour, and so on. Probably no automobile ever ran in such a way as that. The expression "20 mi. an hour" may be understood as meaning that a fictitious automobile traveling in the steady manner just described would actually cover the 100 mi. in just 5 hr.; but for the actual automobile which made the trip, "20 mi. an hour" gives only a certain average speed.

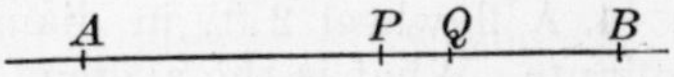

So if a man walks 9 mi. in 3 hr., he has an average speed of 3 mi. an hour. If a stone falls 144 ft. in 3 sec., it has an average speed of 48 ft. per second. In neither of these cases, however, does the average speed tell us what we should properly call the true speed at any given instant. In other words, we do not yet know how fast the body is actually moving at a given instant.

The point we are making is so important, and it is so often overlooked, that we repeat it in the following statement:

If a body traverses a distance in a certain time, the average speed of the body in that time is given by the formula

$$\text{Average speed} = \frac{\text{distance}}{\text{time}},$$

but this formula does not in general give the true speed at any given time.

EXERCISES

1. A man runs a quarter mile in 50 sec. What is his average speed in feet per second?

2. A man runs a mile in 4 min. 25 sec. What is his average speed in yards per second?

3. A stone is thrown directly downward from the edge of a vertical cliff. Three seconds afterwards it passes a point 204 ft. down the side of the cliff, and 6 sec. after it is thrown it passes a point 696 ft. down the side of the cliff. What is the average speed of the stone in falling between the two mentioned points?

4. A flywheel 2 ft. in diameter is making 1500 revolutions per minute. What is the average speed in feet per second of any point on the outer rim of the wheel?

5. A bead slides on a wire bent into a circle of radius 4 ft. If the plane of the circle is vertical and it takes the bead one minute to go from the highest point to the lowest point of the circle, what is its average speed in inches per second?

6. A man rows across a river $\frac{3}{4}$ mi. wide and lands at a point 1 mi. farther down the river. If the banks of the river are parallel straight lines and he takes $\frac{3}{4}$ hr. to cross, what is his average speed in feet per minute if his course is a straight line?

7. A trolley car is running along a straight street at an average speed of 10 mi. per hour. A house is 60 yd. back from the car track and 150 yd. up the street from a car station. A man comes out of the house when a car is 300 yd. away from the station. What must be the average speed of the man in yards per minute if he goes in a straight line to the station and arrives at the same instant as the car?

8. AB is the diameter of a circular track and is 100 yd. long. Two men, C and D, start from A at the same time. C goes directly to B at an average speed of 300 yd. per minute. D goes around the track. What must be D's average speed in yards per minute if he arrives at B at the same moment as C?

3. True speed. How, then, shall we determine the speed at which a moving body passes any given fixed point P in its motion (Fig. 1)? In answering this question the mathematician begins exactly as does the policeman in setting a trap for speeding. He takes a point Q near P and determines the distance PQ and the time it takes to pass over that distance.

Suppose, for example, that the distance PQ is $\frac{1}{2}$ mi. and the time is 1 min. Then, by § 2, the average speed with which the distance is traversed is

$$\frac{\frac{1}{2}\text{ mi.}}{1\text{ min.}} = \frac{\frac{1}{2}\text{ mi.}}{\frac{1}{60}\text{ hr.}} = 30\text{ mi. per hour.}$$

This is merely the average speed, however, and can no more be taken for the true speed at the point P than could the 20 mi. an hour which we obtained by considering the entire distance AB. It is true that the 30 mi. an hour obtained from the interval PQ is likely to be nearer the true speed at P than was the 20 mi. an hour obtained from AB, because the interval PQ is shorter.

The last statement suggests a method for obtaining a still better measure of the speed at P; namely, by taking the interval PQ still smaller. Suppose, for example, that PQ is taken as $\frac{1}{16}$ mi. and that the time is $6\frac{1}{4}$ sec. A calculation shows that the average speed at which this distance was traversed was 36 mi. an hour. This is a better value for the speed at P.

Now, having seen that we get a better value for the speed at P each time that we decrease the size of the interval PQ, we can find no end to the process except by means of the idea of a limit defined in § 1. We have, then, the definition:

The speed of a moving body at any point of its path is the limit approached by the average speed computed for a small distance beginning at that point, the limit to be determined by taking this distance smaller and smaller.

This definition may seem to the student a little intricate, and we shall proceed to explain it further.

In the case of the automobile, which we have been using for an illustration, there are practical difficulties in taking a very small distance, because neither the measurement of the distance nor that of the time can be exact. This does not alter the fact, however, that theoretically to determine the speed of the car we ought to find the time it takes to go an extremely minute distance, and the more minute the distance the better the result. For example, if it were possible to discover that an automobile ran $\frac{1}{10}$ in. in $\frac{1}{5280}$ sec., we should be pretty safe in saying that it was moving at a speed of 30 mi. an hour.

Such fineness of measurement is, of course, impossible; but if an algebraic formula connecting the distance and the time is known, the calculation can be made as fine as this and finer. We will therefore take a familiar case in which such a formula is known; namely, that of a falling body.

Let us take from physics the formula for a body falling from rest,
$$s = 16\,t^2, \tag{1}$$
where s is the distance from the point O (Fig. 2) from which the body fell and t is the time which has elapsed since the body began to fall, and let us ask what is the speed of the body at the instant when $t = 2$. In Fig. 2 let P_1 be its position when $t = 2$, and P_2 its position a short time later. The average speed with which the body falls through the distance P_1P_2 is, by § 2, that distance divided by the time it takes to traverse it. We shall proceed to make several successive calculations of this average speed, assuming P_1P_2 and the corresponding time smaller and smaller.

In so doing it will be convenient to introduce a notation as follows: Let t_1 represent the time at which the body reaches P_1, and t_2 the time at which it reaches P_2. Also let s_1 equal the distance OP_1, and s_2 the distance OP_2.

Fig. 2

Then $s_2 - s_1 = P_1P_2$, and $t_2 - t_1$ is the time it takes to traverse the distance P_1P_2. Then the average speed at which the body traverses P_1P_2 is
$$\frac{s_2 - s_1}{t_2 - t_1}. \tag{2}$$

Now, by the statement of our particular problem,
$$t_1 = 2.$$

Therefore, from (1), $\qquad s_1 = 16(2)^2 = 64.$

We shall assume a value of t_2 a little larger than 2 and compute s_2 from (1) and the average speed from (2). That having been done, we shall take t_2 a little nearer to 2 than it was at first, and again compute the average speed. This we shall do repeatedly, each time taking t_2 nearer to 2.

Our results can best be exhibited in the form of a table, as follows:

t_2	s_2	$t_2 - t_1$	$s_2 - s_1$	$\dfrac{s_2 - s_1}{t_2 - t_1}$
2.1	70.56	.1	6.56	65.6
2.01	64.6416	.01	.6416	64.16
2.001	64.064016	.001	.064016	64.016
2.0001	64.00640016	.0001	.00640016	64.0016

It is fairly evident from the above arithmetical work that as the time $t_2 - t_1$ and the corresponding distance $s_2 - s_1$ become smaller, the more nearly is the average speed equal to 64. Therefore we are led to infer, in accordance with § 1, that the speed at which the body passes the point P_1 is 64 ft. per second.

In the same manner the speed of the body may be estimated at any point of its path by means of a purely arithmetical calculation. In the next section we shall go farther with the same problem and employ algebra.

We may, however, sum up what we have now obtained in the formula

$$\text{Speed} = \text{limit of } \frac{\text{change in distance}}{\text{change in time}}.$$

EXERCISES

1. Estimate the speed of a falling body at the end of the fourth second, given that $s = 16\, t^2$, exhibiting the work in a table.

2. Estimate the speed of the body in Ex. 1 at the end of the fifth second, exhibiting the work in a table.

3. The distance of a falling body from a fixed point at any time is given by the equation $s = 150 + 16\, t^2$. Estimate the speed of the body at the end of the third second, exhibiting the work in a table.

4. A body is falling so that its distance s from a fixed point O at any time t is given by the equation $s = 16\, t^2 + 20\, t$. Estimate the speed of the body when $t = 2$ sec., exhibiting the work in a table.

5. A body is thrown upward with such a speed that at any time its distance from the surface of the earth is given by the equation $s = 200\, t - 16\, t^2$. Estimate its speed at the end of the third second, exhibiting the work in a table.

6. The distance of a falling body from a fixed point at any time is given by the equation $s = 100 + 10\,t + 16\,t^2$. Estimate its speed at the end of the first second, exhibiting the work in a table.

7. A body is thrown upward with such a speed that at any time t its distance from the surface of the earth is given by the equation $s = 100 + 70\,t - 16\,t^2$. Estimate its speed when $t = 2$, exhibiting the work in a table.

4. Algebraic method. In this section we shall show how it is possible to derive an algebraic formula for the speed, still confining ourselves to the special example of the falling body whose equation of motion is

$$s = 16\,t^2. \tag{1}$$

Instead of taking a definite numerical value for t_1, we shall keep the algebraic symbol t_1. Then

$$s_1 = 16\,t_1^2.$$

Also, instead of adding successive small quantities to t_1 to get t_2, we shall represent the amount added by the algebraic symbol h. That is,

$$t_2 = t_1 + h,$$

and, from (1), $s_2 = 16\,t_2^2 = 16(t_1 + h)^2.$

Hence $s_2 - s_1 = 16(t_1 + h)^2 - 16\,t_1^2 = 32\,t_1h + 16\,h^2.$

This is a general expression for the distance P_1P_2 in Fig. 2. Now $t_2 - t_1 = h$, and therefore the average speed with which the body traverses P_1P_2 is represented by the expression

$$\frac{32\,t_1h + 16\,h^2}{h} = 32\,t_1 + 16\,h.$$

It is obvious that if h is taken smaller and smaller, the average speed approaches $32\,t_1$ as a limit. In fact, the quantity $32\,t_1$ satisfies exactly the definition of limit given in § 1. For if e is any number, no matter how small, we have simply to take $16\,h < e$ in order that the average speed should differ from $32\,t_1$ by less than e; and after that, for still smaller values of h, this difference remains less than e.

We have, then, the result that if the distance of a falling body from a fixed point is given by the formula

$$s = 16 \, t^2,$$

the speed of the body at any time is given by the formula

$$\text{Speed} = 32 \, t.$$

It may be well to emphasize that this is not the result which would be obtained by dividing s by t.

EXERCISES

1. Find the speed in each of the problems 3–7 of § 3 by the method explained in this section.

In each of the following equations s is the distance of a body moving along a straight line from a fixed point O of that line at any time t. In each case find an expression for the true speed of the body at any time t.

2. $s = 3 \, t^2 + 4 \, t + 6.$ 4. $s = t^3.$ ✗6. $s = \frac{1}{3} \, t^3 + \frac{1}{2} \, t^2.$

✗3. $s = \frac{1}{2} \, t^2 + 2 \, t + 10.$ ✗5. $s = 2 \, t^3 + t.$ 7. $s = t^3 + 3 \, t + 7.$

5. Acceleration. Let us consider the case of a body which is supposed to move along a straight line so that if s is the distance in feet from a fixed point of that line and t is the time in seconds,

$$s = t^3. \tag{1}$$

Then, by the method of § 4, we find that if v is the speed in feet per second, $$v = 3 \, t^2. \tag{2}$$

We see that when $t = 1$, $v = 3$; when $t = 2$, $v = 12$; when $t = 3$, $v = 27$; and so on. That is, the body is gaining speed with each second. We wish to find how fast it is gaining speed. To find this out, let us take a specific time

$$t_1 = 4.$$

The speed at this time we call v_1, so that, by (2),

$$v_1 = 3(4)^2 = 48 \text{ ft. per second.}$$

Take $t_2 = 5$;

then $v_2 = 3(5)^2 = 75 \text{ ft. per second.}$

Therefore the body has gained $75 - 48 = 27$ units of speed in 1 sec. This number, then, represents the average rate at which the body is gaining speed during the particular second considered. It does not give exactly the rate at which the speed is increasing at the beginning of the second, because the rate is constantly changing.

To find how fast the body is gaining speed when $t_1 = 4$, we must proceed exactly as we did in finding the speed itself. That is, we must compute the gain of speed in a very small interval of time and compare that with the time.

Let us take $\qquad t_2 = 4.1$.

Then $\qquad v_2 = 50.43$

and $\qquad v_2 - v_1 = 2.43$.

Then the body has gained 2.43 units of speed in .1 sec., which is at the rate of $\dfrac{2.43}{.1} = 24.3$ units per second.

Again, take $\qquad t_2 = 4.01$.

Then $\qquad v_2 = 48.2403$

and $\qquad v_2 - v_1 = .2403$.

A gain of .2403 unit of speed in .01 sec. is at the rate of $\dfrac{.2403}{.01} = 24.03$ units per second. We exhibit these results, and one other obtained in the same way, in a table:

t_2	v_2	$t_2 - t_1$	$v_2 - v_1$	$\dfrac{v_2 - v_1}{t_2 - t_1}$
4.1	50.43	.1	2.43	24.3
4.01	48.2403	.01	.2403	24.03
4.001	48.024003	.001	.024003	24.003

The rate at which a body is gaining speed is called its *acceleration*. Our discussion suggests that in the example before us the acceleration is 24 units of speed per second. But the unit of speed is expressed in feet per second, and so we say that the acceleration is 24 ft. per second per second.

By the method used in determining speed, we may get a general formula to determine the acceleration from equation (2). We take

$$t_2 = t_1 + h.$$

Then $$v_2 = 3 \cdot t_2{}^2 = 3(t_1 + h)^2$$

and $$v_2 - v_1 = 6\, t_1 h + 3\, h^2.$$

The average rate at which the speed is gained is then

$$\frac{6\, t_1 h + 3\, h^2}{h} = 6\, t_1 + 3\, h,$$

and the limit of this, as h becomes smaller and smaller, is obviously $6\, t_1$.

This is, of course, a result which is valid only for the special example that we are considering. A general statement of the meaning of acceleration is as follows:

$$\text{Acceleration} = \text{limit of } \frac{\text{change in speed}}{\text{change in time}}.$$

EXERCISES

1. At any time t the speed v of a moving body is given by the equation $v = 8\, t + 21$. What is the speed when $t = 2$, and how rapidly is the speed changing?

2. At any time t the speed v, measured in feet per second, is given by the equation $v = 5\, t + 10$. By how much does the speed increase during the third second, and how fast is v increasing at the end of the third second?

3. If $v = at + b$, a and b being constants, show that the acceleration is constant.

4. At any time t the speed v is given by the equation $v = 6\, t^2 + t + 3$. What is the speed when $t = 3$ and how rapidly is it changing?

5. If $v = 2\, t^2 + 3\, t + 10$, measured in feet per second, by how much does the speed increase during the fifth second, and how fast is the speed increasing at the beginning of that second?

6. If $v = t^2 + 3\, t + 4$, measured in feet per second, determine the acceleration at the beginning of the fourth and at the end of the fifth second, also the average acceleration during the fourth and fifth seconds.

7. If $v = t^3 + t^2$, measured in feet per second, determine the acceleration at the beginning of the second second and at the end of the third second, also the average acceleration during the second and third seconds.

8. If $s = 2 t^2 + 4 t + 7$, s being measured in feet and t in seconds, how far has the body moved between the times $t = 0$ and $t = 4$? Determine the speed and the acceleration when $t = 4$.

9. If $s = at^2 + bt + c$, a, b, and c being constants, show that the acceleration is constant.

10. If $s = t^3 + t^2 + 2 t + 5$, measured in feet per second, (a) how far will the body move during the third and fourth seconds? (b) how fast will the body be moving at the beginning and the end of the period noted in (a)? (c) how fast will the speed be increasing at the beginning and the end of the period noted in (a)?

6. Rate of change. Let us consider another example which may be solved by processes similar to those used for determining speed and acceleration.

A stone is thrown into still water, forming ripples which travel from the center of disturbance in the form of circles (Fig. 3). Let r be the radius of a circle and A its area. Then

$$A = \pi r^2. \qquad (1)$$

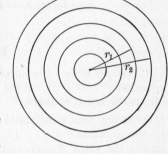

FIG. 3

In Fig. 3 the circles drawn are for the successive values of $r = 1$, 2, 3, and so on. Hence the area of each circular ring is the area which is added to the circle inside the ring as the radius of the circle is increased by unity. It is obvious that these rings increase in area as r increases, and hence the changes in A as r increases from 0 by successive increases of unity are not all the same. How then do the changes in A compare with the changes in r?

To answer this question we first let $r_1 = 3$, whence $A_1 = 9 \pi$. We now give r_2 the successive values noted in the first column of the table on page 13, and compute the corresponding values of A_2, $r_2 - r_1$, $A_2 - A_1$, and finally the ratio $\dfrac{A_2 - A_1}{r_2 - r_1}$ given in the last column.

In the first line we see that a change of .1 in r causes a change of .61 π in A, and the ratio $\dfrac{A_2 - A_1}{r_2 - r_1} = 6.1\ \pi$ is the average change of A per unit change in r, as r increases from 3 to 3.1. In like manner, in the second line we see that the average change in A per unit change in r is 6.01 π as r increases from 3 to 3.01; and finally in the third line the average change of A per unit change in r is found to be 6.001 π as r changes from 3 to 3.001.

r_2	A_2	$r_2 - r_1$	$A_2 - A_1$	$\dfrac{A_2 - A_1}{r_2 - r_1}$
3.1	9.61 π	.1	.61 π	6.1 π
3.01	9.0601 π	.01	.0601 π	6.01 π
3.001	9.006001 π	.001	.006001 π	6.001 π

The average change of A per unit change in r may be called the *average rate of change of A with respect to r* for the interval $r_2 - r_1$ to which it corresponds.

These average rates of change of A with respect to r vary but seem to approach a limit 6 π. Hence we say, as definition, that the limit of the average rate of change of A with respect to r, as the change in r approaches zero, is the true rate, or simply *the rate of change of A with respect to r.*

Using this definition and following the algebraic method of § 4 we determine the rate of change of A with respect to r, starting from any value of r, as r_1. Then

$$A_1 = \pi r_1{}^2.$$

Next take $\qquad\qquad r_2 = r_1 + h.$

Then $\qquad\qquad A_2 = \pi r_2{}^2 = \pi(r_1{}^2 + 2\ r_1 h + h^2)$

and $\qquad\qquad A_2 - A_1 = \pi(2\ r_1 h + h^2);$

so that $\qquad\qquad \dfrac{A_2 - A_1}{r_2 - r_1} = 2\ \pi r_1 + \pi h.$

As $r_2 - r_1 = h$ is taken smaller and smaller, the limit of $\dfrac{A_2 - A_1}{r_2 - r_1}$ is $2\ \pi r_1$, which is accordingly the rate of change of A with respect to r when $r = r_1$. As this is an entirely general statement, we may drop the subscript 1 and state the general result that the rate of change of A with respect to r is $2\pi r$. In case $r = 3$, $2\pi r = 6\pi$, the limit that was inferred from the table.

The above is only one of many cases. For example, it may be desired to compare the change of length of an iron bar with the change in temperature which causes the bar to change in length, or it may be desired to compare the change in the temperature of a gas with the change in the pressure to which it is subjected. In these, and all similar cases, we have two related quantities such that a change in one causes a change in the other. In such a case, if we denote the quantities by x and y, and if the change in x causes the change in y, we write the following definition:

$$\left.\begin{array}{c}\text{Rate of change of } y \\ \text{with respect to } x\end{array}\right\} = \text{limit of } \frac{\text{change in } y}{\text{change in } x}.$$

In the above discussion the element of time does not enter. We are concerned only in comparing the changes in two quantities without considering how fast in respect to time either is changing. The latter question will be taken up in a subsequent section.

EXERCISES

1. In the example of the text find a general expression for the rate of change of the area with respect to the circumference.

2. A soap bubble is expanding, always remaining spherical. Find the general expression for the rate of change of the volume with respect to the radius.

3. In Ex. 2 find the general expression for the rate of change of the surface with respect to the radius.

4. A cube of metal is expanding under the influence of heat. Assuming that the metal retains the form of a cube, find the rate of change at which the volume is increasing with respect to an edge.

5. The altitude of a right circular cylinder is always equal to the diameter of the base. If the cylinder is assumed to expand, always retaining its form and proportions, what is the rate of change of the volume with respect to the radius of the base?

6. Find the rate of change of the area of a sector of a circle of radius 6 ft. with respect to the angle at the center of the circle.

7. Find the rate of change of the area of a sector of a circle with respect to the radius of the circle if the angle at the center of the circle is always $\frac{\pi}{4}$. What is the value of the rate when the radius is 8 in.?

8. Find the rate of change of the area of an equilateral triangle with respect to its side as the side varies in length.

9. The kinetic energy of a body of mass m moving with a velocity v is $\frac{mv^2}{2}$. Find the rate of change of the kinetic energy with respect to the velocity.

10. The slant height of a certain right circular cone is always 6 ft. in length. Find the rate of change of the volume of the cone with respect to its altitude as the vertex of the cone settles toward the base.

11. The length of a bar of metal at different temperatures is given by the formula $L = L_0(1 + at + bt^2)$, where t is the temperature, L_0 is the length of the bar at zero temperature, and a and b are small constants depending upon the nature of the metal. Find the rate of change of the length with respect to the temperature.

12. A balloon is in the form of a right circular cone with a hemispherical top. The radius of the largest cross section is equal to the altitude of the cone. The shape and proportions of the balloon are assumed to be unaltered as the balloon is inflated. Find the rate of increase of the volume with respect to the total height of the balloon.

13. A spherical shell of ice surrounds a spherical iron ball concentric with it. The radius of the iron ball is 6 in. As the ice melts, how fast is the mass of the ice decreasing with respect to its thickness?

CHAPTER II

DIFFERENTIATION

7. The derivative. The examples we have been considering in the foregoing sections of the book are alike in the methods used to solve them. We shall proceed now to examine this method so as to bring out its general character.

In the first place, we notice that we have to do with two quantities so related that the value of one depends upon the value of the other. Thus the distance traveled by a moving body depends upon the time, and the area of a circle depends upon the radius. In such a case one quantity is said to be a *function* of the other. That is, *a quantity y is said to be a function of another quantity, x, if the value of y is determined by the value of x.*

The fact that y is a function of x is expressed by the equation

$$y = f(x),$$

and the particular value of the function when x has a definite value a is then expressed as $f(a)$. Thus, if

$$f(x) = x^3 - 3\,x^2 + 4\,x + 1,$$
$$f(2) = 2^3 - 3(2)^2 + 4(2) + 1 = 5,$$
$$f(0) = 0 - 3(0) + 4(0) + 1 = 1.$$

It is in general true that a change in x causes a change in the function y, and that if the change in x is sufficiently small, the change in y is small also. Some exceptions to this may be noticed later, but this is the general rule. A change in x is called an *increment* of x and is denoted by the symbol Δx (read "delta x"). Similarly, a change in y is called an increment of y and is denoted by Δy. For example, consider

$$y = x^2 + 3\,x + 2.$$

16

When $x = 2$, $y = 12$. When $x = 2.1$, $y = 12.71$. The change in x is .1, and the change in y is .71, and we write

$$\Delta x = .1, \quad \Delta y = .71.$$

So, in general, if x_1 is one value of x, and x_2 a second value of x, then $\quad \Delta x = x_2 - x_1, \quad$ or $\quad x_2 = x_1 + \Delta x;$ (1)

and if y_1 and y_2 are the corresponding values of y, then

$$\Delta y = y_2 - y_1, \quad \text{or} \quad y_2 = y_1 + \Delta y. \tag{2}$$

The word *increment* really means "increase," but as we are dealing with algebraic quantities, the increment may be negative when it means a decrease. For example, if a man invests $1000 and at the end of a year has $1200, the increment of his wealth is $200. If he has $800 at the end of the year, the increment is $- $200. So, if a thermometer registers 65° in the morning and 57° at night, the increment is $- 8°$. The increment is always the second value of the quantity considered minus the first value.

Now, having determined increments of x and of y, the next step is to compare them by dividing the increment of y by the increment of x. This is what we did in each of the three problems we have worked in §§ 3–6. In finding speed we began by dividing an increment of distance by an increment of time, in finding acceleration we began by dividing an increment of speed by an increment of time, and in discussing the ripples in the water we began by dividing an increment of area by an increment of radius.

The quotient thus obtained is $\dfrac{\Delta y}{\Delta x}$. That is,

$$\frac{\Delta y}{\Delta x} = \frac{\text{increment of } y}{\text{increment of } x} = \frac{\text{change in } y}{\text{change in } x}.$$

An examination of the tables of numerical values in §§ 3, 5, and 6 shows that the quotient $\dfrac{\Delta y}{\Delta x}$ depends upon the magnitude of Δx, and that in each problem it was necessary to determine its limit as Δx approached zero. This limit is called the *derivative of y with respect to x*, and is denoted by the symbol $\dfrac{dy}{dx}$. We have then

$$\frac{dy}{dx} = \text{limit of } \frac{\text{change in } y}{\text{change in } x} = \operatorname*{Lim}_{\Delta x \to 0} \frac{\Delta y}{\Delta x}.$$

At present the student is to take the symbol $\dfrac{dy}{dx}$ not as a fraction but as one undivided symbol to represent the derivative. Later we shall consider what meaning may be given to dx and dy separately. At this stage the form $\dfrac{dy}{dx}$ suggests simply the fraction $\dfrac{\Delta y}{\Delta x}$, which has approached a definite limiting value.

We may accordingly write the results of the previous chapter as follows:

$$\text{Speed} = \frac{ds}{dt} = v,$$

$$\text{Acceleration} = \frac{dv}{dt},$$

$$\left.\begin{array}{l}\text{Rate of change of } y \\ \text{with respect to } x\end{array}\right\} = \frac{dy}{dx}.$$

The process of finding the derivative is called *differentiation* and we are said to *differentiate* y with respect to x. From the definition and from the examples with which we began the book, the process is seen to involve the following four steps:

1. The assumption at pleasure of Δx.

2. The determination of the corresponding Δy.

3. The division of Δy by Δx to form $\dfrac{\Delta y}{\Delta x}$.

4. The determination of the limit approached by the quotient in step 3 as the increment assumed in step 1 approaches zero.

Let us apply this method to finding $\dfrac{dy}{dx}$ when $y = \dfrac{1}{x}$. Let x_1 be a definite value of x, and $y_1 = \dfrac{1}{x_1}$ the corresponding value of y.

1. Take $\qquad\qquad\qquad \Delta x = h.$

Then, by (1), $\qquad\qquad x_2 = x_1 + h.$

2. Then $\qquad\quad y_2 = \dfrac{1}{x_2} = \dfrac{1}{x_1 + h}\,;$

whence, by (2), $\qquad \Delta y = \dfrac{1}{x_1 + h} - \dfrac{1}{x_1} = -\dfrac{h}{x_1{}^2 + h x_1}.$

3. By division, $\dfrac{\Delta y}{\Delta x} = -\dfrac{1}{x_1^2 + hx_1}.$

4. By inspection it is evident that the limit, as h approaches zero, is $-\dfrac{1}{x_1^2}$, which is the value of the derivative when $x = x_1$. But x_1 may be any value of x; so we may drop the subscript 1 and write as a general formula

$$\frac{dy}{dx} = -\frac{1}{x^2}.$$

EXERCISES

Find from the definition the derivatives of the following expressions:

1. $y = 5(x^2 + x - 1)$.

2. $y = 3x^3 - x^2 + 3$.

3. $y = x^4 - 2x$.

4. $y = \dfrac{1}{x^2}$.

5. $y = x^3 - \dfrac{1}{x}$.

6. $y = \dfrac{2}{x+4}$.

7. $y = \dfrac{x-2}{x+2}$.

8. $y = \dfrac{x}{x^2+1}$.

8. Differentiation of a polynomial. We shall now obtain formulas by means of which the derivative of a polynomial may be written down quickly. In the first place we have the theorem:

The derivative of a polynomial is the sum of the derivatives of its separate terms.

This follows from the definition of a derivative if we recognize that the change in a polynomial is the sum of the changes in its terms. A more formal proof will be given later.

We have then to consider the terms of a polynomial, which have in general the form ax^n. Since we wish to have general formulas, we shall omit the subscript 1 in denoting the first values of x and y. We have, then, the theorem:

If $y = ax^n$, where n is a positive integer and a is a constant, then

$$\frac{dy}{dx} = anx^{n-1}. \tag{1}$$

To prove this, apply the method of § 7:

1. Take $\qquad\qquad \Delta x = h$;

whence $\qquad\qquad x_2 = x + h$.

2. Then $\qquad\qquad y_2 = ax_2^n = a(x+h)^n$;

whence $\qquad\qquad \Delta y = a(x+h)^n - ax^n$

$$= a(nx^{n-1}h + \frac{n(n-1)}{2} x^{n-2}h^2 + \cdots + h^n).$$

3. By division, $\dfrac{\Delta y}{\Delta x} = a(nx^{n-1} + \dfrac{n(n-1)}{2} x^{n-2}h + \cdots + h^{n-1}).$

4. By inspection, the limit approached by $\dfrac{\Delta y}{\Delta x}$, as h approaches zero, is seen to be anx^{n-1}.

Therefore $\dfrac{dy}{dx} = anx^{n-1}$, as was to be proved.

The polynomial may also have a term of the form ax. This is only a special case of (1) with $n = 1$, but for clearness we say explicitly,

If $y = ax$, where a is a constant, then

$$\frac{dy}{dx} = a. \qquad (2)$$

Finally, a polynomial may have a constant term c. For this we have the theorem:

If $y = c$, where c is a constant, then

$$\frac{dy}{dx} = 0. \qquad (3)$$

The proof of this is that as c is constant, Δc is always zero, no matter what the value of Δx is. Hence

$$\frac{\Delta c}{\Delta x} = 0,$$

and therefore $\qquad\qquad \dfrac{dc}{dx} = 0.$

As an example of the use of the theorems, consider

$$y = 6\,x^4 + 4\,x^3 - 2\,x + 7.$$

We write at once

$$\frac{dy}{dx} = 24\,x^3 + 12\,x^2 - 2.$$

EXERCISES

Find the derivative of each of the following polynomials:

1. $x^2 + 2x - 4$.

2. $\frac{1}{2}x^2 + 5x - 7$.

3. $3x^3 + 6x^2 + 21x - 15$.

4. $x^4 + 3x^2 + 10x - 21$.

5. $\frac{1}{5}x^5 - \frac{1}{3}x^3 + x$.

6. $2 - x + 3x^2 + 4x^4$.

7. $8 + 2x^2 - \frac{1}{4}x^4 + x^6$.

8. $21 + x - x^3 + x^5$.

9. $ax^3 + bx^2 + cx + d$.

10. $a + bx^2 + cx^4 + dx^6$.

9. Sign of the derivative. *If, for a given value of x, $\frac{dy}{dx}$ is positive, an increase in the value of x causes an increase in the value of y; if $\frac{dy}{dx}$ is negative, an increase in the value of x causes a decrease in the value of y.*

To prove this theorem, let us consider that $\frac{dy}{dx}$ is positive. Then, since $\frac{dy}{dx}$ is the limit of $\frac{\Delta y}{\Delta x}$, it follows that $\frac{\Delta y}{\Delta x}$ is positive for sufficiently small values of Δx; that is, if Δx is assumed positive, Δy is also positive, and therefore an increase of x causes an increase of y. Similarly, if $\frac{dy}{dx}$ is negative, it follows that $\frac{\Delta y}{\Delta x}$ is negative for sufficiently small values of Δx; that is, if Δx is positive, Δy must be negative, so that an increase of x causes a decrease of y.

In case the derivative is a polynomial, its sign may be conveniently determined by breaking it up into factors and considering the sign of each factor. It is obvious that a factor of the form $x - a$ is positive when x is greater than a, and negative when x is less than a.

Suppose, then, we wish to determine the sign of

$$(x + 3)(x - 1)(x - 6).$$

There are three factors to consider, and three numbers are important; namely, those which make one of the factors equal to zero. These numbers arranged in order of size are -3, 1, and 6. We have the four cases:

1. $x < -3$. All factors are negative and the product is negative.

2. $-3 < x < 1$. The first factor is positive and the others are negative. Therefore the product is positive.

3. $1 < x < 6$. The first two factors are positive and the last is negative. Therefore the product is negative.

4. $x > 6$. All factors are positive and the product is positive. As an example of the use of the theorem, suppose we have

$$y = x^3 - 3x^2 - 9x + 27,$$

and ask for what values of x an increase in x will cause an increase or a decrease in y. We form the derivative and factor it. Thus,

$$\frac{dy}{dx} = 3x^2 - 6x - 9 = 3(x+1)(x-3).$$

Proceeding as above, we have the following three cases:

1. $x < -1$. $\frac{dy}{dx}$ is positive, and therefore an increase in x increases y.

2. $-1 < x < 3$. $\frac{dy}{dx}$ is negative, and therefore an increase in x decreases y.

3. $x > 3$. $\frac{dy}{dx}$ is positive, and therefore an increase in x increases y.

These results may be checked by substituting values of x in the derivative.

EXERCISES

Find for what values of x each of the following expressions will increase if x is increased, and for what values of x they will decrease if x is increased:

1. $x^2 - 6x + 7$.

2. $3x^2 + 4x + 7$.

3. $2 + 3x - 2x^2$.

4. $4 + 6x + 3x^2$.

5. $x^3 - 9x^2 + 24x + 20$.

6. $x^3 - 3x^2 - 9x + 3$.

7. $x^3 - 2x^2 + 1$.

8. $1 + 3x - 4x^2 - x^3$.

9. $8 + 36x + 54x^2 + 27x^3$.

10. $1 + 2x^2 - x^4$.

11. $1 - 2x^8 + x^4$.

12. $3 + 54x + 27x^2 - 8x^3 - 6x^4$.

10. Velocity and acceleration. The method by which the speed of a body was determined in § 4 was in reality a method of differentiation, and the speed, as there determined, was the derivative of the distance with respect to the time. In that discussion, however, we so arranged each problem that the result was positive and gave a numerical measure (feet per second, miles per hour, etc.) for the rate at which the body was moving. Since we may now expect, on occasion, negative signs, we will replace the word *speed* by the word *velocity*, which we denote by the letter v. In accordance with the previous work, we have

$$v = \frac{ds}{dt}. \tag{1}$$

The distinction between speed and velocity, as we use the words, is simply one of algebraic sign. The speed is the numerical measure of the velocity and is always positive, but the velocity may be either positive or negative.

From (1) and § 9, we have the following theorem:

When the velocity is positive, the body moves so as to increase s. When the velocity is negative, the body moves so as to decrease s.

For example, consider a stone dropped from the top of a building. If s is measured from the top of the building and t is the time which has elapsed since the body began to fall,

$$s = 16\,t^2\,;$$

whence $$v = \frac{ds}{dt} = 32\,t.$$

The velocity is positive and the stone moves so as to increase the distance from the top of the building.

Suppose now for the same falling stone we measure s from the ground. If the building is 100 ft. high, we have

$$s = 100 - 16\,t^2,$$

whence $$v = \frac{ds}{dt} = -32\,t.$$

The velocity is now negative, and the stone moves so as to decrease its distance from the ground. The actual motion of the stone is the same as before. The change in the sign of the velocity is caused by the change in the way s is measured.

In § 5 we have defined acceleration by using the speed and have so arranged the work that the acceleration is always positive. We shall now extend the definition using velocity instead of speed. Letting a represent the acceleration, we have, by definition,

$$a = \frac{dv}{dt}. \tag{2}$$

We must now expect to find negative accelerations on occasion. Accordingly, in accordance with § 9, we have the theorem:

If the acceleration is positive, the body is moving with increasing velocity. If the acceleration is negative, the body is moving with decreasing velocity.

But it must be emphasized that if the velocity is negative, an increasing velocity means a decreasing speed and a decreasing velocity means an increasing speed. This is because, if a negative number increases, its numerical value decreases, while if a negative number decreases, its numerical value increases. Thus, if a number changes from − 8 to − 5 it increases, since 3 has been added, while if it changes from − 5 to − 8 it decreases, since 3 has been subtracted. We have accordingly the following table:

v	a	s	v	SPEED
+	+	increasing	increasing	increasing
+	−	increasing	decreasing	decreasing
−	+	decreasing	increasing	decreasing
−	−	decreasing	decreasing	increasing

As an example, suppose a body thrown vertically into the air with a velocity of 96 ft. per second. From physics, if s is measured up from the earth, we have

$$s = 96\,t - 16\,t^2.$$

From this equation we compute

$$v = 96 - 32\,t,$$
$$a = -32.$$

If $t = 2$, $v = 32$ and $a = -32$. The distance from the earth is increasing (the body is going up), the speed is decreasing. If $t = 4$, $v = -32$, $a = -32$. The distance from the earth is decreasing (the body is coming down) and the speed is increasing, although the velocity is decreasing.

In the following examples find the direction of the motion:

1. $s = 3 t^2 - 4 t + 7.$

2. $s = 2 t^2 + 5 t - 7.$

3. $s = 5 + 8 t - 5 t^2.$

4. $s = 5 + 12 t - 9 t^2 + 2 t^3.$

5. $s = 8 - 4 t - 2 t^2 + t^3.$

6. $s = 3 t^4 - 4 t^3 + 12.$

In the following examples find when the velocity is increasing and when decreasing:

7. $s = 4 t^2 + t + 4.$

8. $s = t^3 - 2 t^2 + 5 t + 1.$

9. $s = 2 - 4 t + 4 t^2 - 2 t^3.$

10. $s = t^4 - 4 t^3 - 4 t + 1.$

11. $s = 3 t^4 + 4 t^3 - 4 t - 3.$

12. $s = 3 t^4 + 7 t^3 - 9 t^2 + 7 t + 3.$

In the following examples find when the speed is increasing and when decreasing:

13. $s = t^2 - 3 t + 1.$

14. $s = 1 - 3 t - t^2.$

15. $s = 3 t^3 - 6 t^2 + 4 t - 6.$

16. $s = 1 + 3 t^2 - t^3.$

17. $s = t^3 - 6 t^2 + 9 t - 12.$

18. $s = 8 + 8 t - t^2 - t^3.$

11. Graphs. The relation between a variable x and a function y may be pictured to the eye by a *graph*. It is expected that students will have acquired some knowledge of the graph in the study of algebra, and the following brief discussion is given for a review.

Take two lines OX and OY (Fig. 4), intersecting at right angles at O, which is called the *origin of coördinates*. The line OX is called the axis of x, and the line OY the axis of y; together they are called the *coördinate axes*, or *axes of reference*. On OX we lay off a distance OM equal to any given value of x, measuring to the right if x is positive and to the left if x is negative. From M we erect a perpendicular MP, equal in length to the value of y, measured up if y is positive and down if y is negative.

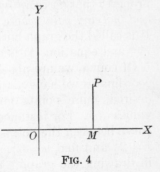

FIG. 4

The point P thus determined is said to have the coördinates x and y and is denoted by (x, y). It follows that the numerical value of x measures the distance of the point P from OY, and the numerical value of y measures the distance of P from OX. The coördinate x is called the *abscissa*, and the coördinate y the *ordinate*. It is evident that any pair of coördinates (x, y) fix a single point P, and that any point P has a single pair of coördinates. The point P is said to be plotted when its position is fixed in this way, and the plotting is conveniently carried out on paper ruled for that purpose into squares.

If y is a function of x, values of x may be assumed at pleasure and the corresponding values of y computed. Then each pair of values (x, y) may be plotted and a series of points found. The locus of these points is a curve called the *graph* of the function.

It may happen that the locus consists of distinct portions not connected in the graph. In this case it is still customary to say that these portions together form a single curve.

For example, let
$$y = 5\,x - x^2. \tag{1}$$

We assume values of x and compute values of y. The results are exhibited in the following table:

x	-1	0	1	2	3	4	5	6
y	-6	0	4	6	6	4	0	-6

These points are plotted and connected by a smooth curve, giving the result shown in Fig. 5. This curve should have the property that *the coördinates of any point on it satisfy equation* (1) *and that any point whose coördinates satisfy* (1) *lies on the curve.* It is called the graph both of the function y and of the equation (1), and equation (1) is called the *equation of the curve*.

Of course we are absolutely sure of only those points whose coördinates we have actually computed. If greater accuracy is desired, more points must be found by assuming fractional values of x. For instance, there is doubt as to the shape of the curve between the points (2, 6) and (3, 6). We take, therefore, $x = 2\frac{1}{2}$ and find $y = 6\frac{1}{4}$. This gives us another point to aid us in drawing the graph. Later, by use of the calculus, we can show that this last point is really the highest point of the curve.

The curve (Fig. 5) gives us a graphical representation of the way in which y varies with x. We see, for example, that when x varies from -1 to 2, y is increasing; that when x varies from 3 to 6, y is decreasing, and that at some point between (2, 6) and (3, 6), not yet exactly determined, y has its largest value.

It is also evident that the steepness of the curve indicates in some way the rate at which y is increasing with respect to x. For example, when $x = -1$, an increase of 1 unit in x causes an increase of 6 units in y; while when $x = 1$, an increase of 1 unit in x causes an increase of only 2 units in y. The curve is therefore steeper when $x = -1$ than it is when $x = 1$.

Now we have seen that the derivative $\dfrac{dy}{dx}$ measures the rate of change

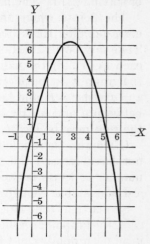

FIG. 5

of y with respect to x. Hence we expect the derivative to be connected in some way with the steepness of the curve. We shall therefore discuss this connection in § 13.

EXERCISES

Plot the graphs of the following functions:

1. $x = 4$.
2. $3y + 5 = 0$.
3. $y = 3x + 7$.
4. $y = 10 - 3x$.
5. $y = x^2 - 2x - 3$.
6. $y = x^2 + 6x + 8$.
7. $y = 10 + x - 3x^2$.
8. $y = 3x^3$.
9. $y = 2x^3 - 24x$.
10. $y = x^3 - 3x^2$.
11. $y = x^3 + 6x^2 + 12x + 8$.
12. $y = x^4 - 4x^3$.

12. Real roots of an equation. Let

$$y = f(x) \qquad (1)$$

be any equation for which we have a graph. When the graph crosses the axis of x we have a point at which $y = 0$ and hence x satisfies the equation $\qquad f(x) = 0$. $\qquad (2)$

Hence *some of the roots of equation (2) may be found by finding the points at which the graph crosses the axis of x.*

We cannot find in this way the imaginary roots of (2) nor the real roots which correspond to points where the graph of (1) touches the axis of x without crossing it. However, this method of solving (2) is very useful.

The points where the graph crosses the axis of x, and the corresponding roots of (2), may be found by trial as follows: Take any two values of x, say $x = a$ and $x = b$, and substitute each in (1). If the values of y thus found have opposite signs, the graph must have crossed the axis of x at least once between $x = a$ and $x = b$, and hence at least one root of the equation lies between a and b. By narrowing the interval between a and b the root may be located as accurately as desired.

Of course, there is no absolute certainty that the curve may not have crossed the axis of x more than once and an odd number of times between $x = a$ and $x = b$, but if these values are taken close enough together, this is not probable.

Similarly, if the values of y for $x = a$ and $x = b$ have the same sign, the graph has either not crossed the axis of x, or has crossed it an even number of times, or has touched it without crossing. The graph will usually distinguish between these cases.

Example. Find a real root of the equation

$$x^3 + 2x - 17 = 0$$

accurate to two decimal places.

We will arrange the work in tables, placing

$$y = x^3 + 2x - 17.$$

I

x	y
0	-17
1	-14
2	-5
3	16

II

x	y
2.1	-3.539
2.2	-1.952
2.3	$-.233$
2.4	1.624

III

x	y
2.31	$-.054$
2.32	.127

In Table I we try integral values of x and discover that a root lies between 2 and 3.

In Table II we try values of x between 2 and 3 differing by tenths. We are lead to suspect that the root is nearer 2 than 3 because the value of y for $x = 2$ is smaller numerically than that for $x = 3$. We find that the root lies between 2.3 and 2.4 and apparently is nearer 2.3.

In Table III we need to try only two values of x to see that the root lies between 2.31 and 2.32. The root apparently lies nearer 2.31, but to make sure we substitute $x = 2.315$ and find $y = .037 \cdots$. Hence the root lies between 2.31 and 2.315, and therefore it is 2.31, accurate to two decimal places.

EXERCISES

Find the real roots of the following equations, accurate to two decimal places:

1. $x^3 - x^2 - 5 = 0$.   4. $x^3 + 4x + 2 = 0$.   7. $x^4 - 12x + 4 = 0$.
2. $x^3 + 3x - 6 = 0$.   5. $x^3 - 6x^2 + 9x - 6 = 0$.   8. $x^4 + x^3 - 3 = 0$.
3. $x^3 + 2x^2 + 1 = 0$.   6. $x^3 - 3x + 1 = 0$.   9. $x^4 + x - 1 = 0$.

13. Slope. We shall discuss in this section a quantity, called the *slope*, which may be used to measure the steepness of a graph. We begin with a straight line.

Let $P_1(x_1, y_1)$ and $P_2(x_2, y_2)$ (Figs. 6 and 7) be any two points on a straight line LK. If we imagine a point to move along the

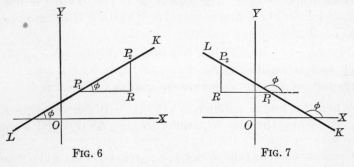

FIG. 6   FIG. 7

line from P_1 to P_2 the change in x is $x_2 - x_1 = \Delta x$ (§ 7) and the change in y is $y_2 - y_1 = \Delta y$ (§ 7). We define the slope as the ratio of the change in y to the change in x and shall denote it by the letter m. We have then, by definition,

$$m = \frac{y_2 - y_1}{x_2 - x_1} = \frac{\Delta y}{\Delta x}. \tag{1}$$

In Fig. 6, since x_2 is greater than x_1, Δx is positive, and since y_2 is greater than y_1, Δy is positive, and hence m is positive. If the points P_1 and P_2 are interchanged it is evident that Δx and Δy both become negative but their ratio m remains positive.

In Fig. 7, since x_2 is less than x_1, Δx is negative, and since y_2 is greater than y_1, Δy is positive, and hence m is negative. If the points P_1 and P_2 are interchanged, it is evident that Δx becomes positive and Δy becomes negative, but their ratio m remains negative.

Let us now draw through P_1 a straight line parallel to OX and through P_2 a straight line parallel to OY and denote by R the point in which the two lines intersect. Then $x_2 - x_1 = \Delta x = P_1R$, where P_1R is positive if drawn from left to right (Fig. 6) and is negative if drawn from right to left (Fig. 7). In like manner $y_2 - y_1 = \Delta y = RP_2$, where RP_2 is positive if drawn upward and negative if drawn downward. It follows that

$$m = \frac{RP_2}{P_1R}. \tag{2}$$

If any other two points are chosen on the given line LK, it can be shown by similar triangles that the ratio m is not changed in magnitude or sign. The sign of m is positive if the line is situated as in Fig. 6 and is negative if the line is situated as in Fig. 7; that is,

The slope of a straight line is positive if the line runs up to the right and is negative if the line runs down to the right. The magnitude of the slope measures the steepness of the line.

When the line is parallel to OX, $\Delta y = 0$ and consequently $m = 0$. When the line is parallel to OY, $\Delta x = 0$ and we say $m = \infty$.

Consider now the general case of a curve AB (Figs. 8 and 9) and let P_1 and P_2 be two points on it. Draw the straight line P_1P_2 and prolong it to form the secant P_1S. Then, as in (1), $\frac{\Delta y}{\Delta x}$ is the slope of P_1S and may be called the average slope of the curve between P_1 and P_2.

To obtain a number which may be used for the actual slope of the curve at the point P_1, it is necessary to use the limit process (with which the student should now be familiar), by which we allow Δx to become smaller and smaller and the point

P_2 to approach P_1 along the curve. The result is the derivative of y with respect to x, and we have the following result:

The slope of a curve at any point is given by the value of the derivative $\dfrac{dy}{dx}$ at that point.

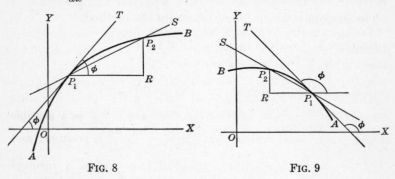

FIG. 8   FIG. 9

From this and §9 we may at once deduce the theorem:

If the derivative is positive, the curve runs up to the right. If the derivative is negative, the curve runs down to the right.

The values of x which make $\dfrac{dy}{dx}$ zero are of particular interest in the plotting of a curve. If the derivative changes its sign at such a point, the curve will change its direction from down to up or from up to down. Such a point will be called a *turning-point*.

This is illustrated in Fig. 10, where the derivative is positive to the left of A, is negative between A and B, and is positive to the right of B. The points A and B are turning-points. To find the turning-points we solve the equation

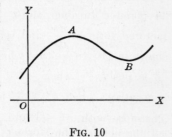

FIG. 10

$$\frac{dy}{dx} = 0$$

and examine the sign of the derivative for values of x less and greater than the roots of the equation to see if we have a change of sign. It is to be noted that a solution of the equation does not give a turning-point if the derivative does not change sign.

In rare cases a turning-point may occur when $\dfrac{dy}{dx} = \infty$, but this cannot happen in the case of a polynomial and will not be discussed here.

The examples which follow illustrate the method.

Example 1. Consider equation (1) of § 11,

$$y = 5\,x - x^2.$$

Here $$\frac{dy}{dx} = 5 - 2\,x = 2\left(\frac{5}{2} - x\right).$$

Equating $\dfrac{dy}{dx}$ to zero and solving, we have $x = \dfrac{5}{2}$ as a possible turning-point. It is evident that when $x < \dfrac{5}{2}$, $\dfrac{dy}{dx}$ is positive; and when $x > \dfrac{5}{2}$, $\dfrac{dy}{dx}$ is negative. Therefore $x = \dfrac{5}{2}$ gives a turning-point of the curve at which the latter changes its direction from up to down. It may be called a *high point* of the curve.

Example 2. Consider

$$y = \frac{1}{8}(x^3 - 3\,x^2 - 9\,x + 32).$$

Here $$\frac{dy}{dx} = \frac{3}{8}(x^2 - 2\,x - 3) = \frac{3}{8}(x - 3)(x + 1).$$

Equating $\dfrac{dy}{dx}$ to zero and solving, we have $x = -1$ and $x = 3$ as possible turning-points. From the factored form of $\dfrac{dy}{dx}$, and reasoning as shown in § 9, we see that when $x < -1$, $\dfrac{dy}{dx}$ is positive; when $-1 < x < 3$, $\dfrac{dy}{dx}$ is negative; when $x > 3$, $\dfrac{dy}{dx}$ is positive. Therefore both $x = -1$ and $x = 3$ give turning-points, the former giving a high point, and the latter a low point. Substituting these values of x in the

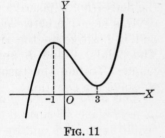

FIG. 11

equation of the curve, we find the high point to be $(-1, 4\frac{5}{8})$ and the low point to be $(3, \frac{5}{8})$. The graph is shown in Fig. 11.

The case in which a solution of the equation $\frac{dy}{dx} = 0$ does not give a turning-point is illustrated in the next example.

Example 3. Consider

$$y = \tfrac{1}{3}(x^3 - 9\,x^2 + 27\,x - 19).$$

Here $\dfrac{dy}{dx} = x^2 - 6\,x + 9 = (x-3)^2.$

Solving $\dfrac{dy}{dx} = 0$, we have $x = 3$; but since

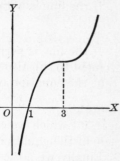

the derivative is a perfect square, it is never negative. Therefore $x = 3$ does not give a turning-point, although when $x = 3$ the tangent to the curve is parallel to OX. The curve is shown in Fig. 12.

FIG. 12

EXERCISES

Locate the turning-points and then plot the following curves:

1. $y = 3\,x^2 - 5\,x - 2.$

2. $y = 3 - x - x^2.$

3. $y = x^3 - 12\,x.$

4. $y = 4 + 2\,x^2 - x^3.$

5. $y = x^3 - x^2 - 5\,x + 5.$

6. $y = x^3 - 7\,x^2 + 15\,x - 6.$

7. $y = 8 + 4\,x - 2\,x^2 - x^3.$

8. $y = x^4 - 4\,x^3 + 16.$

9. $y = x^4 - 2\,x^3 - 2\,x^2 + 1.$

10. $y = x^4 - 4\,x^3 + 6\,x^2 - 4\,x + 6.$

14. Straight line. Let a given straight line pass through a fixed point $P_1(x_1, y_1)$ with a given slope m. Let $P(x, y)$ be any point of this line. We may then substitute x and y for x_2 and y_2 respectively in (1), § 13, and clearing of fractions have

$$y - y_1 = m(x - x_1). \tag{1}$$

This is *the equation of a line through a fixed point (x_1, y_1) with a fixed slope m*, since it is satisfied by the coördinates of any point on the line and by those of no other point.

In particular, $P_1(x_1, y_1)$ may be taken as the point with coördinates $(0, b)$ in which the line cuts OY. Then equation (1) becomes

$$y = mx + b. \tag{2}$$

Since any straight line not parallel ~~to OX~~ or to OY intersects OY somewhere and has a definite slope, the equation of any such line may be written in the form (2).

If the line is parallel to OX, $m = 0$ and equation (1) becomes

$$y = y_1. \tag{3}$$

If the line is perpendicular to OX, $m \overset{\text{is undefinable}}{=} \infty$, and it is not convenient to substitute in (1). However, it is evident from a figure that the equation of the line is

$$x = x_1, \tag{4}$$

a result which we could get from (1) by placing m on the other side of the equation and then allowing it to approach ∞.

Finally we notice that *any equation of the form*

$$Ax + By + C = 0 \tag{5}$$

represents a straight line. This follows from the fact that the equation may be written either as (2), (3), or (4).

The straight line LK (Figs. 6 and 7) makes with OX an angle ϕ which we shall always take as marked in the figures, namely, above OX and to the right of LK. Then it is at once evident from the figures that

$$\tan \phi = m. \tag{6}$$

Formula (6) is also true for a line perpendicular to OX, when $\phi = 90°$, or for a line parallel to OX, when we shall say that $\phi = 0$.

If two lines are parallel they make equal angles with OX, and conversely. Hence if m_1 and m_2 are the slopes of the two lines, we have

$$m_2 = m_1 \tag{7}$$

as *the condition for parallelism.*

Consider now two lines making angles ϕ_2 and ϕ_1 ($\phi_2 > \phi_1$) with OX (Fig. 13). They intersect at a point P.

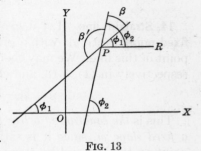

FIG. 13

Through P draw PR parallel to OX. Then, as is evident from the figure, if β is the angle as shown between the two lines,

$$\beta = \phi_2 - \phi_1. \tag{8}$$

If $\beta = 90°$, we have $\phi_2 = 90° + \phi_1$,

whence $\tan \phi_2 = -\operatorname{ctn} \phi_1.$ (9)

Conversely, if this condition is fulfilled and ϕ_2 and ϕ_1 are as in the figure, we have $\phi_2 = 90° + \phi_1$.

Hence we have, from (9),

$$m_2 = -\frac{1}{m_1}$$ (10)

is the condition for perpendicularity.

Consider now the general case (8). Then

$$\tan \beta = \tan (\phi_2 - \phi_1)$$
$$= \frac{\tan \phi_2 - \tan \phi_1}{1 + \tan \phi_2 \tan \phi_1} = \frac{m_2 - m_1}{1 + m_2 m_1}.$$ (11)

If $\tan \beta$ is positive, β is acute. If $\tan \beta$ is negative, β is obtuse and β' (Fig. 13) is acute. Then $\tan \beta' = \tan (180° - \beta)$ $= -\tan \beta$.

If the slope of a line whose equation is in form (5) is needed in using the above formulas, it may be found by placing the equation in form (2) and taking the coefficient of x.

EXERCISES

1. Find the equation of the straight line which passes through $(1, -4)$ with the slope 2.

2. Find the equation of the straight line which passes through $(-2, 3)$ with the slope $-\frac{5}{2}$.

3. Find the equation of the straight line passing through the points $(2, 3)$ and $(\frac{5}{2}, -4)$.

4. Find the equation of the straight line passing through the points $(3, -1)$ and $(3, 4)$.

5. Find the equation of the straight line passing through the points $(1, 5)$ and $(-4, 5)$.

6. Find the equation of the straight line passing through the point $(1, -4)$ and making an angle of $30°$ with OX.

7. Find the equation of the straight line passing through the point $(\frac{3}{2}, -\frac{2}{3})$ and making an angle of $135°$ with OX.

8. Find the equation of the straight line passing through the point $(-1, \frac{3}{4})$ and parallel to the line $2x - 3y + 7 = 0$.

9. Find the equation of the straight line passing through the point $(-2, -3)$ and perpendicular to the line $3x + 4y - 12 = 0$.

10. Find the equation of the straight line passing through the point $(3, 3)$ and parallel to the straight line determined by the two points $(-2, 4)$ and $(2, -1)$.

11. Find the equation of the straight line passing through $(2, -3)$ and perpendicular to the straight line determined by the points $(-3, -1)$ and $(2, \frac{7}{2})$.

12. Find the angle between the lines $2x - y = 0$ and $5x - y - 3 = 0$.

13. Find the angle between the lines $x - 2y - 3 = 0$ and $6x - 2y - 13 = 0$.

14. Find the angle between the lines $2x + y + 4 = 0$ and $5x - y + 17 = 0$.

15. Find the angle between the lines $2x - 6y - 11 = 0$ and $4x + 2y + 13 = 0$.

16. Find the angle between the line $3x + 4y = 12$ and the line determined by the points $(-1, 1)$ and $(3, 3)$.

17. Find the angle between the line determined by the points $(-4, 0)$ and $(1, 6)$ and the line determined by the points $(0, 5)$ and $(4, 0)$.

18. The vertices of a triangle are at the points $A(-1, 1)$, $B(4, -2)$, and $C(2, 2)$. Find the internal angles of the triangle.

19. Find the foot of the perpendicular drawn from the vertex C of the triangle of Ex. 18 to the side AB.

20. Prove that the lines $3x + 5y - 8 = 0$ and $3x - 5y + 2 = 0$ form with the axis of x an isosceles triangle, and determine its area.

15. Tangent line to a curve. In determining the slope of a curve (§ 13) we allowed the point P_2 to approach P_1 (Figs. 8 and 9).

As this limit process takes place, it appears from the figures that the secant $P_1 S$ approaches a limiting position $P_1 T$. The line $P_1 T$ is called a *tangent* to the curve, a tangent being by definition *the line approached as a limit by a secant through two points of the curve as the two points approach coincidence.* It follows that the slope of the tangent is the limit of the slope of the secant. Therefore,

The slope of the tangent to a curve at any point is the same as the slope of the curve at that point.

From (6), § 14, it also follows that if ϕ is the angle which the tangent at any point of a curve makes with OX, then

$$\tan \phi = \frac{dy}{dx}. \tag{1}$$

The equation of the tangent to a curve at a point (x_1, y_1) is easily written down. We let $\left(\frac{dy}{dx}\right)_1$ represent the value of $\frac{dy}{dx}$ at the point (x_1, y_1). Then $m = \left(\frac{dy}{dx}\right)_1$, and, from (1), § 14, the equation of the tangent is

$$y - y_1 = \left(\frac{dy}{dx}\right)_1 (x - x_1). \tag{2}$$

Example. Find the equation of the tangent at $(1, -1)$ to the curve
$$y = x^2 - 4x + 2.$$

We have
$$\frac{dy}{dx} = 2x - 4,$$

and
$$x_1 = 1, \ y_1 = -1, \left(\frac{dy}{dx}\right)_1 = -2.$$

Therefore the equation of the tangent is
$$y + 1 = -2(x - 1),$$
which reduces to
$$2x + y - 1 = 0.$$

EXERCISES

1. Find the equation of the tangent line drawn to the curve $y = 4x^3 + 7x^2 - 6x + 5$ at the point for which $x = 1$.

2. Find the equations of the tangent lines drawn to the curve $y = x^3 - 3x + 4$ at the points for which $x = -2$ and $x = 2$ respectively.

3. Find the equations of the tangent lines drawn to the curve $y = 8 + 4x - 2x^2 - x^3$ at the points which are on OX and OY.

4. Find the equations of the tangent lines drawn to the curve $y = x^3 - 5x^2 - 8x$ at the points whose abscissas are respectively $-\frac{1}{3}$ and $\frac{1}{3}$, and find the acute angle between the tangents.

5. Find the equations of the tangent lines drawn to the curve $y = x^3 + x^2 - x + 2$ which make an angle of $135°$ with OX.

6. At what points on the curve $y = x^3 - x^2 - 5x + 5$ will the tangents be parallel to $3x - y + 5 = 0$? What are the equations of these tangents?

7. Tangents are drawn to the curve $y = x^3 + 3\,x^2 - 9\,x - 10$ perpendicular to the straight line determined by the points $(8, 1)$ and $(\frac{1}{2}, \frac{3}{2})$. Find their equations.

8. Find the equation of the tangent line to the curve $8\,y = x^3$ at the point $(1, \frac{1}{8})$. Find where the tangent again intersects the curve.

16. The second derivative. The derivative of the derivative is called the *second derivative* and is indicated by the symbol $\frac{d}{dx}\left(\frac{dy}{dx}\right)$ or $\frac{d^2y}{dx^2}$.

The acceleration of a body moving in a straight line may be expressed as a second derivative. For, by definition, $a = \frac{dv}{dt}$ and $v = \frac{ds}{dt}$, whence

$$a = \frac{d}{dt}\left(\frac{ds}{dt}\right) = \frac{d^2s}{dt^2}.$$

The second derivative may also be used in studying the slope of a curve; for since $\frac{dy}{dx}$ is equal to the slope of the graph, we have

$$\frac{d^2y}{dx^2} = \frac{d}{dx}\,(\text{slope}).$$

From this and § 9 we have the following theorem:

If the second derivative is positive, the slope is increasing as x increases; and if the second derivative is negative, the slope is decreasing as x increases.

We may accordingly use the second derivative to distinguish between the high turning-points and the low turning-points of a curve, as follows:

If, when $x = a$, $\frac{dy}{dx} = 0$ and $\frac{d^2y}{dx^2}$ is positive, it is evident that $\frac{dy}{dx}$ is increasing through zero; hence, when $x < a$, $\frac{dy}{dx}$ is negative, and when $x > a$, $\frac{dy}{dx}$ is positive. The point for which $x = a$ is therefore a low turning-point, by § 13.

Similarly, if, when $x = a$, $\frac{dy}{dx} = 0$ and $\frac{d^2y}{dx^2}$ is negative, it is evident that $\frac{dy}{dx}$ is decreasing through zero; hence, when $x < a$, $\frac{dy}{dx}$ is positive, and when $x > a$, $\frac{dy}{dx}$ is negative. The point for which $x = a$ is therefore a high turning-point of the curve, by § 13.

These conclusions may be stated as follows:

If $x = a$ is a root of the equation $\dfrac{dy}{dx} = 0$ and $\dfrac{d^2y}{dx^2}$ is positive when $x = a$, the point corresponding to $x = a$ is a low turning-point of the curve; but if $\dfrac{d^2y}{dx^2}$ is negative when $x = a$, the corresponding point is a high turning-point of the curve.

EXERCISES

Plot the following curves after determining their high and low turning-points by the use of $\dfrac{dy}{dx}$ and $\dfrac{d^2y}{dx^2}$:

1. $y = 4x^3 - 3x + 4$.

2. $y = 5x^3 - x^2 - 8x + 2$.

3. $y = 1 + 12x + 3x^2 - x^3$.

4. $y = x^3 + 3x^2 - 3x + 1$.

5. $y = 3 + 3x - x^2 - x^3$.

6. $y = x^3 + 2x^2 - 5x - 5$.

17. Maxima and minima. If $f(a)$ is a value of $f(x)$ which is greater than the values obtained either by increasing or by decreasing x by a small amount, $f(a)$ is called a *maximum* value of $f(x)$. If $f(a)$ is a value of $f(x)$ which is smaller than the values of $f(x)$ found either by increasing or by decreasing x by a small amount, $f(a)$ is called a *minimum* value of $f(x)$.

It is evident that if we place

$$y = f(x)$$

and make the graph of this equation, a maximum value of $f(x)$ occurs at a high point of the curve and a minimum value at a low point. Hence we deduce the following rule:

To find the values of x which give maximum or minimum values of y, solve the equation
$$\frac{dy}{dx} = 0.$$

If $x = a$ is a root of this equation, it must be tested to see if it gives a maximum or a minimum. We have two tests:

Test I. *If the sign of $\dfrac{dy}{dx}$ changes from $+$ to $-$ as x increases through a, then $x = a$ gives a maximum value of y. If the sign of $\dfrac{dy}{dx}$ changes from $-$ to $+$ as x increases through a, then $x = a$ gives a minimum value of y.*

TEST II. *If $x = a$ makes $\dfrac{dy}{dx} = 0$ and $\dfrac{d^2y}{dx^2}$ negative, then $x = a$ gives a maximum value of y. If $x = a$ makes $\dfrac{dy}{dx} = 0$ and $\dfrac{d^2y}{dx^2}$ positive, then $x = a$ gives a minimum value of y.*

Either of these tests may be applied according to convenience. It may be noticed that Test I always works and is readily applicable in case $\dfrac{dy}{dx}$ can be factored; if $\dfrac{dy}{dx}$ is not easily factored Test II is to be preferred unless $\dfrac{d^2y}{dx^2} = 0$ when $x = a$, in which case the test fails to give the required information. It is also frequently possible by the application of common sense to a problem to determine whether the result is a maximum or minimum, and neither of the formal tests need then be applied.

Example 1. A rectangular box is to be formed by cutting a square from each corner of a rectangular piece of cardboard and bending the resulting figure. If the dimensions of the piece of cardboard are 20 in. by 30 in., find the largest box which can be made.

Let x be the side of the square cut out. Then, if the cardboard is bent along the dotted lines of Fig. 14, the dimensions of the box are $30 - 2x$, $20 - 2x$, x. Let V be the volume of the box.

Then $V = x(20 - 2x)(30 - 2x)$
$$= 600x - 100x^2 + 4x^3.$$
$$\frac{dV}{dx} = 600 - 200x + 12x^2.$$

Equating $\dfrac{dV}{dx}$ to zero, we have

$$3x^2 - 50x + 150 = 0;$$

whence $x = \dfrac{25 \pm 5\sqrt{7}}{3} = 3.9$ or 12.7.

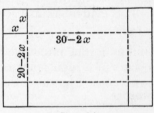

FIG. 14

The result 12.7 is impossible, since that amount cannot be cut twice from the side of 20 in. The result 3.9 corresponds to a possible maximum, and the tests are to be applied.

To apply Test I we write $\dfrac{dV}{dx}$ in the factored form

$$\frac{dV}{dx} = 12(x - 3.9)(x - 12.7),$$

when it appears that $\dfrac{dV}{dx}$ changes from $+$ to $-$ as x increases through 3.9. Hence $x = 3.9$ gives a maximum value of V.

To apply Test II we find $\dfrac{d^2V}{dx^2} = -200 + 24\,x$ and substitute $x = 3.9$. The result is negative. Therefore $x = 3.9$ gives a maximum value of V.

The maximum value of V is 1056 cu. in., approximately, found by substituting $x = 3.9$ in the equation for V.

Example 2. A piece of wood is in the form of a right circular cone, the altitude and the radius of the base of which are each equal to 12 in. What is the volume of the largest right circular cylinder that can be cut from this piece of wood, the axis of the cylinder to coincide with the axis of the cone?

Let x be the radius of the base of the required cylinder, y its altitude, and V its volume. Then

$$V = \pi x^2 y. \tag{1}$$

We cannot, however, apply our method directly to this value of V, since it involves two variables x and y. It is necessary to find a connection between x and y and eliminate one of them. To do so, consider Fig. 15, which shows a cross section of cone and cylinder. From similar triangles we have

$$\frac{FE}{EC} = \frac{AD}{DC};$$

that is, $\quad \dfrac{y}{12 - x} = \dfrac{12}{12};$

whence $\quad y = 12 - x.$

Substituting in (1), we have

$$V = 12\,\pi x^2 - \pi x^3;$$

whence $\quad \dfrac{dV}{dx} = 24\,\pi x - 3\,\pi x^2.$

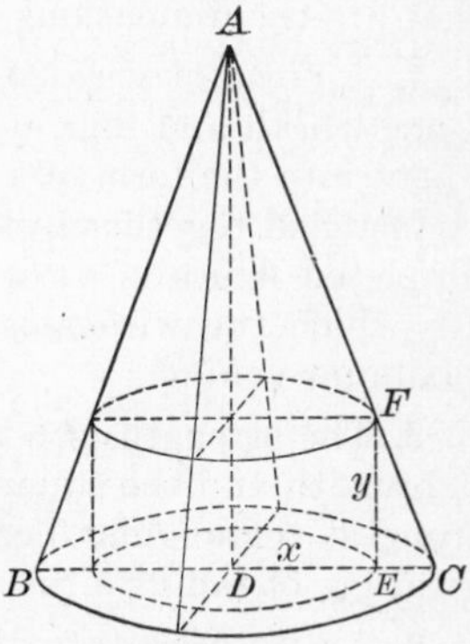

Fig. 15

Equating $\dfrac{dV}{dx}$ to zero and solving, we find $x = 0$ or 8. The value $x = 0$ is evidently not a solution of the problem, but $x = 8$ is a possible solution.

Applying Test I, we find that as x increases through the value 8, $\dfrac{dV}{dx}$ changes its sign from $+$ to $-$. Applying Test II, we find that $\dfrac{d^2V}{dx^2} = 24\,\pi - 6\,\pi x$ is negative when $x = 8$. Either test shows that $x = 8$ corresponds to a maximum value of V. To find V substitute $x = 8$ in the expression for V. We have $V = 256\,\pi$ cu. in.

EXERCISES

1. A piece of wire of length 30 in. is bent into a rectangle. Find the maximum area.

2. A gardener has a certain length of wire fencing with which to fence three sides of a rectangular plot of land, the fourth side being made by a wall already constructed. Required the dimensions of the plot which contains the maximum area.

3. A gardener is to lay out a flower bed in the form of a sector of a circle. If he has 40 ft. of wire with which to inclose it, what radius will he take for the circle to have his garden as large as possible?

4. In a given isosceles triangle of base 30 and altitude 10 a rectangle is inscribed. Find the rectangle of maximum area.

5. A right circular cylinder is inscribed in a sphere of radius a. Find the cylinder of maximum volume.

6. A rectangular box with a square base and open at the top is to be made out of a given amount of material. If no allowance is made for the thickness of the material or for waste in construction, what are the dimensions of the largest box that can be made?

7. A piece of wire 24 ft. in length is cut into six portions, two of one length and four of another. Each of the two former portions is bent into the form of a square, and the corners of the two squares are fastened together by the remaining portions of wire, so that the completed figure is a rectangular parallelepiped. Find the lengths into which the wire must be divided so as to produce a figure of maximum volume.

8. The strength of a rectangular beam varies as the product of its breadth and the square of its depth. Find the dimensions of the strongest rectangular beam that can be cut from a circular cylindrical log of radius a inches.

9. An isosceles triangle of constant perimeter is revolved about its base to form a solid of revolution. What are the altitude and the base of the triangle when the volume of the solid generated is a maximum?

10. The combined length and girth of a parcel is 60 in. Find the maximum volume (1) when the parcel is rectangular with square cross section; (2) when it is cylindrical.

11. A piece of galvanized iron b feet long and a feet wide is to be bent into a U-shaped water drain b feet long. If we assume that the cross section of the drain is exactly represented by a rectangle on top of a semicircle, what must be the dimensions of the rectangle and the semicircle in order that the drain may have the greatest capacity (1) when the drain is closed on top? (2) when it is open on top?

12. A circular filter paper 12 in. in diameter is folded into a right circular cone. Find the height of the cone when it has the greatest volume.

18. Differentials. The derivative has been defined as the limit of $\frac{\Delta y}{\Delta x}$ and has been denoted by the symbol $\frac{dy}{dx}$. This symbol is in the fractional form to suggest that it is the *limit* of a fraction, but thus far we have made no attempt to treat it as a fraction.

It is, however, desirable in many cases to treat the derivative as a fraction and to consider dx and dy as separate quantities. These quantities are called *differentials,* and it is necessary to define them in such a manner that their quotient shall be the derivative. We shall begin by defining dx, when x is the independent variable; that is, the variable whose values can be assumed independently of any other quantity.

We shall define dx, the *differential* of x, as a change in x which may have any magnitude, but which is generally regarded as small and may be made to approach zero as a limit. In other words, *the differential of the independent variable x is identical with the increment of x;* that is,

$$dx = \Delta x. \tag{1}$$

After dx has been defined, it is necessary to define dy so that its quotient by dx is the derivative. Therefore, if $y = f(x)$ and $\frac{dy}{dx} = f'(x)$, we have

$$dy = f'(x)dx. \tag{2}$$

That is, *the differential of the function y is equal to the derivative times the differential of the independent variable x.*

In equation (2) the derivative appears as the coefficient of dx. For this reason it is sometimes called the *differential coefficient.*

It is important to notice the distinction between dy and Δy. The differential dy is not the limit of the increment Δy, since both dy and Δy have the same limit, zero. Neither is dy equal to a very small increment Δy, since it generally differs in value from Δy. It is true, however, that when dy and Δy both become small, they differ by a quantity which is small compared with each of them. These statements may best be understood from the following examples:

Example 1. Let A be the area of a square with the side x, so that

$$A = x^2.$$

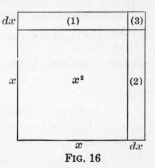

FIG. 16

If x is increased by $\Delta x = dx$, A is increased by ΔA, where

$$\Delta A = (x + dx)^2 - x^2 = 2\,x\,dx + (dx)^2.$$

Now, by (2), $\quad dA = 2\,x\,dx,$

so that ΔA and dA differ by $(dx)^2$.

Referring to Fig. 16, we see that dA is represented by the rectangles (1) and (2), while ΔA is represented by the rectangles (1) and (2) together with the square (3); and it is obvious from the figure that the square (3) is very small compared with the rectangles (1) and (2), provided dx is taken small. For example, if $x = 5$ and $dx = .001$, the rectangles (1) and (2) have together the area $2\,x\,dx = .01$ and the square (3) has the area $.000001$.

Example 2. Let $\quad\quad s = 16\,t^2,$

where s is the distance traversed by a moving body in the time t.

If t is increased by $\Delta t = dt$, we have

$$\Delta s = 16(t + dt)^2 - 16\,t^2 = 32\,t\,dt + 16(dt)^2,$$

and, from (2), $\quad\quad\quad\quad ds = 32\,t\,dt\,;$

so that Δs and ds differ by $16(dt)^2$. The term $16(dt)^2$ is very small compared with the term $32\,t\,dt$, if dt is small. For example, if $t = 4$ and $dt = .001$, then $32\,t\,dt = .128$, while $16(dt)^2 = .000016$.

In this problem Δs is the actual distance traversed in the time dt, and ds is the distance which would have been traversed if the body had moved throughout the time dt with the same velocity which it had at the beginning of the time dt.

In general, if $y = f(x)$ and we make a graphical representation, we may have two cases, as shown in Figs. 17 and 18.

In each figure, $MN = PR = \Delta x = dx$ and $RQ = \Delta y$, since RQ is the total change in y caused by a change of $dx = MN$ in x. If PT is the tangent to the curve at P, then, by § 15,

$$\frac{dy}{dx} = f'(x) = \tan RPT;$$

so that, by (2), $dy = (\tan RPT)(PR) = RT$.

In Fig. 17, $dy < \Delta y$, and in Fig. 18, $dy > \Delta y$; but in each case the difference between dy and Δy is represented in magnitude by the length of QT.

This shows that $RQ = \Delta y$ is the change in y as the point P is supposed to move along the curve $y = f(x)$, while $RT = dy$ is

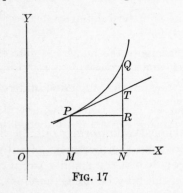

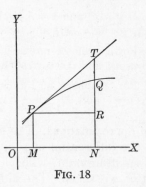

FIG. 17 FIG. 18

the change in the value of y as the point P is supposed to move along the tangent to that curve. Now, as a very small arc does not deviate much from its tangent, it is not hard to see graphically that if the point Q is taken close to P, the difference between RQ and RT, namely, QT, is very small compared with RT.

A more rigorous examination of the difference between the increment and the differential lies outside the range of this book.

EXERCISES

1. If $y = x^3 - 4x^2 + 4x - 1$, find dy.

2. If $y = x^4 + 5x^3 - x^2 + 7x$, find dy.

3. If V is the volume of a cube of edge x, find both ΔV and dV and interpret geometrically.

4. If A is the area of a circle of radius r, find both ΔA and dA. Show that ΔA is the exact area of a ring of width dr, and that dA is the product of the inner circumference of the ring by its width.

5. If V is the volume of a sphere of radius r, find ΔV and dV. Show that ΔV is the exact volume of a spherical shell of thickness dr, and that dV is the product of the area of the inner surface of the shell by its thickness.

6. If s is the distance traversed by a moving body, t the time, and v the velocity, show that $ds = v\, dt$. How does ds differ from Δs?

7. If $y = x^2$ and $x = 3$, find the numerical difference between dy and Δy, with successive assumptions of $dx = .01$, $dx = .001$, and $dx = .0001$.

8. If $y = x^3$ and $x = 5$, find the numerical difference between dy and Δy for $dx = .001$ and for $dx = .0001$.

9. For a circle of radius 8 in. compute the numerical difference between dA and ΔA corresponding to an increase of r by .001 in.

10. For a sphere of radius 2 ft. find the numerical difference between dV and ΔV when r is increased by 1 in.

19. Approximations. The previous section brings out the fact that the differential of y differs from the increment of y by a very small amount, which becomes less the smaller the increment of x is taken. The differential may be used, therefore, to make certain approximate calculations, especially when the question is to determine the effect upon a function caused by small changes in the independent variable. This is illustrated in the following examples:

Example 1. Find approximately the change in the area of a square of side 2 in. caused by an increase of .002 in. in the side.

Let x be the side of the square, A its area. Then

$$A = x^2 \quad \text{and} \quad dA = 2\, x\, dx.$$

Placing $x = 2$ and $dx = .002$, we find $dA = .008$, which is approximately the required change in the area.

If we wish to know how nearly correct the approximation is, we may compute $\Delta A = (2.002)^2 - (2)^2 = .008004$, which is the exact change in A. Our approximate change is therefore in error by .000004, a very small amount.

Example 2. Find approximately the volume of a sphere of radius 1.9.

The volume of a sphere of radius 2 is $\frac{32}{3}\pi$, and the volume of the required sphere may be found by computing the change in the volume of a sphere of radius 2 caused by decreasing its radius by .1.

If r is the radius of the sphere and V its volume, we have

$$V = \tfrac{4}{3}\pi r^3 \quad \text{and} \quad dV = 4\pi r^2\, dr.$$

Placing $r = 2$ and $dr = -.1$, we find $V = \frac{32}{3}\pi$ and $dV = -1.6\pi$. Hence the volume of the required sphere is approximately

$$\tfrac{32}{3}\pi - 1.6\pi = 9.0667\pi.$$

To find how much this is in error we may compute exactly the volume of the required sphere by the formula

$$V = \tfrac{4}{3}\pi(1.9)^3 = 9.1453\pi.$$

The approximate volume is therefore in error by $.0786\pi$, which is less than 1 per cent of the true volume.

EXERCISES

1. The side of a square is measured as 4 ft. long. If this length is in error by 1 in., find approximately the resulting error in the area of the square.

2. The diameter of a spherical ball is measured as $2\frac{1}{3}$ in., and the volume and the surface are computed. If an error of $\frac{1}{10}$ in. has been made in measuring the diameter, what is the approximate error in the volume and the surface?

3. The radius and the altitude of a right circular cone are measured as 3 in. and 5 in. respectively. What is the approximate error in the volume if an error of $\frac{1}{25}$ in. is made in the radius? What is the approximate error in the volume if an error of $\frac{1}{25}$ in. is made in the altitude?

4. Find approximately the volume of a cube with 2.0003 in. on each edge.

5. The altitude of a certain right circular cone is the same as the radius of the base. Find approximately the volume of the cone if the altitude is 3.00003 in.

6. The distance s of a moving body from a fixed point of its path, at any time t, is given by the equation $s = 16\,t^2 + 100\,t - 50$. Find approximately the distance when $t = 4.0002$.

7. Find the approximate value of $x^3 + x - 2$ when $x = 1.0001$.

8. Find approximately the value of $x^4 + x^2 + 4$ when $x = .99988$.

20. Integration. It is often desirable to reverse the process of differentiation. For example, if the velocity or the acceleration of a moving body is given, we may wish to find the distance traversed; or, if the slope of a curve is given, we may wish to find the curve.

The inverse operation to differentiation is called *integration*, and the result of the operation is called an *integral*. In the case of a polynomial it may be performed by simply working the formulas of differentiation backwards. Thus, if n is a positive integer and

$$\frac{dy}{dx} = ax^n,$$

then
$$y = \frac{ax^{n+1}}{n+1} + C. \tag{1}$$

The first term of this formula is justified by the fact that if it is differentiated, the result is exactly ax^n. The second term is justified by the fact that the derivative of a constant is zero. The constant C may have any value whatever and cannot be determined by the process of integration. It is called the *constant of integration* and can only be determined in a given problem by special information given in the problem. The examples will show how this is to be done.

Again, if
$$\frac{dy}{dx} = a,$$

then •
$$y = ax + C. \tag{2}$$

This is only a special case of (1) with $n = 0$.

Finally, if
$$\frac{dy}{dx} = a_0x^n + a_1x^{n-1} + \cdots + a_{n-1}x + a_n,$$
$$y = \frac{a_0x^{n+1}}{n+1} + \frac{a_1x^n}{n} + \cdots + \frac{a_{n-1}x^2}{2} + a_nx + C. \tag{3}$$

Example 1. The velocity v with which a body is moving along a straight line AB (Fig. 19) is given by the equation

$$v = 16\,t + 5.$$

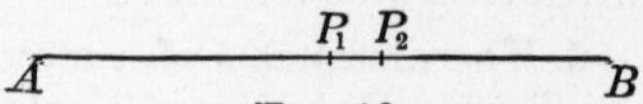

Fig. 19

How far will the body move in the time from $t = 2$ to $t = 4$?

If when $t = 2$ the body is at P_1, and if when $t = 4$ it is at P_2, we are to find P_1P_2.

By hypothesis, $\dfrac{ds}{dt} = 16\,t + 5.$

Therefore $\qquad s = 8\,t^2 + 5\,t + C.$ (1)

We have first to determine C. As a matter of fact, the value of C depends upon the point from which s is measured. This point is not given in the problem, so that we may take it anywhere we please. If s is measured from P_1, it follows that when

$$t = 2, \qquad s = 0.$$

Therefore, substituting in (1), we have

$$0 = 8(2)^2 + 5(2) + C;$$

whence $\qquad C = -42,$

and (1) becomes $\qquad s = 8\,t^2 + 5\,t - 42.$ (2)

This is the distance of the body from P_1 at any time t. Accordingly, it remains for us to substitute $t = 4$ in (2) to find the required distance P_1P_2. There results

$$P_1P_2 = 8(4)^2 + 5(4) - 42 = 106.$$

If the velocity is in feet per second, the required distance is in feet.

Example 2. Required the curve the slope of which at any point is twice the abscissa of the point.

By hypothesis, $\dfrac{dy}{dx} = 2\,x.$

Therefore $\qquad y = x^2 + C.$ **(1)**

FIG. 20

Any curve whose equation can be derived from (1) by giving C a definite value satisfies the condition of the problem (Fig. 20). If it is required that the curve should pass through the point $(2, 3)$, we have, from (1), $3 = 4 + C;$

whence $\qquad C = -1,$

and therefore the equation of the curve is

$$y = x^2 - 1.$$

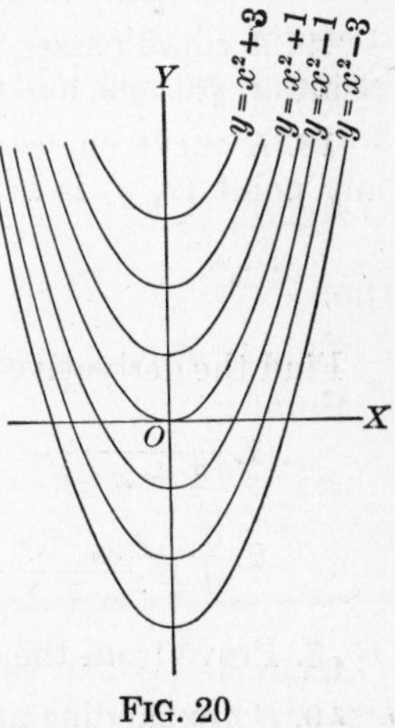

But if it is required that the curve should pass through $(-3, 10)$, we have, from (1), $10 = 9 + C;$

whence $\qquad C = 1,$

and the equation is $\qquad y = x^2 + 1.$

EXERCISES

In the following problems v is the velocity, in feet per second, of a moving body at any time t:

1. If $v = 32\,t - 64$, how far will the body move in the time from $t = 2$ to $t = 5$?

2. If $v = 3\,t^2 + 4\,t + 3$, how far will the body move in the time from $t = 1$ to $t = 3$?

3. If $v = 20\,t - 25$, how far will the body move in the fourth second?

4. If $v = t^2 + 2\,t + 6$, how far will the body move in the fifth and sixth seconds?

5. If $v = 160 - 32\,t$, how far will the body move before $v = 0$?

6. A curve passes through the point $(-1, 1)$, and its slope at any point (x, y) is 3 more than twice the abscissa of the point. What is its equation?

7. The slope of a curve at any point (x, y) is $3\,x^2 + x - 4$, and the curve passes through the point $(2, 2)$. What is its equation?

8. The slope of a curve at any point (x, y) is $6 - 5\,x - x^2$, and the curve passes through the point $(-6, 1)$. What is its equation?

9. A curve passes through the point $(-5, 2)$, and its slope at any point (x, y) is one half the abscissa of the point. What is its equation?

10. A curve passes through the point $(-6, -4)$, and its slope at any point (x, y) is $x^2 - x + 1$. What is its equation?

GENERAL EXERCISES

Find the derivatives of the following functions from the definition:

1. $\dfrac{2 + 3\,x}{1 - x}$. **3.** $\dfrac{2}{x^2 - 1}$. **5.** $\sqrt{x}$.*

6. $\dfrac{1}{\sqrt{x}}$.*

2. $\dfrac{a - x}{a + x}$. **4.** $\dfrac{x^2 + 1}{x^2 - 1}$. **7.** $\sqrt{x^2 + 1}$.*

8. Prove from the definition that the derivative of $\dfrac{a}{x^n}$ is $\dfrac{-na}{x^{n+1}}$.

9. By expanding and differentiating, prove that the derivative of $(x + a)^n$ is $n(x + a)^{n-1}$, where n is a positive integer.

10. By expanding and differentiating, prove that the derivative of $(x^2 + a^2)^n$ is $2\,nx(x^2 + a^2)^{n-1}$, where n is a positive integer.

*HINT. In these examples make use of the relation $\sqrt{A} - \sqrt{B} = \dfrac{A - B}{\sqrt{A} + \sqrt{B}}$.

11. A particle is moving along a straight line so that at any time t its distance s from a fixed point A of the line is given by the equation $s = t^3 - 2\,t^2 - 4\,t + 8$. During what intervals of time is the body moving toward A?

12. A particle is moving in a straight line in such a manner that its distance x from a fixed point A of the straight line, at any time t, is given by the equation $x = t^3 - 9\,t^2 + 15\,t + 25$. When will the particle be approaching A?

13. A particle is moving along a straight line so that at any time t its velocity in feet per second is given by the equation $v = 16 + 2\,t - 3\,t^2$. How far does the body move in the direction in which s is increasing?

14. At any time t the velocity v of a body is given by the equation $v = t^2 - 6\,t + 5$. When is the body moving in the direction in which s is decreasing? How far does it move in that direction?

15. If a stone is thrown up from the surface of the earth with a velocity of 300 ft. per second, the distance traversed in t seconds is given by the equation $s = 300\,t - 16\,t^2$. Find when the stone moves up and when down.

16. The distance s of a certain moving body from a fixed point in its path is given by the equation $s = 10 + 5\,t - 5\,t^2 - 10\,t^3$, where t is the time. When is its velocity increasing and when decreasing?

17. At any time t the distance of a certain moving body from a fixed point in its path is given by the equation $s = t^3 - t^2 - 5\,t + 6$. When is its velocity increasing and when decreasing?

18. At any time t the distance s of a certain moving body from a fixed point in its path is given by the equation $s = t^3 + 2\,t^2 - 55\,t + 60$. When is the speed of the body increasing and when decreasing?

19. At any time t the distance s of a certain moving body from a fixed point in its path is given by the equation $s = 48 + 24\,t - 3\,t^2 - t^3$. When is its speed increasing and when decreasing?

20. Show that the equation of any straight line not parallel or perpendicular to OX may be written $y = m(x - a)$, where m is the slope and a the intercept on OX.

21. Show that if a straight line intersects OX at a distance a from O and intersects OY at a distance b from O, its equation may be written $\dfrac{x}{a} + \dfrac{y}{b} = 1$.

22. Show that two straight lines whose equations agree in the coefficients of x and y are parallel.

[handwritten in top margin:]
$Bx - Ay + F = 0$
$Ax + By + C = 0$

23. Show that two straight lines are perpendicular when their equations are such that the coefficient of x in one is the negative of the coefficient of y in the other, and the coefficient of y in the first is the coefficient of x in the other.

24. Find the equation of a straight line through the point (x_1, y_1) parallel to the line $Ax + By + C = 0$.

25. Find the equation of a straight line through the point (x_1, y_1) perpendicular to the line $Ax + By + C = 0$.

26. Find the equation of the straight line determined by the two points (x_1, y_1) and (x_2, y_2).

27. Find the turning-points of the curve $y = 27 + 9\,x - 3\,x^2 - x^3$, and draw the graph.

28. Find the turning-points of the curve $y = 4\,x^3 - 7\,x^2 - 6\,x + 5$, and draw the graph.

29. Find the turning-points of the curve $y = 2\,x^3 + 3\,x^2 - 36\,x$, and draw the graph.

30. Find the turning-point of the curve $y = ax^2 + bx + c$. From this deduce the condition that the equation $ax^2 + bx + c = 0$ has equal roots.

31. Find the turning-points of the curve $y = ax^3 + bx + c$, and find the conditions that there should be two or none. Hence show that if a and b have the same sign the equation $ax^3 + bx + c = 0$ has only one real root.

32. Show graphically that the cubic equation $ax^3 + bx^2 + cx + d = 0$ has always at least one real root.

33. Find the equations of the tangents to the curve $y = x^3 + x$ which are perpendicular to the line $2\,x + 8\,y - 7 = 0$.

34. Tangents are drawn to the curve $y = 4\,x^3 - 7\,x^2 - 6\,x + 5$ at the points for which $x = -1$ and $x = 1$, respectively. Find the acute angle between these tangents.

35. Find the points of the curve $y = 2 + 3\,x + 4\,x^2 - x^3$ where the tangents make an angle of $45°$ with OX.

36. Find the area of the triangle included between the coördinate axes and the straight line tangent to the curve $y = x^3 + 4\,x^2$ at the point for which $x = 2$.

37. Find the equations of the tangent lines drawn to the curve $y = 2\,x^3 + 3\,x^2 - 3\,x$ at the points where the ordinate is twice the abscissa.

38. Find the area of the triangle formed by the axis of x and the tangents to the curve $y = 4 - x^2$ at the points for which $x = -2$ and $x = 2$.

39. Show that the equation of the tangent drawn to the curve $y = ax^2 + 2bx + c$ at the point (x_1, y_1) is $y = 2(ax_1 + b)x - ax_1^2 + c$.

40. Show that the equation of the tangent drawn to the curve $y = x^3 + ax + b$ at the point (x_1, y_1) is $y = (3x_1^2 + a)x - 2x_1^3 + b$.

41. Find the equation of the tangent to the curve $y = ax^2$ at the point $P_1(x_1, y_1)$. If A is the point where the tangent intersects OY and N is the foot of the perpendicular from P_1 to OY, show that O is halfway between A and N.

42. A length l of wire is to be cut into two portions which are to be bent into the forms of a circle and a square, respectively. Show that the sum of the areas of these figures will be least when the wire is cut in the ratio $\pi : 4$.

43. A log in the form of a frustum of a cone is 10 ft. long, the diameters of the bases being 4 ft. and 2 ft. A beam with a square cross section is cut from it so that the axis of the beam coincides with the axis of the log. Find the beam of greatest volume that can be so cut.

44. Required the right circular cone of greatest volume which can be inscribed in a given sphere.

45. The total surface of a regular triangular prism is to be k. Find its altitude and the side of its base when its volume is a maximum.

46. A piece of wire 9 in. long is cut into five pieces, two of one length and three of another. Each of the two equal pieces is bent into an equilateral triangle, and the vertices of the two triangles are connected by the remaining three pieces so as to form a regular triangular prism. How is the wire cut when the prism has the largest volume?

47. The perimeter of a rectangle is constant and equal to 30 in. What must be its dimensions when the volume of the right circular cylinder formed by revolving the rectangle about one of its sides is a maximum?

48. A post is in the form of a right circular cylinder of radius r surmounted by a right circular cone of altitude $\frac{3}{4}r$ and base equal to that of the cylinder. If the outside area of the post is 9π sq. ft., what is its radius when the volume is a maximum?

49. From a rectangle whose perimeter is 120 in. a semicircle is cut, the diameter of the semicircle coinciding with one of the shorter sides of the rectangle. What are the dimensions of the rectangle when the area of the remainder of the rectangle is a maximum?

50. A piece of wire 36 in. long is to be cut into two pieces, one of which is to be bent into the form of a square and the other into the form of an equilateral triangle. Prove that the sum of the areas of the square and the triangle is a minimum when the side of the square is to the side of the triangle as $1 : \sqrt{3}$.

51. The hypotenuse of a right triangle is 10 in. What must be the lengths of the other two sides of the triangle in order that the volume of the solid formed by revolving the triangle about the hypotenuse shall be a maximum?

52. Compute the difference between ΔA and dA for the area A of a circle of radius 5, corresponding to an increase of .01 in the radius.

53. Compute the difference between ΔV and dV for the volume V of a sphere of radius 5, corresponding to an increase of .01 in the radius.

54. If a cubical shell is formed by increasing each edge of a cube by dx, where x is the length of an edge, show that the volume of the shell is approximately equal to its inside surface multiplied by its thickness.

55. Show that the volume of a thin cylindrical shell is approximately equal to the area of its inner surface times its thickness.

56. If V is the volume and S the curved area of a right circular cone the radius of whose base is r and whose vertical angle is 2α, show that $V = \frac{1}{3} \pi r^3 \operatorname{ctn} \alpha$ and $S = \pi r^2 \csc \alpha$. Thence show that the volume of a thin conical shell is approximately equal to the area of its inner surface multiplied by its thickness.

57. A solid sphere of radius x is cut out of a cube of edge $2x$. If by error of measurement the value of x is made too small by 1 per cent, find approximately the percentage of the error caused in the amount of material left in the hollow cube.

58. Find an expression for the area of a square inscribed in a circle of radius r. Find approximately the area remaining if such a square is cut out of a circle of radius 3.99.

59. The height of a post in the form of a right circular cylinder is known to be eight times its diameter. By use of differentials find approximately the volume of the post if its diameter is 5.98 in.

60. The strength of a rectangular beam varies as the product of its breadth and the square of its depth. A rectangular beam of breadth 2.99 in. is cut from a circular cylindrical log of 6-inch radius. By using differentials find approximately the strength of this beam.

61. A rough wooden model is in the form of a regular quadrangular pyramid 3 in. tall and 3 in. on each side of the base. After it is smoothed down, its dimensions are all decreased by .01 in. What is the approximate volume of the material removed?

62. The edge of a cube is 1.999 in. long. Find the approximate volume.

63. The distance s of a body from a fixed point in its path at any time t is given by $s = 100 - 45\,t + 12\,t^2 - t^3$. Find approximately how far the body moves in the time from $t = 4$ to $t = 4.2$.

64. A particle moves in a straight line according to the law $s = t^3 + 3\,t^2 - 6\,t + 4$, where s is in feet and t is in seconds. Its velocity when $t = 10$ is to be found. If an error of .01 is made in measuring t, what is the approximate error in the computed velocity?

65. Find approximately the value of $x^4 + 4\,x^2 + 1$ when $x = 2.0003$ and when $x = 1.9997$.

66. The edge of a cube is 2.0001 in. Find approximately its surface.

67. If t is time in seconds, v the velocity of a moving body in feet per second, and $v = 200 - 32\,t$, how far will the body move in the first 5 sec.?

68. If $v = 200 - 32\,t$, where v is the velocity of a moving body in feet per second and t is time in seconds, how far will the body move in the fifth second?

69. A curve passes through the point $(2, -3)$, and its slope at any point is equal to 3 more than twice the abscissa of the point. Find the equation of the curve.

70. At any point of a curve its slope is $8 - 2\,x - 3\,x^2$. Find the equation of the curve which passes through the point $(-2, 4)$, and sketch the curve.

71. The slope of a curve at any point is $3\,x^2 - 2\,x - 1$, and the curve passes through the point $(1, 0)$. Find the equation of the curve and sketch the curve.

72. The slope of a curve at any point is $12 - 3\,x^2$, and the curve crosses the axis of x at the point $x = 4$. Find the equation of the curve and sketch the curve.

CHAPTER III

SUMMATION

21. Area. An important application of integration occurs in the problem of finding an area bounded as follows:

Let RS (Fig. 21) be any curve with the equation $y = f(x)$, and let ED and BC be any two ordinates. It is required to find the area bounded by the curve RS, the two ordinates ED and BC, and the axis of x.

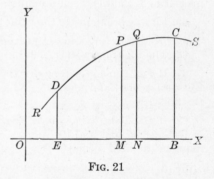

FIG. 21

Take MP, any variable ordinate between ED and BC, and let us denote by A the area $EMPD$ bounded by the curve, the axis of x, the fixed ordinate ED, and the variable ordinate MP.

It is evident that as values are assigned to $x = OM$, different positions of MP and corresponding values of A are determined. Hence A is a function of x. To determine this function we shall first find $\dfrac{dA}{dx}$.

Take $MN = \Delta x$ and draw the corresponding ordinate NQ. Then the area $MNQP = \Delta A$. If L is the length of the longest ordinate of the curve between MP and NQ, and l is the length of the shortest ordinate in the same region, it is evident that

$$l\,\Delta x \leq \Delta A \leq L\,\Delta x,$$

for $L\,\Delta x$ is the area of a rectangle entirely surrounding ΔA, and $l\,\Delta x$ is the area of a rectangle entirely included in ΔA.

Dividing by Δx, we have

$$l < \frac{\Delta A}{\Delta x} < L.$$

56

As Δx approaches zero, NQ approaches coincidence with MP, and hence l and L, which are always between NQ and MP, approach coincidence with MP. Hence at the limit we have

$$\frac{dA}{dx} = MP = y = f(x). \tag{1}$$

Therefore, by integrating,

$$A = F(x) + C, \tag{2}$$

where $F(x)$ is used simply as a symbol for any function whose derivative is $f(x)$.

We must now find C. As in § 20, the value of C is not determined by the integration but depends upon the position of the left-hand boundary from which A is measured. If we wish to measure the area from ED and let $OE = a$, then when MP coincides with ED, the area is zero. That is, when

$$x = a, \ A = 0.$$

Substituting in (2), we have

$$0 = F(a) + C;$$

whence $\qquad\qquad C = -F(a),$

and therefore (2) becomes

$$A = F(x) - F(a) \tag{3}$$

and we have A expressed as a function of x.

If in (3) we place $x = b$, we have

$$A = F(b) - F(a), \tag{4}$$

a formula in which A is now the area bounded on the left by the ordinate $x = a$ and on the right by the ordinate $x = b$. If, in Fig. 21, $OB = b$, then (4) is the area $EBCD$ which we set out to find.

In solving problems the student is advised to begin with formula (1) and follow the method of the text, as shown in the following example:

Example. Find the area bounded by the axis of x, the curve $y = \frac{1}{3} x^2$, and the ordinates $x = 1$ and $x = 3$.

In Fig. 22, BE is the line $x = 1$, CD is the line $x = 3$, and the required area is the area $BCDE$.

Then, by (1),

$$\frac{dA}{dx} = \frac{1}{3} x^2;$$

whence $A = \frac{1}{9} x^3 + C.$

When $x = 1$, $A = 0$, and therefore

$$0 = \frac{1}{9} + C;$$

whence $C = -\frac{1}{9},$

and $A = \frac{1}{9} x^3 - \frac{1}{9}.$

Finally, when $x = 3$,

$$A = \frac{1}{9}(3)^3 - \frac{1}{9} = 2\frac{8}{9}.$$

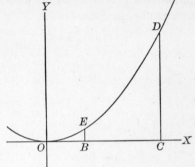

Fig. 22

EXERCISES

1. Find the area bounded by the curve $y = 10\,x - 3\,x^2$, the axis of x, and the lines $x = 1$ and $x = 3$.

2. Find the area bounded by the curve $y = x^2 - 6\,x + 18$, the axis of x, and the lines $x = -4$ and $x = -1$.

3. Find the area bounded by the curve $y = 16 + 12\,x - x^3$, the axis of x, and the lines $x = -1$ and $x = 3$.

4. Find the area bounded by the curve $y + x^2 - 4 = 0$ and the axis of x.

5. Find the area bounded by the curve $y + 2\,x + x^2 = 0$ and the axis of x.

6. Find each of the areas bounded by the curve $y = 6\,x^2 - x^3$, the axis of x, and the line $x = 2$.

7. Find the area bounded by the axis of x, the axis of y, and the curve $9\,y = x^2 + 4\,x + 4$.

8. Find the area bounded by the curve $y = 8 + 4\,x - 2\,x^2 - x^3$ and the axis of x.

22. Area by summation. Let us consider the problem of finding the area bounded by the curve $y = \frac{1}{5} x^2$, the axis of x, and the ordinates $x = 2$ and $x = 3$ (Fig. 23). This may be solved by the method of § 21; but we wish to show that it may also be considered as a problem in summation, since the area is approximately equal to the sum of the areas of a number of rectangles constructed as follows:

We divide the axis of x between $x = 2$ and $x = 3$ into 10 equal parts, each of which we call Δx, so that $\Delta x = \dfrac{3 - 2}{10} = .1$. If x_1 is the first point of divi-

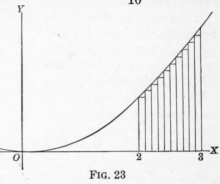

sion, x_2 the second point, and so on, and rectangles are constructed as shown in the figure, then the altitude of the first rectangle is $\frac{1}{5}(2)^2$, that of the second rectangle is $\frac{1}{5} x_1{}^2 = \frac{1}{5}(2.1)^2 = .882$, and so on. The area of the first rectangle is $\frac{1}{5}(2)^2 \Delta x = .08$, that of

FIG. 23

the second rectangle is $\frac{1}{5} x_1{}^2 \Delta x = \frac{1}{5}(2.1)^2 \Delta x = .0882$, and so on.

Accordingly we make the following calculation:

$x = 2,$	$\frac{1}{5}(2)^2 \Delta x = \ .08$
$x_1 = 2.1,$	$\frac{1}{5}(x_1)^2 \Delta x = \ .0882$
$x_2 = 2.2,$	$\frac{1}{5}(x_2)^2 \Delta x = \ .0968$
$x_3 = 2.3,$	$\frac{1}{5}(x_3)^2 \Delta x = \ .1058$
$x_4 = 2.4,$	$\frac{1}{5}(x_4)^2 \Delta x = \ .1152$
$x_5 = 2.5,$	$\frac{1}{5}(x_5)^2 \Delta x = \ .1250$
$x_6 = 2.6,$	$\frac{1}{5}(x_6)^2 \Delta x = \ .1352$
$x_7 = 2.7,$	$\frac{1}{5}(x_7)^2 \Delta x = \ .1458$
$x_8 = 2.8,$	$\frac{1}{5}(x_8)^2 \Delta x = \ .1568$
$x_9 = 2.9,$	$\frac{1}{5}(x_9)^2 \Delta x = \ \underline{.1682}$
	1.2170

This is a first approximation to the area.

For a better approximation the axis of x between $x = 2$ and $x = 3$ may be divided into 20 parts with $\Delta x = .05$. The result is 1.2418. If the base of the required figure is divided into 100 parts with $\Delta x = .01$, the sum of the areas of the 100 rectangles constructed as above is 1.26167.

The larger the number of parts into which the base of the figure is divided, the more nearly is the required area obtained. In fact, the required area is the limit approached as the number of parts is indefinitely increased and the size of Δx approaches zero.

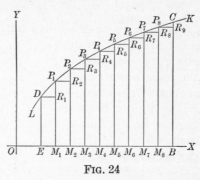

We shall now proceed to generalize the problem just handled. Let LK (Fig. 24) be a curve with equation $y = f(x)$, and let $OE = a$ and $OB = b$. It is required to find the area bounded by the curve LK, the axis of x, and the ordinates at E and B.

FIG. 24

For convenience we assume in the first place that $a < b$ and that $f(x)$ is positive for all values of x between a and b. We will divide the line EB into n equal parts by placing $\Delta x = \dfrac{b-a}{n}$ and laying off lengths $EM_1 = M_1M_2 = M_2M_3 = \cdots = M_{n-1}B = \Delta x$ (in Fig. 24, $n = 9$).

Let $OM_1 = x_1$, $OM_2 = x_2$, $\cdots$, $OM_{n-1} = x_{n-1}$. Draw $ED = f(a)$, $M_1P_1 = f(x_1)$, $M_2P_2 = f(x_2)$, $\cdots$, $M_{n-1}P_{n-1} = f(x_{n-1})$, and BC; also DR_1, P_1R_2, P_2R_3, $\cdots$, $P_{n-1}R_n$, parallel to OX. Then

$f(a)\Delta x =$ the area of the rectangle EDR_1M_1,

$f(x_1)\Delta x =$ the area of the rectangle $M_1P_1R_2M_2$,

$f(x_2)\Delta x =$ the area of the rectangle $M_2P_2R_3M_3$,

· · · · · · · · · · ·

$f(x_{n-1})\Delta x =$ the area of the rectangle $M_{n-1}P_{n-1}R_nB$.

The sum

$$f(a)\Delta x + f(x_1)\Delta x + f(x_2)\Delta x + \cdots + f(x_{n-1})\Delta x \qquad (1)$$

is then the sum of the areas of these rectangles and equal to the area of the polygon $EDR_1P_1R_2 \cdots R_{n-1}P_{n-1}R_nB$. It is evident that the limit of this sum as n is indefinitely increased is the area bounded by ED, EB, BC, and the arc DC.

The sum (1) is expressed concisely by the notation

$$\sum_{i=0}^{i=n-1} f(x_i)\Delta x,$$

where Σ (sigma), the Greek form of the letter S, stands for the word "sum," and the whole expression indicates that the sum is to be taken of all terms obtained from $f(x_i)\Delta x$ by giving to i in succession the values 0, 1, 2, 3, $\cdots$, $n-1$, where $x_0 = a$.

The limit of this sum as n is indefinitely increased is expressed by the symbol

$$\int_a^b f(x)dx,$$

where $\int$ is a modified form of S; that is,

$$\int_a^b f(x)dx = \operatorname*{Lim}_{n\to\infty} \sum_{i=0}^{i=n-1} f(x_i)\Delta x, \tag{2}$$

and therefore if we denote the area $EBCD$ by A,

$$A = \int_a^b f(x)dx. \tag{3}$$

We have found in § 21 that the area $EBCD$ is $F(b) - F(a)$, and shall express this as $[F(x)]_a^b$, where $F(x)$ is any function whose derivative is $f(x)$. We have then, finally,

$$A = \int_a^b f(x)dx = [F(x)]_a^b = F(b) - F(a). \tag{4}$$

It is evident that the result is not vitiated if ED or BC is of length zero.

The expression $f(x)dx$ which appears in formula (3) is called the *element of area*. It is obviously equal to $dF(x)$. In fact, it follows at once from § 21 that

$$dA = y\,dx = f(x)dx. \tag{5}$$

In applying (4) it is usually desirable to take a as the smaller of the two quantities a and b. Then Δx in (2) is positive. If the curve $y = f(x)$ lies above the axis of x, as in Fig. 24, all the factors $f(x_i)$ are positive and all the products $f(x_i)\Delta x$ in (2) are positive, and hence the area A in (4) is positive. If the curve lies entirely below the axis of x, $f(x_i)$ is negative, all products $f(x_i)\Delta x$

are negative, and hence A computed from (4) has a negative sign. If the curve lies partly above and partly below the axis of x, it is necessary to find each area separately, as formula (4) would give the algebraic sum of the areas (see Example 2).

Example 1. The example of the text may now be completely solved. The required area is

$$\int_2^3 \frac{x^2}{5} dx = \left[\frac{x^3}{15}\right]_2^3 = \frac{27}{15} - \frac{8}{15} = \frac{19}{15} = 1\frac{4}{15}.$$

Example 2. Find the area bounded by the curve $y = x^3 - x^2 - 6x$ and the axis of x.

Plotting the curve (Fig. 25), we see that it crosses the axis of x at the points $B(-2, 0)$, $O(0, 0)$, and $C(3, 0)$. Hence part of the area is above the axis of x and part below. Accordingly, we shall find it necessary to solve the problem in two parts, first finding the area above the axis of x and then finding that below. To find the first area we proceed as in the text, dividing the area up into elementary rectangles for each of which

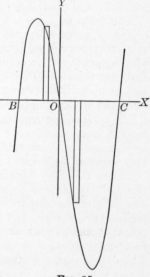

$$dA = y\, dx = (x^3 - x^2 - 6x)dx;$$

whence $A = \int_{-2}^{0} (x^3 - x^2 - 6x)dx$

$$= \left[\tfrac{1}{4} x^4 - \tfrac{1}{3} x^3 - 3x^2\right]_{-2}^{0}$$

$$= 0 - \left[\tfrac{1}{4}(-2)^4 - \tfrac{1}{3}(-2)^3 - 3(-2)^2\right] = 5\tfrac{1}{3}.$$

Similarly, for the area below the axis of x we find, as before,

$$dA = y\, dx = (x^3 - x^2 - 6x)dx.$$

But in this case $y = x^3 - x^2 - 6x$ is negative and hence dA is negative, for we are making x vary from 0 to 3, and

FIG. 25

therefore dx is positive. Therefore we expect to find the result of the summation negative. In fact, we have

$$A = \int_0^3 (x^3 - x^2 - 6x)dx = \left[\tfrac{1}{4} x^4 - \tfrac{1}{3} x^3 - 3x^2\right]_0^3$$

$$= \left[\tfrac{1}{4}(3)^4 - \tfrac{1}{3}(3)^3 - 3(3)^2\right] - 0 = -15\tfrac{3}{4}.$$

As we are asked to compute the total area bounded by the curve and the axis of x, we discard the negative sign in the last summation and add $5\frac{1}{3}$ and $15\frac{3}{4}$, thus obtaining $21\frac{1}{12}$ as the required result.

If we had computed the definite integral

$$\int_{-2}^{3}(x^3 - x^2 - 6\,x)dx,$$

we should have obtained the result $-10\frac{5}{12}$, which is the algebraic sum of the two portions of area computed separately.

Example 3. Find the area bounded by the two curves $y = x^2$ and $y = 8 - x^2$.

We draw the curves (Fig. 26)

$$y = x^2 \tag{1}$$

and $\qquad y = 8 - x^2, \tag{2}$

and by solving their equations we find that they intersect at the points $P_1(2, 4)$ and $P_2(-2, 4)$.

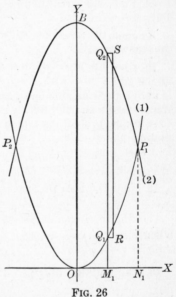

FIG. 26

The required area OP_1BP_2O is evidently twice the area OP_1BO, since both curves are symmetrical with respect to OY. Accordingly, we shall find the area OP_1BO and multiply it by 2. This latter area may be found by subtracting the area ON_1P_1O from the area ON_1P_1BO, each of these areas being found as in the previous example; or we may proceed as follows:

Divide ON_1 into n parts dx, and through the points of division draw straight lines parallel to OY, intersecting both curves. Let one of these lines be $M_1Q_1Q_2$. Through the points Q_1 and Q_2 draw straight lines parallel to OX until they meet the next vertical line to the right, forming the rectangle Q_1RSQ_2. The area of such a rectangle may be taken as dA and may be computed as follows: its base is dx and its altitude is $Q_1Q_2 = M_1Q_2 - M_1Q_1 = (8 - x^2) - x^2 = 8 - 2\,x^2$; for M_1Q_2 is the ordinate of a point on the curve (2) and M_1Q_1 the ordinate of a point on (1).

Therefore $\qquad dA = (8 - 2\,x^2)dx;$

whence $\qquad A = \int_{0}^{2}(8 - 2\,x^2)dx = [8\,x - \frac{2}{3}\,x^3]_{0}^{2}$

$$= [16 - \tfrac{1}{3}(16)] - 0 = 10\tfrac{2}{3}.$$

Finally, the required area is $2(10\frac{2}{3}) = 21\frac{1}{3}$.

EXERCISES

1. Find the area bounded by the curve $3y - x^2 - 3 = 0$, the axis of x, and the lines $x = -3$ and $x = 3$.

2. Find the area bounded by the curve $y = x^3 - 5x^2 + 3x + 10$, the axis of x, and the lines $x = 1$ and $x = 2$.

3. Find the area bounded by the curve $y = 16x - 8x^2 + x^3$ and the axis of x.

4. Find the area bounded by the axis of x and the curve $3y = 9 - x^2$.

5. Find the area bounded by the curve $y = 4x^2 - 4x - 15$ and the axis of x.

6. Find the area bounded below by the axis of x and above by the curve $y = x^3 - x^2 - 4x + 4$.

7. Find the area bounded by the curve $y = 4x^3 - 3x^2 - 16x + 12$ and the axis of x.

8. Find the area bounded by the curve $x^2 + 3y - 7 = 0$ and the straight line $2x + 3y - 4 = 0$.

9. Find the area bounded by the curve $3y = x^2 + 5$ and the straight line $x - 3y + 7 = 0$.

10. Find the area of the crescent-shaped figure bounded by the two curves $y = x^2 + 13$ and $y = 2x^2 + 4$.

11. Find the area bounded by the curves $y = 2x^2$ and $y = 36 - 2x^2$.

12. Find the area bounded by the curves $4y - x^2 - 4x - 4 = 0$ and $y = 1 - 4x - x^2$.

23. The definite integral. The formula

$$\int_a^b f(x)dx = F(b) - F(a), \tag{1}$$

obtained by the study of an area, may be given a much more general application. For if $f(x)$ is any function of x whatever, it may be graphically represented by the curve $y = f(x)$. The rectangles of Fig. 24 are then the graphical representations of the products $f(x)dx$, and the symbol $\int_a^b f(x)dx$ represents the limit of the sum of these products. We may accordingly say:

Any problem which requires the determination of the limit of the sum of products of the type $f(x)dx$ may be solved by the use of formula (1).

The limit of the sum (1), § 22, which is denoted by $\int_a^b f(x)dx$, is called a *definite integral*, and the numbers a and b are called the *lower limit* and the *upper limit*,* respectively, of the definite integral. The quantity $f(x)dx$ is called the *element of integration*.

On the other hand, the symbol $\int f(x)dx$ is called an *indefinite integral* and indicates the process of integration, as already defined in § 20.

Thus, from that section, we have

$$\int ax^n dx = \frac{ax^{n+1}}{n+1} + C,$$

$$\int a\,dx = ax + C,$$

and, in general, $\qquad \int f(x)dx = F(x) + C,$

where $F(x)$ is any function whose derivative is $f(x)$.

We may therefore express formula (1) in the following rule:

To find the value of $\int_a^b f(x)dx$, evaluate $\int f(x)dx$, substitute $x = b$ and $x = a$ successively, and subtract the latter result from the former.

It is to be noticed that in evaluating $\int f(x)dx$ the constant of integration is to be omitted, because if it is added, it disappears in the subtraction, since

$$[F(b) + C] - [F(a) + C] = F(b) - F(a).$$

Let us illustrate this by considering again the problem, already solved in § 20, of determining the distance traveled in the time from $t = t_1$ to $t = t_2$ by a body whose velocity v is known. Since

$$v = \frac{ds}{dt},$$

we have $\qquad\qquad ds = v\,dt,$

which is approximately the distance traveled in a small interval of time dt. Let the whole time from $t = t_1$ to $t = t_2$ be divided

---

* The student should notice that the word "limit" is here used in a sense quite different from that in which it is used when a variable is said to approach a limit (§ 1).

into a number of intervals each equal to dt. Then the total distance traveled is equal to the sum of the distances traveled in the several intervals dt, and hence is equal approximately to the sum of the several terms $v\,dt$. This approximation becomes better as the size of the intervals dt becomes smaller and their number larger, and we conclude that the limit of the sum of the terms $v\,dt$ is the actual distance traveled by the body. Hence we have, if s is the total distance traveled,

$$s = \int_{t_1}^{t_2} v\,dt.$$

If, now, we know v in terms of t, we may apply formula (1), but, as in the case of area, we must determine whether or not v has the same sign throughout the interval of time considered.

Example 1. If $v = 16\,t + 5$, find the distance traveled in the time from $t = 2$ to $t = 4$.

Since v is positive throughout the interval of time from $t = 2$ to $t = 4$, we have directly

$$s = \int_2^4 (16\,t + 5)dt = [8\,t^2 + 5\,t]_2^4 = 106.$$

Example 2. If $v = 10\,t - 30$, find the distance traveled in the time from $t = 1$ to $t = 4$.

Writing $v = 10(t - 3)$, we see that v is negative before $t = 3$, and accordingly we set

$$s_1 = \int_1^3 (10\,t - 30)dt = [5\,t^2 - 30\,t]_1^3 = -20,$$

and

$$s_2 = \int_3^4 (10\,t - 30)dt = [5\,t^2 - 30\,t]_3^4 = 5.$$

Hence the total distance traveled is 25, 20 in the direction in which s decreases and 5 in the direction in which s increases.

EXERCISES

1. At any time t the velocity of a moving body is $6\,t^2 + 2\,t$ ft. per second. How far will it move in the first 4 sec.?

2. How far will the body in Ex. 1 move during the sixth second?

3. At any time t the velocity of a moving body is $4 + 3\,t - t^2$ ft. per second. Show that this velocity is positive during the interval from $t = -1$ to $t = 4$, and find how far the body moves during that interval.

4. At any time t the velocity of a moving body is $4\,t^2 - 6\,t - 4$ ft. per second. During what interval of time is the velocity negative, and how far will the body move during that interval?

5. At any time t the velocity of a moving body in feet per second is $64 - 2\,t$. How many feet will the body move in the first 40 sec.?

6. At any time the velocity of a moving body in feet per second is $3\,t^2 - 20\,t + 32$. How far does the body move in the time from $t = 3$ to $t = 5$?

7. The number of foot-pounds of work done in lifting a weight is the product of the weight in pounds and the distance in feet through which the weight is lifted. A cubic foot of water weighs $62\frac{1}{2}$ lb. Compute the work done in emptying a cylindrical tank of depth 6 ft. and radius 2 ft., considering it as the limit of the sum of the pieces of work done in lifting each thin layer of water to the top of the tank.

8. By the method of Ex. 7 find the work done in pumping to a distance of 10 ft. above the top of the tank the contents of a cylindrical tank of depth 10 ft. and radius 4 ft.

9. By the method of Ex. 7 find the work done in emptying of water a full conical receiver of altitude 12 ft. and radius 4 ft., the vertex of the cone being down and the water being emptied from the top.

24. Pressure. It is shown in physics that the pressure on one side of a plane surface of area A, immersed in a liquid at a uniform depth of h units below the surface of the liquid, is equal to whA, where w is the weight of a unit volume of the liquid. This may be remembered by noticing that whA is the weight of the column of the liquid which would be supported by the area A.

Since the pressure is the same in all directions, we can also determine the pressure on one side of a plane surface which is perpendicular to the surface of the liquid and hence is not at a uniform depth.

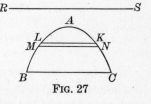

FIG. 27

Let ABC (Fig. 27) represent such a surface and RS the line of intersection of the plane of ABC with the surface of the liquid. Divide ABC into strips by drawing straight lines parallel to RS. Call the area of one of these strips dA, as in § 22, and the depth of one edge h. Then, since the strip is narrow and horizontal, the depth of every point differs only slightly from h, and the pressure on the strip is then approximately $wh\,dA$. Taking P as the total pressure, we write

$$dP = wh\,dA.$$

The total pressure P is the sum of the pressures on the several strips and is therefore the limit of the sum of terms of the form $wh\,dA$, the limit being approached as the number of the strips is indefinitely increased and the width of each indefinitely decreased. Therefore

$$P = \int wh\,dA,$$

where the limits of integration are to be taken so as to include the whole area on which the pressure is to be determined. To evaluate the integral it is necessary to express both h and dA in terms of the same variable.

Example 1. Find the pressure on one side of a rectangle $BCDE$ (Fig. 28), where the sides BC and ED are each 4 ft. long, the sides BE and CD are each 3 ft. long, immersed in water so that the plane of the rectangle is perpendicular to the surface of the water, and the side BC is parallel to the surface of the water and 2 ft. below it.

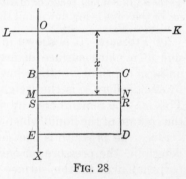

Fig. 28

In Fig. 28, LK is the line of intersection of the surface of the water and the plane of the rectangle. Let O be the point of intersection of LK and BE produced. Then, if x is measured downward from O along BE, x has the value 2 at the point B and the value 5 at the point E.

We now divide BE into parts dx, and through the points of division draw straight lines parallel to BC, thus dividing the given rectangle into elementary rectangles such as $MNRS$.

Therefore $\quad dA = $ area of $MNRS = MN \cdot MS = 4\,dx$.

Since MN is at a distance x below LK, the pressure on the elementary rectangle $MNRS$ is approximately $wx(4\,dx)$. Accordingly, we have $\qquad dP = 4\,wx\,dx$

and $\quad P = \displaystyle\int_2^5 4\,wx\,dx = [2\,wx^2]_2^5 = 2\,w(5)^2 - 2\,w(2)^2 = 42\,w.$

For water, $w = 62\frac{1}{2}$ lb. $= \frac{1}{32}$ T.

Hence we have, finally, $P = 2625$ lb. $= 1\frac{5}{16}$ T.

Example 2. The base CD (Fig. 29) of a triangle BCD is 7 ft., and its altitude from B to CD is 5 ft. This triangle is immersed in water with its plane perpendicular to the surface of the water and with CD parallel to the surface and 1 ft. below it, B being below CD. Find the total pressure on one side of this triangle.

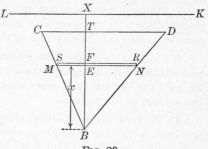

FIG. 29

Let LK represent the line of intersection of the plane of the triangle and the surface of the water. Then B is 6 ft. below LK. Let BX be perpendicular to LK and intersect CD at T. We will measure distances from B in the direction BX and denote them by x. Then, at the point B, x has the value 0; and at T, x has the value 5.

Divide the distance BT into parts dx; through the points of division draw straight lines parallel to CD, and on each of these lines as lower base construct a rectangle such as $MNRS$, where E and F are two consecutive points of division on BX.

Then $\qquad\qquad BE = x,$

$\qquad\qquad\qquad\quad EF = dx,$

and, by similar triangles, $\quad \dfrac{MN}{CD} = \dfrac{BE}{BT}$;

whence $\qquad\qquad\qquad \dfrac{MN}{7} = \dfrac{x}{5}$

and $\qquad\qquad\qquad MN = \frac{7}{5}x.$

Then $\qquad dA = $ the area of $MNRS = \frac{7}{5}x\,dx.$

Since B is 6 ft. below LK, and $BE = x$, it follows that E is $(6-x)$ ft. below LK.

Hence the pressure on the rectangle is approximately

$$dP = \left(\tfrac{7}{5}x\,dx\right)(6-x)w = \left(\tfrac{42}{5}wx - \tfrac{7}{5}wx^2\right)dx,$$

and $\quad P = \int_0^5 \left(\tfrac{42}{5}wx - \tfrac{7}{5}wx^2\right)dx = \left[\tfrac{21}{5}wx^2 - \tfrac{7}{15}wx^3\right]_0^5$

$\qquad = (105\,w - \tfrac{175}{3}w) - 0 = \tfrac{140}{3}w = 2916\frac{2}{3}$ lb. $= 1\frac{11}{24}$ T.

EXERCISES

1. A gate in the side of a dam is in the form of a square 3 ft. on a side, the upper side being parallel to and 12 ft. below the surface of the water in the reservoir. What is the pressure on the gate?

2. Find the total pressure on one side of a triangle of base 3 ft. and altitude 9 ft., submerged in water so that the altitude is vertical and the vertex is in the surface of the water.

3. Find the total pressure on one side of a triangle of base 8 ft. and altitude 6 ft., submerged in water so that the base is horizontal, the altitude vertical, and the vertex above the base and 8 ft. below the surface of the water.

4. The base of an isosceles triangle is 6 ft. and the equal sides are each 5 ft. The triangle is completely immersed in water, its base being parallel to and 8 ft. below the surface of the water, its altitude being perpendicular to the surface of the water, and its vertex being above the base. Find the total pressure on one side of the triangle.

5. Find the pressure on one side of an equilateral triangle 8 ft. on a side, if it is partly submerged in water so that one vertex is 2 ft. above the surface of the water, the corresponding altitude being perpendicular to the surface of the water.

6. The gate in Ex. 1 is strengthened by a brace which runs diagonally from one corner to another. Find the pressure on each of the two portions of the gate — one above, the other below, the brace.

7. A dam is in the form of a trapezoid, with its two horizontal sides 200 and 100 ft. respectively, the longer side being at the top; and the height is 20 ft. What is the pressure on the dam when the water is level with the top of the dam?

8. Compare the pressures on the two portions of the dam in Ex. 7 respectively above and below a straight line parallel to the top and the bottom of the dam and midway between them.

9. What is the pressure on the dam of Ex. 7 when the water reaches halfway to the top of the dam?

10. If it had been necessary to construct the dam of Ex. 7 with the shorter side at the top instead of the longer side, how much pressure would the dam have had to sustain when the reservoir was full of water?

11. The centerboard of a yacht is in the form of a trapezoid in which the two parallel sides are 2 ft. and 4 ft., respectively, in length, and a side perpendicular to these two is 3 ft. in length. Assuming that the last-named side is parallel to the surface of the water at a depth of 3 ft., and that the parallel sides are vertical, find the pressure on one side of the board.

12. Where shall a horizontal line be drawn across the gate of Ex. 1 so that the pressure on the portion above the line shall equal the pressure on the portion below?

25. Volume. The volume of a solid may be computed by dividing it into n elements of volume, dV, and taking the limit of the sum of these elements as n is increased indefinitely, the magnitude of each element at the same time approaching zero. The question in each case is the determination of the form of the element dV. We shall discuss a comparatively simple case of a solid such as is shown in Fig. 30.

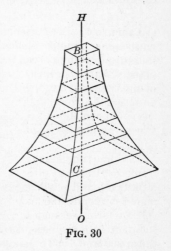

In this figure let OH be a straight line, and let the distance of any point of it from O be denoted by h. At one end the solid is bounded by a plane perpendicular to OH at C, where $OC = a$, and at the other end it is bounded by a plane perpendicular to OH at B, where $OB = b$, so that it has *parallel bases*.

Fig. 30

The solid is assumed to be such that the area A of any plane section made by a plane perpendicular to OH at a point distant h from O can be expressed as a function of h.

To find the volume of such a solid we divide the distance CB into n parts dh, and through the points of division pass planes perpendicular to OH. We have thus divided the solid into slices of which the thickness is dh.

Since A is the area of the base of a slice, and since the volume of the slice is approximately equal to the product of its base and thickness, we write

$$dV = A\,dh.$$

The volume of the solid is then the limit of the sum of terms of this type, and therefore

$$V = \int_a^b A \, dh.$$

It is clear that the foregoing discussion is valid even when one or both of the bases corresponding to $h = a$ and $h = b$, respectively, reduces to a point.

This method of finding volumes is particularly useful when the sections of the solid made by parallel planes are bounded by circles or by concentric circles. If such a solid is generated by the revolution of a plane area around an axis in its plane, it is called a *solid of revolution*.

Example 1. Let OY (Fig. 31) be an edge of a solid such that all its sections made by planes perpendicular to OY are rectangles, the sides of a rectangle in a plane distant y from O being respectively $2y$ and y^2. We shall find the volume included between the planes $y = 0$ and $y = 2\frac{1}{2}$.

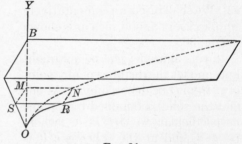

FIG. 31

Dividing the distance from $y = 0$ to $y = 2\frac{1}{2}$ into n parts dy, and passing planes perpendicular to OY, we form rectangles such as $MNRS$, where, if $OM = y$, $MN = y^2$, and $MS = 2y$. Hence the area $MNRS = 2y^3$, and the volume of the slice standing on $MNRS$ as a base is $2y^3 \, dy$; that is,

$$dV = 2y^3 \, dy.$$

Therefore $\qquad V = \int_0^{2\frac{1}{2}} 2y^3 \, dy = [\tfrac{1}{2}y^4]_0^{2\frac{1}{2}} = 19\tfrac{17}{32}.$

Example 2. The axes of two equal right circular cylinders of radius a intersect at right angles. Required the volume common to the two cylinders.

Let OA and OB (Fig. 32) be the axes of the cylinders and OY the common perpendicular to OA and OB at their point of intersection O. Then OAD and OBD are quadrants of two equal circles cut from the two cylinders by the planes through OY perpendicular to the axes OB and OA, and $OD = a$. Then the figure represents one eighth of the required volume.

We divide the distance OD into n parts dy, and through the points of division pass planes perpendicular to OY. Any section, such as $LMNP$, is a square, of which one side NP is equal to $\sqrt{\overline{OP}^2 - \overline{ON}^2}$. $OP = a$, being a radius of one of the cylinders, and hence, as $ON = y$,

$$NP = \sqrt{a^2 - y^2}.$$

Accordingly, the area of $LMNP = a^2 - y^2$, and the volume of the slice standing on $LMNP$ as a base is

$$dV = (a^2 - y^2)dy;$$

whence

$$V = \int_0^a (a^2 - y^2)dy = [a^2 y - \tfrac{1}{3} y^3]_0^a = \tfrac{2}{3} a^3.$$

Hence the total volume is $\tfrac{16}{3} a^3$.

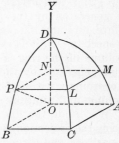

FIG. 32

Example 3. Find the volume of the solid generated by revolving about OX the area bounded by the curve $y^2 = 4\,x$, the axis of x, and the line $x = 3$.

The generating area is shown in Fig. 33, where AB is the line $x = 3$. Hence $OA = 3$.

Divide OA into n parts dx, and through the points of division pass straight lines parallel to OY, meeting the curve. When the area is revolved about OX, each of these lines, as MP, NQ, etc., generates a circle, the plane of which is perpendicular to OX. The area of the circle generated by MP, for example, is $\pi\overline{MP}^2$, which is equal to $\pi y^2 = \pi(4\,x)$ if $OM = x$.

Hence the area of any plane section of the solid made by a plane perpendicular to OX can be expressed in terms

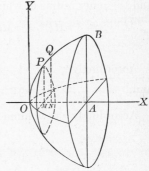

FIG. 33

of its distance from O, and we may apply the previous method for finding the volume.

Since the base of any slice is $4\,\pi x$ and its thickness is dx, we have

$$dV = 4\,\pi x\,dx.$$

Hence $\qquad V = \int_0^3 4\,\pi x\,dx = [2\,\pi x^2]_0^3 = 18\,\pi.$

Example 4. Find the volume of the ring solid generated by revolving about the axis of x the area bounded by the line $y = 5$ and the curve $y = 9 - x^2$.

The line and the curve (Fig. 34) are seen to intersect at the points $P_1(-2, 5)$ and $P_2(2, 5)$, and the ring is generated by the area $P_1BP_2P_1$. Since this area is symmetrical with respect to OY, it is evident that the volume of the ring is twice the volume generated by the area AP_2BA. Accordingly we shall find the latter volume and multiply it by 2.

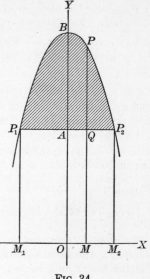

FIG. 34

We divide the line $OM_2 = 2$ (M_2 being the projection of P_2 on OX) into n parts dx, and through the points of division draw straight lines parallel to OY and intersecting the straight line and the curve. One of these lines, as MQP, will, when revolved about OX, generate a circular ring, the outer radius of which is $MP = y = 9 - x^2$ and the inner radius of which is $MQ = y = 5$. Hence the area of the ring is

$$\pi \overline{MP}^2 - \pi \overline{MQ}^2 = \pi(9 - x^2)^2 - \pi(5)^2$$

$$= \pi(56 - 18\,x^2 + x^4).$$

Accordingly, $\qquad dV = \pi(56 - 18\,x^2 + x^4)dx,$

and $\quad V = \int_0^2 \pi(56 - 18\,x^2 + x^4)dx = \pi\,[56\,x - 6\,x^3 + \tfrac{1}{5}\,x^5]_0^2 = 70\tfrac{2}{5}\,\pi.$

Accordingly the volume of the ring is $2(70\tfrac{2}{5}\,\pi) = 140\tfrac{4}{5}\,\pi.$

EXERCISES

1. The section of a certain solid made by any plane perpendicular to a given line OH is a circle with one point in OH and its center on a straight line OB intersecting OH at an angle of 60°. If the height of this solid measured from O along OH is 4 ft., find its volume by integration.

2. A solid is such that any cross section perpendicular to an axis is an equilateral triangle of which each side is equal to the square of the distance of the plane of the triangle from a fixed point on the axis. The total length of the axis from the fixed point is 6. Find the volume.

3. Find the volume of the solid generated by revolving about OX the area bounded by OX and the curve $y = 3x - x^2$.

4. Find the volume of the solid generated by revolving about OX the area included between the axis of x and the curve $y = 2x^2 + x^3$.

5. Find the volume of the solid generated by revolving about the line $y = -3$ the area bounded by the axis of y, the lines $x = 5$ and $y = -3$, and the curve $y = 5x^2$.

6. On a spherical ball of radius 3 in. two great circles are drawn intersecting at right angles at the points A and B. The material of the ball is then cut away so that the sections perpendicular to AB are squares with their vertices on the two great circles. Find the volume left.

7. Find the volume generated by revolving about the line $x = 2$ the area bounded by the curve $y^2 = 8x$, the axis of x, and the line $x = 2$.

8. Any plane section of a certain solid made by a plane perpendicular to OY is a square of which the center lies on OY and two opposite vertices lie on the curve $y = 3x^2$. Find the volume of the solid if the extreme distance along OY is 6.

9. Find the volume generated by revolving about OY the area bounded by the curve $y^2 = 8x$ and the line $x = 2$.

10. Find the volume of the solid generated by revolving about OX the area bounded by the curves $y = 4x - x^2$ and $y = x^2 - 4x + 6$.

11. The cross section of a certain solid made by any plane perpendicular to OX is a circle with the ends of one of its diameters on the curves $y = x^2$ and $2y = x^2 + 4$. Find the volume of this solid between the points of intersection of the curves.

GENERAL EXERCISES

1. If A denotes the area bounded by the axis of y, the curve $x = f(y)$, and two straight lines $y = a$ and $y = b$ parallel to OX, show that
$$A = \int_a^b f(y)dy.$$

2. If A denotes the area bounded above by the curve $y = f(x)$ and below by the curve $y = F(x)$, show that
$$A = \int_a^b (f(x) - F(x))dx,$$

where $x = a$ and $x = b$ are either the abscissas of the points of intersection of the two curves, or the equations of two straight lines bounding the area at the left and the right. Show that the formula is correct even if part of the area is above OX and part below OX.

3. The curve $y = ax^2$ is known to pass through the point (h, k). Prove that the area bounded by the curve, the axis of x, and the line $x = h$ is $\frac{1}{3} hk$.

4. The curve $y^2 = ax$ is known to pass through the point (h, k). Prove that the area bounded by the curve, the axis of x, and the line $x = h$ is $\frac{2}{3} hk$.

5. Find the total area bounded by the curves $y^2 = 4 ax$ and $y^2 = 4 a^2 - 4 ax$.

6. Find the total area bounded by the curve $y^2 - 4y - x = 0$ and the axis of y.

✓**7.** Find the total area bounded by the curve $x = y^3 + y^2 - 6y$ and the axis of y.

8. Find the area bounded by the curve $y = x^2$ and the line $y = x + 12$.

9. Find the area bounded by the curve $y + 4x + x^2 = 0$ and the line $y = x$.

10. Find the area bounded by the curve $y = x^2 - 6x + 5$ and the line $3x + y - 15 = 0$.

✓**11.** Find the area bounded by the curves $x^2 + 2x + y - 2 = 0$ and $3x^2 + 6x - 4y - 13 = 0$.

12. The velocity in feet per second of a moving body at any time t is $t^2 - 4t + 6$. Show that the body is always moving in the direction in which s increases, and find how far it will move during the fourth second.

13. The velocity in feet per second of a moving body at any time t is $t^2 - 6t$. Show that after $t = 6$ the body will always move in the direction in which s increases, and find how far it will move in the time from $t = 7$ to $t = 9$.

✓**14.** At any time t the velocity in feet per second of a moving body is $t^2 - 8t + 15$. How many feet will the body move in the direction in which s decreases?

15. At any time t the velocity in feet per second of a moving body is $3 + 2t - t^2$. Find the total distance traversed in the first 5 sec.

16. At any time t the velocity in feet per second of a moving body is $t^2 - 10t + 21$. Find the total distance traversed in the first 10 sec.

17. At any time t the velocity in feet per second of a moving body is $10 - 7t + t^2$. Find the distance traversed in the interval from $t = 1$ to $t = 7$.

18. The water is 15 ft. deep in a well which is 50 ft. deep and 6 ft. in diameter. How much work must be done in pumping the well dry?

19. Find the work done in pumping all the water from a full hemispherical bowl of diameter 4 ft. to a height of 10 ft. above the level of the top of the bowl.

20. A tank is in the form of the frustum of a right circular cone, 10 ft. across the top, 6 ft. across the bottom, and 8 ft. deep. If the tank is full of water, how much work will be done in pumping the tank dry?

21. If a force of F pounds moves a body through a small distance, dx, measured in feet, the work done is $F\,dx$ foot-pounds. Show that if the force F is a function of x, the work done in moving the body from $x = a$ to $x = b$ is $\int_{a}^{b} F\,dx$.

22. Apply Ex. 21 to find the work done in stretching a spring $1\frac{1}{2}$ ft. from the unstretched position, it being known that the force needed at any time is proportional to the amount that the spring has been stretched.

23. Apply Ex. 21 to find the work done in lifting a bag of sand 100 ft., if the bag weighed originally 50 lb. and the sand leaked out so that the amount in the bag at any time was $50 - \frac{1}{2}x$, where x is the distance the bag had been lifted.

24. Prove that the pressure on one side of a rectangle completely submerged with its plane vertical is equal to the area of the rectangle multiplied by the depth of its center and by w (consider only the case in which one side of the rectangle is parallel to the surface).

25. Prove that the pressure on one side of a triangle completely submerged with its plane vertical is equal to its area multiplied by the depth of its median point and by w (consider only the case in which one side of the triangle is parallel to the surface).

26. Show by Ex. 24 that the pressure on a vertical strip of breadth dx and with one end at the surface of the liquid and the other at the depth y is $\dfrac{wy^2}{2}\,dx$.

27. Use Ex. 26 to find the pressure on a semicircle of radius a, the diameter of the semicircle being in the surface of the liquid and its plane being vertical.

28. The equal sides of an isosceles triangle are each 5 ft. long, and the length of the base is 6 ft. It is held in a vertical position in water, the vertex above the base, with its base parallel to and 2 ft. below the surface of the water. Find the pressure of the water on the part of the triangle which is under water.

29. The cross section of a ditch is in the form of an equilateral triangle, vertex down. The ditch is closed by a vertical dam. Determine the pressure on the dam when the water in the ditch is 3 ft. deep.

30. A square 4 ft. on a side is immersed in water, with one vertex in the surface of the water and with the diagonal through that vertex perpendicular to the surface of the water. How much greater is the pressure on the lower half of the square than that on the upper half?

31. The parallel sides of a trapezoid are, respectively, 2 ft. and 8 ft. long, and the nonparallel sides are each 5 ft. long. Find the pressure on one side of this trapezoid when it is immersed in water with its parallel sides vertical and its highest vertex 2 ft. below the surface of the water.

32. Find the pressure on one side of an area the equations of whose boundary lines are $x = 4$, $y = 0$, and $y^2 = 4\,x$ respectively, where the axis of x is taken in the surface of the water and where the positive direction of the y-axis is downward and vertical.

33. Derive by integration the formula $V = \frac{1}{3}\,\pi r^2 h$, where V is the volume of a right circular cone whose altitude is h and the radius of whose base is r.

34. Derive by integration the formula $V = \frac{1}{3}\,h(A_1 + A_2 + \sqrt{A_1 A_2})$, where V is the volume of the frustum of a right circular cone whose altitude is h and the areas of whose bases are, respectively, A_1 and A_2.

35. Derive by integration the formula $V = \frac{4}{3}\,\pi r^3$, where V is the volume of a sphere of radius r.

36. Derive by integration the formula $V = \pi(rh^2 - \frac{1}{3}\,h^3)$, where V is the volume of a segment of one base, and altitude h, cut from a sphere of radius r.

37. Derive by integration the formula $V = \frac{1}{6}\,\pi h(3\,r_1{}^2 + 3\,r_2{}^2 + h^2)$, where V is the volume of the segment of a sphere, the altitude of the segment and the radii of its bases being, respectively, h, r_1, and r_2.

38. Show that the volume of the solid generated by revolving about OY the area bounded by OX and the curve $y = a - bx^2$ is equal to the area of the base of the solid multiplied by half its altitude.

39. An axman makes a wedge-shaped cut in the trunk of a tree. Assuming that the trunk is a right circular cylinder of radius 8 in.,

that the lower surface of the cut is a horizontal plane, and that the upper surface is a plane inclined at an angle of 45° to the horizontal and intersecting the lower surface of the cut in a diameter, find the amount of wood cut out.

40. AB is a diameter of a spherical ball of radius 10 in. Through A and B are drawn semicircumferences of three great circles so that the diedral angle between the planes of each pair of adjacent semicircumferences is 120°. The material of the ball is then cut away so that the plane sections perpendicular to AB are equilateral triangles with their vertices on the semicircumferences. Find the volume left.

41. The cross section of a certain solid made by any plane perpendicular to OX is a square with the ends of one of its diagonals on the curves $y = 4 + x^2$ and $y = 2 x^2 - 5$. Find the volume of the solid between the points of intersection of the curves.

42. Find the volume generated by revolving about OX the area bounded by OX and the curve $y = 3 x - x^2$.

43. Find the volume generated by revolving about OX the area bounded by OX and the curve $y = x^3 - x^2 - 2 x$.

44. Find the volume generated by revolving about the line $y = -1$ the area bounded by the curves $y = 5 x^2$ and $y = 2 x^2 + 12$.

45. On a system of parallel chords of a circle of radius 3 there are constructed equilateral triangles with their planes perpendicular to the plane of the circle and on the same side of that plane, thus forming a solid. Find the volume of the solid.

46. A solid is such that any cross section perpendicular to an axis is a circle, with its radius equal to the square root of the distance of the section from a fixed point of the axis. The total length of the axis from the fixed point is 6. Find the volume of the solid.

47. The cross section of a certain solid made by any plane perpendicular to OY is a right isosceles triangle with the ends of its base on the curve $y = x^2 - 2$. Find the volume of this solid between the planes $y = -2$ and $y = 2$.

48. All sections of a certain solid made by planes perpendicular to OY are isosceles triangles. The base of each triangle is a line drawn perpendicular to OY, with its ends in the curve $y = 4 - x^2$. The altitude of each triangle is equal to its base. Find the volume of the solid included between the planes for which $y = 0$ and $y = 4$.

49. Compare the volumes generated by revolving the area bounded by OX and the curve $y = 3 x - x^2$ about the lines $y = -3$ and $y = 3$ as axes.

CHAPTER IV

ALGEBRAIC FUNCTIONS

26. Graphs. In the previous chapters we have used only polynomials in explaining and illustrating the fundamental ideas of differentiation and integration. We now wish to apply the same principles to general algebraic functions which may involve sums, products, fractions, and roots. We begin with the study of graphs which are more complicated than those of Chapter II.

In making any graph the final step is to substitute values of one variable in the equation of the graph, compute the corresponding values of the other variable, plot the corresponding points, and draw a curve through them. But a preliminary study of the equation will often give a general idea of the appearance of the graph and aid in determining what particular points should be found. It is accordingly suggested that the following plan of work be followed :

1. *Solve the equation* for one coördinate in terms of the other. We shall suppose in the following directions that the equation has been solved for y in terms of x.

2. Find the *axis of symmetry* parallel to OX if such exists. When y is equal to plus or minus the square root of a function of x, the graph is symmetrical with respect to OX. When y is equal to a constant, c, plus or minus the square root of a function of x, the line $y = c$ is an axis of symmetry.

3. Find the *intersections* with the axis of symmetry, or with the axis of x if no symmetry exists. This may be done by placing $y = c$ or $y = 0$, where c is as in 2.

4. Find *impossible values* of x. Values of x which make negative the expression under the square-root sign referred to in 2, cannot be used since they make y imaginary.

5. Find *asymptotes* parallel to OY if such exist. These may occur when the value of y found in 1 contains a fraction. If the denominator of such a fraction is zero when $x = a$, the value of y

is not defined, since we cannot divide by zero. We may, however, let $x \rightarrow a$. Then the value of y increases indefinitely and is said to become infinite. The graph then runs up or down indefinitely, approaching the line $x = a$ indefinitely near but never reaching it.

Now, *when a straight line has such a position with respect to a curve that as the two are indefinitely prolonged they do not meet, but the distance between them approaches zero as a limit, the straight line is called an asymptote of the curve.* Hence the line $x = a$ is an asymptote.

It may sometimes be more convenient to solve the equation for x in terms of y. In such a case x and y should be interchanged in the above directions. While it is generally sufficient to solve for either x or y alone, there are cases in which it is desirable to make both solutions, as the second solution may give us information which could not be obtained from the first solution.

Example 1. $y^2 = 8(x - 2)$.

Solving for y, we have $y = \pm \sqrt{8(x - 2)}$.

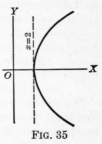

FIG. 35

The axis of x is an axis of symmetry since any value of x gives two values of y equal in magnitude but opposite in sign. The graph intersects the axis of x when $x = 2$. Any value of x less than 2 makes the quantity under the square-root sign negative and the value of y imaginary. Hence such values of x are impossible and the curve lies entirely to the right of the line $x = 2$. Assigning values to x greater than 2, computing values of y, and plotting points, we draw the curve (Fig. 35). This curve is a *parabola* (§ 33).

Example 2. $(y + 3)^2 = (x - 2)^2(x + 1)$.

Solving for y, we have
$$y = -3 \pm (x - 2)\sqrt{x + 1}.$$

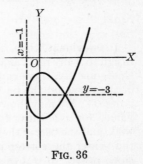

FIG. 36

In the first place we see that the line $y = -3$ is an axis of symmetry. The curve meets the axis of symmetry when $x = -1$ and $x = 2$. Since any value of x less than -1 makes y imaginary, only values of x greater than -1 can be used, and hence the curve lies entirely to the right of the line $x = -1$. Assigning values of x and locating the points determined, we have the curve (Fig. 36).

Example 3. $x^2 + 4y^2 - 2x - 8y + 1 = 0.$

Solving for y, we have

$$y = 1 \pm \tfrac{1}{2} \sqrt{(3 - x)(1 + x)}.$$

It appears that $y = 1$ is an axis of symmetry, which the curve intersects when $x = -1$ and $x = 3$. Values of x less than -1 or greater than 3 make the quantity under the radical sign negative, but values of x between -1 and 3 make the quantity under the radical sign positive. Hence the curve lies between the lines $x = -1$ and $x = 3$.

Again, solving for x, we have

$$x = 1 \pm 2 \sqrt{y(2 - y)}.$$

It appears that $x = 1$ is an axis of symmetry, which the curve intersects when $y = 0$ and $y = 2$. Values of y less than zero or greater than

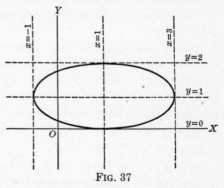

Fig. 37

2 make the quantity under the radical sign negative, while values of y between 0 and 2 make the quantity under the radical sign positive. Hence the curve lies between the axis of x and the line $y = 2$.

We now have the curve boxed up inside a certain rectangle, and we also know two axes of symmetry. It is necessary to compute only a few points and draw the rest of the curve by symmetry (Fig. 37).

Example 4. $xy = 4.$

Solving for y, we have

$$y = \frac{4}{x}.$$

It is evident, then, that we may assign to x any real value except zero. Consequently, there can be no point of the curve on the line $x = 0$; that is, on OY. We may, however, assume values for x as near to zero as we wish, and the nearer they are to zero,

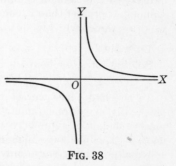

Fig. 38

the nearer the corresponding points are to OY; but as the points come nearer to OY they recede along the curve. Hence OY is an asymptote of the curve.

P_1 draw a straight line parallel to OX, and through P_2 draw a straight line parallel to OY, and denote their point of intersection by R.

Then $\qquad\qquad P_1R = \Delta x = x_2 - x_1$

and $\qquad\qquad RP_2 = \Delta y = y_2 - y_1.$

In the right triangle P_1RP_2

$$P_1P_2 = \sqrt{\overline{P_1R}^2 + \overline{RP_2}^2};$$

whence $\qquad P_1P_2 = \sqrt{(x_2 - x_1)^2 + (y_2 - y_1)^2}.$ $\qquad$ (1)

If $y_2 = y_1$, P_1P_2 is parallel to OX, and the formula reduces to

$$P_1P_2 = x_2 - x_1. \qquad\qquad (2)$$

In like manner, if $x_2 = x_1$, P_1P_2 is parallel to OY, and the formula reduces to $\qquad P_1P_2 = y_2 - y_1.$ $\qquad\qquad$ (3)

In §§ 28–32 we shall use these formulas to obtain general forms for the equations of certain curves. For the present we shall apply the formulas to finding the equations of curves defined by simple numerical data. Some of these examples are special cases of the more general discussions to follow.

Example 1. Find the equation of a circle with center at the point (2, 3) and radius equal to 5.

Let $P(x, y)$ (Fig. 42) be any point on the circle. By (1) the distance of the point from the center is $\sqrt{(x - 2)^2 + (y - 3)^2}$. But this distance is equal to the radius 5. Hence we have

$$\sqrt{(x - 2)^2 + (y - 3)^2} = 5,$$

which reduces to

$$x^2 + y^2 - 4x - 6y - 12 = 0.$$

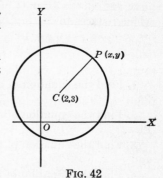

FIG. 42

Example 2. Find the equation of a curve such that the sum of the distances of any point on it from the two points $(-3, 0)$ and $(3, 0)$ is always equal to 8.

Let $P(x, y)$ (Fig. 43) be any point on the curve. Its distance from $(-3, 0)$ is $\sqrt{(x + 3)^2 + y^2}$, and its distance from $(3, 0)$ is $\sqrt{(x - 3)^2 + y^2}$. By the statement of the problem the sum of these distances is 8. Hence we have

$$\sqrt{(x + 3)^2 + y^2}$$
$$+ \sqrt{(x - 3)^2 + y^2} = 8.$$

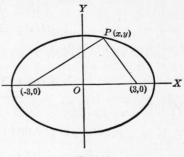

To simplify this equation we transpose the second radical to the right-hand side of the equation and square. A few simple reductions then give

$$3x - 16 = -4\sqrt{x^2 + y^2 - 6x + 9}.$$

Again square and reduce. We have $7x^2 + 16y^2 = 112,$

Fig. 43

the required equation.

Example 3. Find the equation of a curve such that any point on it is equally distant from the axis of x and from the point $(2, 3)$.

Let $P(x, y)$ (Fig. 44) be any point on the curve. Its distance from OX is $\pm y$. Its distance from $(2, 3)$ is $\sqrt{(x - 2)^2 + (y - 3)^2}$. Therefore

$$\pm y = \sqrt{(x - 2)^2 + (y - 3)^2},$$

which reduces to

$$x^2 - 4x - 6y + 13 = 0.$$

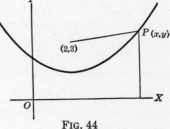

Fig. 44

EXERCISES

1. Find the equation of a circle with radius 6 and center $(-2, 3)$. Plot.

2. Find the equation of a circle with radius 5 and center $(-3, 4)$. Plot.

3. Find the equation of the locus of a point equidistant from $(1, 3)$ and $(-2, 5)$. Plot.

4. Find the equation of the locus of a point equidistant from $(0, 3)$ and $(5, 0)$. Plot.

5. A curve is such that the sum of the distances of any point on it from the two points $(2, 0)$ and $(-2, 0)$ is 12. Find its equation and graph.

6. A curve is such that the sum of the distances of any point on it from the two points $(0, 1)$ and $(0, -1)$ is 3. Find its equation and graph.

7. Find the equation of a curve such that any point on it is equidistant from $(4, 0)$ and the axis of y. Plot.

8. Find the equation of a curve such that any point on it is equidistant from $(4, 0)$ and the line $x = -4$. Plot.

9. Find the equation of a curve such that the distance of any point on it from $(3, 0)$ is twice its distance from OY. Plot.

10. A curve is such that the distance of any point on it from $(4, 0)$ is twice its distance from $(1, 0)$. Find its equation and graph.

28. Circle. Since a *circle* is the locus of a point which is always at a constant distance from a fixed point, formula (1), § 27, enables us to write down immediately the equation of a circle.

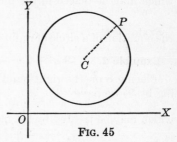

Let $C(h, k)$ (Fig. 45) be the center of a circle of radius r. Then, if $P(x, y)$ is any point of the circle, by (1), § 27, x and y must satisfy the equation

$$(x - h)^2 + (y - k)^2 = r^2. \quad (1)$$

FIG. 45

Moreover, any point the coördinates of which satisfy (1) must be at the distance r from C and hence be a point of the circle. Accordingly (1) is the equation of a circle.

If (1) is expanded, it becomes

$$x^2 + y^2 - 2hx - 2ky + h^2 + k^2 - r^2 = 0, \quad (2)$$

an equation of the second degree with no term in xy and with the coefficients of x^2 and y^2 equal.

Conversely, any equation of the second degree with no xy term and with the coefficients of x^2 and y^2 equal (as

$$Ax^2 + Ay^2 + 2Gx + 2Fy + C = 0, \quad (3)$$

where A, G, F, and C are any constants) may be transformed into the form (1) and represents a circle, unless the number corresponding to r^2 is negative (see Example 3), in which case the equation is satisfied by no real values of x and y and accordingly has no corresponding locus.

The circle is most readily drawn by making such transformation, locating the center, and constructing the circle with compasses.

Example 1. $\qquad x^2 + y^2 - 2\,x - 4\,y = 0.$

This equation may be written in the form
$$(x^2 - 2\,x \quad) + (y^2 - 4\,y \quad) = 0,$$
and the terms in the parentheses may be made perfect squares by adding 1 in the first parenthesis and 4 in the second parenthesis. As we have added a total of 5 to the left-hand side of the equation, we must add an equal amount to the right-hand side of the equation. The result is
$$(x^2 - 2\,x + 1) + (y^2 - 4\,y + 4) = 5,$$

which may be placed in the form
$$(x - 1)^2 + (y - 2)^2 = 5,$$
the equation of a circle of radius $\sqrt{5}$ with its center at the point $(1, 2)$.

Example 2. $\qquad 9\,x^2 + 9\,y^2 - 9\,x + 6\,y - 8 = 0.$

Placing 8 on the right-hand side of the equation and then dividing by 9, we have
$$x^2 + y^2 - x + \tfrac{2}{3}\,y = \tfrac{8}{9},$$

which may be treated by the method used in Example 1. The result is
$$(x - \tfrac{1}{2})^2 + (y + \tfrac{1}{3})^2 = \tfrac{5}{4},$$
the equation of a circle of radius $\tfrac{1}{2}\sqrt{5}$, with its center at $(\tfrac{1}{2}, -\tfrac{1}{3})$.

Example 3. $\qquad 9\,x^2 + 9\,y^2 - 6\,x + 12\,y + 11 = 0.$

Proceeding as in Example 2, we have, as the transformed equation,
$$(x - \tfrac{1}{3})^2 + (y + \tfrac{2}{3})^2 = -\tfrac{2}{3},$$

an equation which cannot be satisfied by any real values of x and y, since the sum of two positive quantities cannot be negative. Hence this equation corresponds to no real curve.

EXERCISES

1. Find the center and the radius of the circle
$$x^2 + y^2 + 4\,x - 10\,y + 13 = 0.$$

2. Find the center and the radius of the circle
$$3\,x^2 + 3\,y^2 - 4\,x + 2\,y - 5 = 0.$$

3. Find the equation of the straight line passing through the center of the circle $x^2 + y^2 + 2x - y + 1 = 0$ and perpendicular to the line
$$2x + 3y - 4 = 0.$$

4. Prove that two circles are concentric if their equations differ only in the constant term.

5. Show that $x^2 + y^2 + ax = 0$ is the equation of a circle with its center on OX and tangent to OY.

6. Find the equation of the locus of a point the square of whose distance from $(3, 0)$ is always twice its distance from OX. Show that the locus is a circle, and find its center and radius.

7. A point moves so that its distance from $(0, 4)$ is always three times its distance from $(0, -4)$. Show that its locus is a circle, and find the center and the radius of the circle.

8. Find the equation of the locus of a point whose distance from $(3, 0)$ is always twice its distance from $(-3, 0)$. Show that the locus is a circle, and find the center and the radius of the circle.

9. Find the length of the tangents drawn from $(4, 5)$ to the circle $x^2 + y^2 - 4x - 6y + 12 = 0$.

10. A point moves so that the squares of the lengths of the tangents drawn from it to the two circles $x^2 + y^2 = 4$ and $x^2 + y^2 = 25$ are inversely as the radii of these circles. Find the locus of the point.

29. Parabola. *The locus of a point equally distant from a fixed point and a fixed straight line is called a parabola.* The fixed point is called the *focus* and the fixed straight line is called the *directrix*.

Let F (Fig. 46) be the focus and RS the directrix of a parabola. Through F draw a straight line perpendicular to RS, intersecting it at D, and let this line be the axis of x. Let the middle point of DF be taken as O, the origin of coördinates, and draw the axis OY. Then, if the distance DF

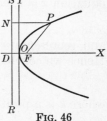

Fig. 46

is $2c$, the coördinates of F are $(c, 0)$ and the equation of RS is $x = -c$.

Let $P(x, y)$ be any point of the parabola, and draw the straight line FP and the straight line NP perpendicular to RS.

Then $\qquad\qquad\qquad NP = c + x,$

and, by § 27, $\qquad\qquad FP = \sqrt{(x - c)^2 + y^2}\,;$

whence, from the definition of the parabola,

$$(x - c)^2 + y^2 = (c + x)^2,$$

which reduces to $\qquad\quad y^2 = 4\,cx.$ $\qquad\qquad\qquad\qquad$ (1)

Conversely, if the coördinates of any point P satisfy (1), it can be shown that the distances FP and NP are equal, and hence P is a point of the parabola.

Solving (1) for y in terms of x, we have

$$y = \pm\, 2\,\sqrt{cx}.$$ $\qquad\qquad\qquad\qquad$ (2)

We assume that c is positive. Then it is evident from (2) that the parabola is symmetrical with respect to OX. Accordingly OX is called the *axis* of the parabola. The point at which a parabola intersects its axis is called the *vertex* of the parabola. Accordingly O is the vertex of the parabola.

It is also evident from (2) that only positive values may be assigned to x, and hence the parabola lies entirely on the positive side of the axis OY.

Accordingly we assign positive values to x, compute the corresponding values of y, and draw a smooth curve through the points thus located.

Returning to Fig. 46, if F is taken at the left of O with the coördinates $(-c, 0)$, and RS is taken at the right of O with the equation $x = c$, equation (1) becomes

$$y^2 = -\,4\,cx$$ $\qquad\qquad\qquad\qquad$ (3)

and represents a parabola lying on the negative side of OY. Hence we conclude that any equation in the form

$$y^2 = kx,$$ $\qquad\qquad\qquad\qquad$ (4)

where k is a positive or a negative constant, is a parabola, with its vertex at O, its axis on OX, its focus at the point $\left(\dfrac{k}{4}, 0\right)$, and its directrix the straight line $x = -\dfrac{k}{4}$.

Similarly, the equation $\quad x^2 = ky$ $\qquad\qquad\qquad$ (5)

represents a parabola, with its vertex at O and with its axis coinciding with the positive or the negative part of OY, according as k is positive or negative. The focus is always the point $\left(0, \dfrac{k}{4}\right)$, and the directrix is the line $y = -\dfrac{k}{4}$, whether k be positive or negative.

30. Parabolic segment. An important property of the parabola is contained in the following theorem :

The squares of any two chords of a parabola which are perpendicular to its axis are to each other as their distances from the vertex of the parabola.

This theorem may be proved as follows:

Let $P_1(x_1, y_1)$ and $P_2(x_2, y_2)$ be any two points of any parabola $y^2 = kx$ (Fig. 47).

Then $\qquad y_1^2 = kx_1$

and $\qquad y_2^2 = kx_2$;

whence $\qquad \dfrac{y_1^2}{y_2^2} = \dfrac{x_1}{x_2}$,

whence $\qquad \dfrac{(2\,y_1)^2}{(2\,y_2)^2} = \dfrac{x_1}{x_2}.$ $\qquad$ (1)

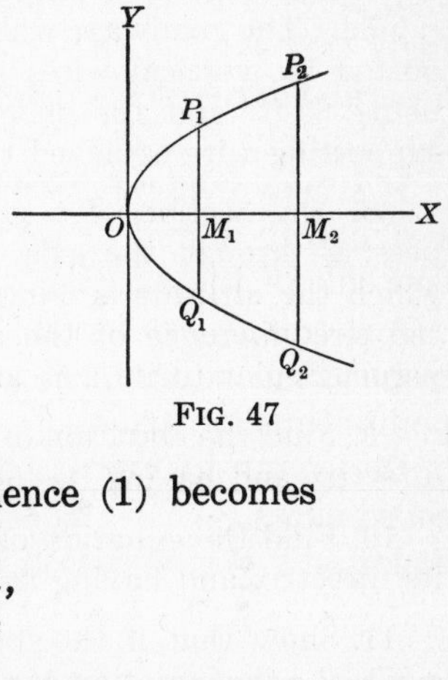

FIG. 47

From the symmetry of the parabola, $2\,y_1 = Q_1P_1$ and $2\,y_2 = Q_2P_2$. But $x_1 = OM_1$ and $x_2 = OM_2$, and hence (1) becomes

$$\frac{\overline{Q_1P_1}^2}{\overline{Q_2P_2}^2} = \frac{OM_1}{OM_2},$$

and the theorem is proved.

The property just proved does not depend upon the position of the parabola. It can therefore be used when the parabola so lies that none of the equations of § 29 applies.

The figure bounded by the parabola and a chord perpendicular to the axis of the parabola, as Q_1OP_1 (Fig. 47), is called a *parabolic segment*. The chord is called the *base* of the segment, the vertex of the parabola is called the *vertex* of the segment, and the distance from the vertex to the base is called the *altitude* of the segment.

EXERCISES

Plot the following parabolas, determining the focus of each:

1. $y^2 = -4x$.   3. $y^2 = 3x$.

2. $x^2 = 8y$.   4. $x^2 = -5y$.

5. The altitude of a parabolic segment is 8 ft., and the length of its base is 16 ft. A straight line drawn across the segment perpendicular to its axis is 12 ft. long. How far is it from the vertex of the segment?

6. An arch in the form of a parabolic curve, the axis being vertical, is 25 ft. across the bottom, and the highest point is 15 ft. above the horizontal. What is the length of a beam placed horizontally across the arch 6 ft. from the top?

7. The cable of a suspension bridge hangs in the form of a parabola. The roadway, which is horizontal and 500 ft. long, is supported by vertical wires attached to the cable, the longest wire being 80 ft. and the shortest being 20 ft. Find the length of a supporting wire attached to the roadway 75 ft. from the middle.

8. Any section of a given parabolic mirror made by a plane passing through the axis of the mirror is a parabolic segment of which the altitude is 6 in. and the length of the base 12 in. Find the circumference of the section of the mirror made by a plane perpendicular to its axis and 4 in. from its vertex.

9. Find the equation of the parabola having the line $x = 5$ as its directrix and having its focus at the origin of coördinates.

10. Find the equation of the parabola having the line $y = -3$ as its directrix and having its focus at the point $(2, 4)$.

11. Show that if the focus is at the origin and the directrix is $x = -2c$ the equation of the parabola is $y^2 = 4cx + 4c^2$.

12. Show that if the vertex of the parabola is at $(a, 0)$ and the focus at $(a + c, 0)$, the equation of the parabola is $y^2 = 4c(x - a)$.

31. Ellipse. *The locus of a point the sum of whose distances from two fixed points is constant is called an ellipse.* The two fixed points are called the *foci.*

Let F and F' (Fig. 48) be the two foci, and let the distance $F'F$ be $2c$. Let the straight line determined by F' and F be taken as the axis of x, and the middle point of $F'F$ be taken as

O, the origin of coördinates, and draw the axis OY. Then the coördinates of F' and F are, respectively, $(-c, 0)$ and $(c, 0)$.

Let $P(x, y)$ be any point of the ellipse, and let $2\,a$ represent the constant sum of its distances from the foci. Then, from the definition of the ellipse, the sum of the distances $F'P$ and FP is $2\,a$, and from the triangle $F'PF$ it is evident that $2\,a > 2\,c$; whence $a > c$.

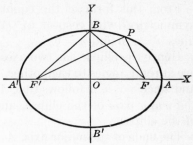

FIG. 48

By § 27,

$$F'P = \sqrt{(x+c)^2 + y^2},$$

and $$FP = \sqrt{(x-c)^2 + y^2};$$

whence, from the definition of the ellipse,

$$\sqrt{(x+c)^2 + y^2} + \sqrt{(x-c)^2 + y^2} = 2\,a. \qquad (1)$$

Clearing (1) of radicals, we have

$$(a^2 - c^2)x^2 + a^2y^2 = a^4 - a^2c^2. \qquad (2)$$

Dividing (2) by $a^4 - a^2c^2$, we have

$$\frac{x^2}{a^2} + \frac{y^2}{a^2 - c^2} = 1. \qquad (3)$$

But since $a > c$, $a^2 - c^2$ is a positive quantity which may be denoted by b^2, and (3) becomes

$$\frac{x^2}{a^2} + \frac{y^2}{b^2} = 1. \qquad (4)$$

Conversely, if the coördinates of any point P satisfy (4), it can be shown that the sum of the distances $F'P$ and FP is $2\,a$, and hence P is a point of the ellipse.

Solving (4) for y in terms of x, we have

$$y = \pm \frac{b}{a} \sqrt{a^2 - x^2}. \qquad (5)$$

From this form of the equation it appears that the ellipse has OX as an axis of symmetry and lies entirely between the lines $x = -a$ and $x = a$.

We may also solve (4) for x in terms of y, with the result

$$x = \pm \frac{a}{b} \sqrt{b^2 - y^2}. \tag{6}$$

From this form of the equation we find that the ellipse is symmetrical with respect to OY and lies entirely between the lines $y = -b$ and $y = b$.

Hence the ellipse has two axes, $A'A$ and $B'B$ (Fig. 48), which are at right angles to each other. But $A'A = 2a$ and $B'B = 2b$; and since $a > b$, it follows that $A'A > B'B$. Hence $A'A$ is called the *major axis* of the ellipse, and $B'B$ is called the *minor axis* of the ellipse.

The ends of the major axis, A' and A, are called the *vertices* of the ellipse, and the point midway between the vertices is called the *center* of the ellipse; that is, O is the center of the ellipse. Since the ellipse is symmetrical both with respect to OX and with respect to OY it follows that any chord of the ellipse which passes through O is bisected by that point.

From B draw lines to F and F'. Since B is a point on the ellipse the sum of the lengths of these lines is equal to $2a$. But these lines are obviously equal. Hence

$$BF = BF' = a.$$

Hence if we describe a circle with the point B as a center and with a radius equal to a, that circle will intersect OX in the foci of the ellipse.

It follows that $\qquad c = OF = \sqrt{a^2 - b^2}, \tag{7}$

which is in agreement with the original algebraic definition of b.

The ratio $\dfrac{OF}{OA}$ (that is, the ratio of the distance of the focus from the center to the distance of either vertex from the center) is called the *eccentricity* of the ellipse and is denoted by e. Hence

$$e = \frac{\sqrt{a^2 - b^2}}{a}; \tag{8}$$

whence it follows that the eccentricity of an ellipse is always less than unity.

Similarly, an equation in form (4) in which $b^2 > a^2$ represents an ellipse with its center at O, its major axis on OY, and its minor axis on OX. Then the vertices are the points $(0, \pm b)$, the foci are the points $(0, \pm \sqrt{b^2 - a^2})$, and $e = \dfrac{\sqrt{b^2 - a^2}}{b}$.

In either case the nearer the foci approach coincidence, the smaller e becomes and the more nearly $b = a$. Hence *a circle may be considered as an ellipse with coincident foci and equal axes.* Its eccentricity is, of course, zero.

EXERCISES

Plot the following ellipses, finding the vertices, the foci, and the eccentricity of each:

1. $9 x^2 + 25 y^2 = 225$.   3. $x^2 + 2 y^2 = 1$.
2. $25 x^2 + 4 y^2 = 100$.   4. $3 x^2 + 5 y^2 = 1$.

5. Find the equation of the ellipse having its foci at the points $(-1, 0)$ and $(7, 0)$ and having the length of its major axis equal to 10.

6. Find the equation of the ellipse having its foci at the points $(0, 0)$ and $(0, 4)$ and having the length of its major axis equal to 6.

7. Find the equation of the ellipse which passes through the point $(7, 0)$ and has its foci at the points $(-6, 0)$ and $(6, 0)$.

8. Find the equation of the ellipse which passes through the point $(4, \frac{12}{5})$ and has its foci at the points $(-3, 0)$ and $(3, 0)$.

9. Find the locus of a point such that its distance from the point $(3, 0)$ is always one half its distance from the line $x = 12$.

10. Find the locus of a point such that its distance from the point $(3, 0)$ is always three fifths of its distance from the line $3 x - 25 = 0$.

32. Hyperbola. *The locus of a point the difference of whose distances from two fixed points is constant is called a hyperbola.* The two fixed points are called the *foci.*

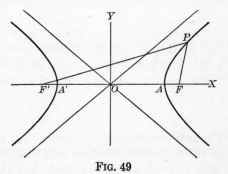

Let F and F' (Fig. 49) be the two foci, and let the distance $F'F$ be $2c$. Let the straight line determined by F' and F be taken as the axis of x, and the middle point of $F'F$ be

FIG. 49

taken as O, the origin of coördinates, and draw the axis OY. Then the coördinates of F' and F are, respectively, $(-c, 0)$ and $(c, 0)$.

Let $P(x, y)$ be any point of the hyperbola and let $2\,a$ represent the constant difference of its distances from the foci. Then, from the definition of the hyperbola, the difference of the distances $F'P$ and FP is $2\,a$, and from the triangle $F'PF$ it is evident that $2\,a < 2\,c$, for the difference of any two sides of a triangle is less than the third side; whence $a < c$.

By § 27, $\qquad F'P = \sqrt{(x+c)^2 + y^2}$

and $\qquad\qquad FP = \sqrt{(x-c)^2 + y^2}$;

whence either

$$\sqrt{(x-c)^2 + y^2} - \sqrt{(x+c)^2 + y^2} = 2\,a \qquad (1)$$

or $\qquad \sqrt{(x+c)^2 + y^2} - \sqrt{(x-c)^2 + y^2} = 2\,a, \qquad (2)$

according as FP or $F'P$ is the greater distance.

Clearing either (1) or (2) of radicals, we obtain the same result:

$$(a^2 - c^2)x^2 + a^2 y^2 = a^4 - a^2 c^2. \qquad (3)$$

Dividing (3) by $a^4 - a^2 c^2$, we have

$$\frac{x^2}{a^2} + \frac{y^2}{a^2 - c^2} = 1. \qquad (4)$$

But since $a < c$, $a^2 - c^2$ is a negative quantity which may be denoted by $-b^2$, and (4) becomes

$$\frac{x^2}{a^2} - \frac{y^2}{b^2} = 1. \qquad (5)$$

Conversely, if the coördinates of any point P satisfy (5), it can be shown that the difference of the distances $F'P$ and FP is $2\,a$, and hence P is a point of the hyperbola.

Solving (5) for y in terms of x, we have

$$y = \pm \frac{b}{a} \sqrt{x^2 - a^2}. \qquad (6)$$

From this equation it appears that OX is an axis of symmetry of the hyperbola, that no part of the hyperbola lies between the lines $x = -a$ and $x = a$, and that as $x \to \infty$, $y \to \infty$.

If we solve (5) for x in terms of y, the result is

$$x = \pm \frac{a}{b} \sqrt{b^2 + y^2} ; \tag{7}$$

from which it appears that OY is also an axis of symmetry of the hyperbola and all values may be assigned to y.

The points A' and A in which one axis of the hyperbola intersects the hyperbola are called the *vertices*, and the portion of the axis extending from A' to A is called the *transverse axis*. The point midway between the vertices is called the *center*; that is, O is the center of the hyperbola, and it can readily be seen that any chord of the hyperbola which passes through O is bisected by that point. The other axis of the hyperbola, which is perpendicular to the transverse axis, is called the *conjugate axis*. This axis does not intersect the curve.

Important information as to the shape of the hyperbola may be obtained by considering a straight line through the center (Fig. 50). The equation of such a line is

$$y = mx. \tag{8}$$

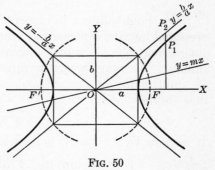

Fig. 50

To find the points of intersection of this line with the hyperbola we must solve equations (5) and (8) simultaneously. Substituting from (8) into (5), and solving for x, we have

$$x = \frac{\pm ab}{\sqrt{b^2 - a^2 m^2}}. \tag{9}$$

This equation shows that if m is so taken that $m^2 > \dfrac{b^2}{a^2}$ the values of x in (9) are imaginary and hence that the line (8) does not intersect the hyperbola; but if $m^2 < \dfrac{b^2}{a^2}$ the line (8) intersects the curve in two real points. Hence if we draw the two straight lines

$$y = \pm \frac{b}{a} x, \tag{10}$$

we divide the plane into four sections, in two of which the curve lies and in the other two of which there is no point of the curve (Fig. 50).

We shall now prove that the lines (10) are *asymptotes* of the hyperbola in the sense of § 26. For that purpose take two points both in the first quadrant, one P_2 on the line $y = \frac{b}{a} x$ and the other P_1 on the hyperbola, and such that P_2 and P_1 have the same abscissa, x. Then if y_2 is the ordinate of P_2 and y_1 is the ordinate of P_1, we have

$$P_1 P_2 = y_2 - y_1 = \frac{b}{a} x - \frac{b}{a} \sqrt{x^2 - a^2}$$

$$= \frac{b(x - \sqrt{x^2 - a^2})}{a}. \tag{11}$$

If we should allow x to increase indefinitely in this expression we should get no information, since the difference between two quantities each of which increases indefinitely is not determinate. We may, however, rationalize the numerator in (11) by multiplying numerator and denominator by $x + \sqrt{x^2 - a^2}$ and obtain

$$P_1 P_2 = \frac{ab}{x + \sqrt{x^2 - a^2}}. \tag{12}$$

If we now let $x \to \infty$, it is evident that $P_1 P_2 \to 0$. Hence the line $y = \frac{b}{a} x$ is an asymptote. From the symmetry of the figure it is evident that the property which we have proved for the first quadrant is true in all quadrants.

In graphing a hyperbola it is best to draw the asymptotes first. This may be done by drawing the rectangle with sides $2\,a$ and $2\,b$ as in Fig. 50. The asymptotes are then the diagonals of this rectangle.

From the definition of b, $c = \sqrt{a^2 + b^2}$, and the coördinates of the foci are $(\pm \sqrt{a^2 + b^2}, 0)$. Therefore

$$OF = \sqrt{a^2 + b^2}. \tag{13}$$

The foci may be found by describing a circle with the center at O and a radius equal to the semidiagonal of the rectangle which determines the asymptotes. This circle intersects the transverse axis in the foci. If we define the eccentricity of the hyperbola as the ratio $\dfrac{OF}{OA}$, we have

$$e = \frac{\sqrt{a^2 + b^2}}{a}, \tag{14}$$

a quantity which is evidently always greater than unity.

Similarly, the equation

$$\frac{y^2}{b^2} - \frac{x^2}{a^2} = 1 \tag{15}$$

is the equation of a hyperbola, with its center at O, its transverse axis on OY, and its conjugate axis on OX. Then the vertices are the points $(0, \pm b)$, the foci are the points $(0, \pm \sqrt{b^2 + a^2})$, the asymptotes are the straight lines $y = \pm \dfrac{b}{a} x$, and $e = \dfrac{\sqrt{b^2 + a^2}}{b}$.

If $b = a$, in either (5) or (15), the equation of the hyperbola assumes the form

$$x^2 - y^2 = a^2 \quad \text{or} \quad y^2 - x^2 = a^2, \tag{16}$$

and the hyperbola is called an *equilateral hyperbola*. The equations of the asymptotes become $y = \pm x$; and as these lines are perpendicular to each other, the hyperbola is also called a *rectangular hyperbola*.

EXERCISES

Plot the following hyperbolas, finding the vertices, the foci, the asymptotes, and the eccentricity of each:

1. $4 x^2 - 25 y^2 = 100$.   3. $2 y^2 - 3 x^2 = 6$.   5. $3 x^2 - 2 y^2 = 1$.

2. $25 x^2 - 4 y^2 = 100$.   4. $x^2 - y^2 = 16$.   6. $y^2 - 4 x^2 = 1$.

7. Find the equation of the hyperbola having its foci at the points $(0, 0)$ and $(3, 0)$, and the difference of the distances of any point on it from the foci equal to 2.

8. The foci of a hyperbola are at the points $(-5, 2)$ and $(5, 2)$, and the difference of the distances of any point on it from the foci is 4. Find the equation of the hyperbola, and plot.

9. Find the locus of a point which has the property that its distance from the point $(4, 0)$ is twice its distance from the line $x = 1$.

10. Find a curve which has the property that the distance of any point on it from the point $(6, 0)$ is three times its distance from the line $3 x - 2 = 0$.

33. Conics. The circle, ellipse, hyperbola, and parabola are called collectively *conics,* or *conic sections.* The name is due to the fact that they may all be obtained by making plane sections of a right circular cone.

The general equation of the circle has been obtained in § 28, and special forms of the equations of the other conics have been derived in §§ 29–32. We shall now proceed to find more general forms of the equations of the ellipse, parabola, and hyperbola, but shall not try to obtain the most general forms of their equations.

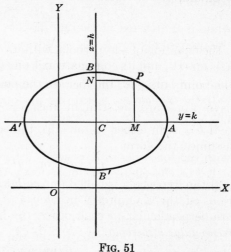

FIG. 51

Let us take first an ellipse with its center at the point (h, k), and with its axes along the lines $x = h$ and $y = k$ (Fig. 51). In the equation of the ellipse obtained in § 31, the coördinates x and y denote the distances of a point on the ellipse from the two axes of the ellipse. In the present case these distances are $NP = x - h$ and $MP = y - k$, respectively. Hence the equation of the ellipse is

$$\frac{(x - h)^2}{a^2} + \frac{(y - k)^2}{b^2} = 1. \tag{1}$$

Similarly, if the center of a hyperbola is at (h, k) and its transverse axis is $y = k$, its equation is

$$\frac{(x - h)^2}{a^2} - \frac{(y - k)^2}{b^2} = 1; \tag{2}$$

while if its center is at (h, k) and its transverse axis is $x = h$, its equation is

$$\frac{(y - k)^2}{b^2} - \frac{(x - h)^2}{a^2} = 1. \tag{3}$$

Similarly, for a parabola, the coördinates y and x in § 29 are the distances of a point on the parabola from the axis of the parabola and from a line perpendicular to the axis through the vertex. If the vertex of the parabola is at the point (h, k) and the axis of the parabola is $y = k$, these distances now become $y - k$ and $x - h$, respectively, and hence the equation of the parabola is

$$(y - k)^2 = 4\,c(x - h)\,; \tag{4}$$

while if the vertex of the parabola is at (h, k) and the axis of the parabola is $x = h$, the equation of the parabola is

$$(x - h)^2 = 4\,c(y - k), \tag{5}$$

where in both (4) and (5) c has the same meaning as in § 29.

If the indicated operations in equations (1)–(5) are carried out and terms are collected, each equation reduces to the form

$$Ax^2 + By^2 + 2\,Gx + 2\,Fy + C = 0 \tag{6}$$

with the following differences:

1. For the ellipse, A and B have the same sign. If $A = B$, the ellipse reduces to the circle as a special case of the ellipse.

2. For the hyperbola, A and B have opposite signs.

3. For the parabola, either $A = 0$ or $B = 0$.

Conversely, if an equation of the form (6) is given, it may usually be reduced to one of the types (1)–(5) by methods similar to those used in handling the circle as shown in the following examples. Occasionally, however, certain exceptional cases may arise, as shown in Example 4.

Equation (6) is obtained when each axis of a conic is parallel to one of the coördinate axes. When this is not true, the equation of the conic will also contain a term with the product xy and will be of the most general form

$$Ax^2 + 2\,Hxy + By^2 + 2\,Gx + 2\,Fy + C = 0. \tag{7}$$

A discussion of this equation lies outside the range of this book. We will notice, however, that in § 26 we have plotted a special, but important, case, namely

$$xy = k, \tag{8}$$

and have said that this was a rectangular hyperbola. This may be verified by showing that the locus of a point the difference of whose distances from the fixed points (a, a) and $(-a, -a)$ is always equal to $2\,a$ is the curve

$$xy = \frac{a^2}{2}.$$

By taking $a = \sqrt{2\,k}$ we have equation (8).

Example 1. Discuss the equation $4\,x^2 + 6\,y^2 + 4\,x - 12\,y - 1 = 0$.

We collect the x-terms in one parenthesis and the y-terms in another, and have
$$4(x^2 + x) + 6(y^2 - 2\,y) = 1.$$

Completing the square in each parenthesis and adding to the right-hand member of the equation the same numbers that are added to the left-hand member, we have

$$4(x^2 + x + \tfrac{1}{4}) + 6(y^2 - 2\,y + 1) = 1 + 1 + 6 = 8,$$

which may be written in the form

$$\frac{(x + \frac{1}{2})^2}{2} + \frac{(y - 1)^2}{\frac{4}{3}} = 1.$$

The equation therefore represents an ellipse with its center at $(-\frac{1}{2}, 1)$ and its major axis parallel to OX.

Example 2. Discuss the equation $9\,x^2 - 4\,y^2 - 36\,x - 24\,y - 36 = 0$.

Proceeding as in Example 1, we have
$$9(x^2 - 4\,x + 4) - 4(y^2 + 6\,y + 9) = 36 + 36 - 36 = 36,$$
which may be written in the form

$$\frac{(x - 2)^2}{4} - \frac{(y + 3)^2}{9} = 1.$$

The equation therefore represents a hyperbola with its center at $(2, -3)$ and its transverse axis parallel to OX.

Example 3. Discuss the equation $4\,y^2 - 8\,x - 6\,y - 3 = 0$.

We collect the terms in y and transpose the other terms to the right-hand side of the equation. We have
$$4(y^2 - \tfrac{3}{2}\,y) = 8\,x + 3.$$

Completing the square of the terms in the parenthesis, we have
$$4(y^2 - \tfrac{3}{2}\,y + \tfrac{9}{16}) = 8\,x + \tfrac{21}{4},$$
which may be written $$(y - \tfrac{3}{4})^2 = 2(x + \tfrac{21}{32}).$$

The equation therefore represents a parabola with its vertex at $(-\frac{21}{32}, \frac{3}{4})$ and its axis parallel to OX.

Example 4. *Exceptional cases.* In discussing an equation of elliptic type 1 we may be led to an equation of either one of the forms

$$\frac{(x-h)^2}{a^2} + \frac{(y-k)^2}{b^2} = 0,$$

or
$$\frac{(x-h)^2}{a^2} + \frac{(y-k)^2}{b^2} = -1.$$

The first equation is satisfied by $x = h$, $y = k$, but by no other real values of x and y. It therefore represents a point as a special case of an ellipse. The second equation can be satisfied by no real values of the variables, and hence no graph exists.

Also, in discussing an equation of the hyperbolic type 2 we may be led to an equation of the form

$$\frac{(x-h)^2}{a^2} - \frac{(y-k)^2}{b^2} = 0.$$

This may be written as

$$y - k = \pm \frac{b}{a}(x - h)$$

and hence represents two straight lines intersecting at (h, k). This may be considered as a special case of a hyperbola when the axes have become zero, just as a point is a special case of an ellipse.

Finally, an equation of parabolic type 3 may have one of the variables missing. For example,

$$Ay^2 + 2\,Gy + C = 0.$$

This represents two straight lines parallel to OX or no lines at all, according as the roots of the equation are real or imaginary. This may be considered a special case of a parabola.

EXERCISES

Discuss the following conics:

1. $3\,x^2 + 2\,y^2 + 6\,x - 8\,y + 5 = 0.$
2. $x^2 + 3\,y^2 - 6\,x + 6\,y + 9 = 0.$
3. $4\,x^2 + 9\,y^2 - 4\,x + 6\,y + 1 = 0.$
4. $5\,x^2 - 2\,y^2 + 50\,x + 16\,y + 83 = 0.$
5. $45\,x^2 - 75\,y^2 - 60\,x + 60\,y + 23 = 0.$
6. $16\,x^2 - 16\,y^2 - 64\,x + 8\,y + 15 = 0.$
7. $y^2 - 2\,y - 2\,x - 5 = 0.$
8. $x^2 + 4\,x + 3\,y + 10 = 0.$
9. $15\,y^2 + 12\,y + 30\,x - 8 = 0.$
10. $b^2x^2 + a^2y^2 - 2\,ab^2x = 0.$

34. Theorems on limits. In obtaining more general formulas for differentiation, the following theorems on limits will be assumed without formal proof:

1. *The limit of the sum of a finite number of variables is equal to the sum of the limits of the variables.*

2. *The limit of the product of a finite number of variables is equal to the product of the limits of the variables.*

3. *The limit of a constant multiplied by a variable is equal to the constant multiplied by the limit of the variable.*

4. *The limit of the quotient of two variables is equal to the quotient of the limits of the variables, provided the limit of the divisor is not zero.*

35. Theorems on derivatives. In order to extend the process of differentiation to functions other than polynomials, we shall need the following theorems:

1. *The derivative of a constant is zero.*

This theorem was proved in § 8.

2. *The derivative of a constant times a function is equal to the constant times the derivative of the function.*

Let u be a function of x which can be differentiated, let c be a constant, and place $\qquad y = cu.$

Give x an increment Δx, and let Δu and Δy be the corresponding increments of u and y. Then

$$\Delta y = c(u + \Delta u) - cu = c\,\Delta u.$$

Hence $$\frac{\Delta y}{\Delta x} = c\,\frac{\Delta u}{\Delta x},$$

and, by theorem 3, § 34, when $\Delta x \to 0$,

$$\operatorname{Lim}\frac{\Delta y}{\Delta x} = c\operatorname{Lim}\frac{\Delta u}{\Delta x}.$$

Therefore $$\frac{dy}{dx} = c\,\frac{du}{dx},$$

by the definition of a derivative.

Example 1. $y = 5(x^3 + 3\,x^2 + 1).$

$$\frac{dy}{dx} = 5\,\frac{d}{dx}\,(x^3 + 3\,x^2 + 1) = 5(3\,x^2 + 6\,x) = 15(x^2 + 2\,x).$$

3. *The derivative of the sum of a finite number of functions is equal to the sum of the derivatives of the functions.*

Let u, v, and w be three functions of x which can be differentiated, and let

$$y = u + v + w.$$

Give x an increment Δx, and let the corresponding increments of u, v, w, and y be Δu, Δv, Δw, and Δy. Then

$$\Delta y = (u + \Delta u + v + \Delta v + w + \Delta w) - (u + v + w)$$
$$= \Delta u + \Delta v + \Delta w;$$

whence $\quad \dfrac{\Delta y}{\Delta x} = \dfrac{\Delta u}{\Delta x} + \dfrac{\Delta v}{\Delta x} + \dfrac{\Delta w}{\Delta x}.$

Now let $\Delta x \to 0$. By theorem 1, § 34,

$$\text{Lim} \, \frac{\Delta y}{\Delta x} = \text{Lim} \, \frac{\Delta u}{\Delta x} + \text{Lim} \, \frac{\Delta v}{\Delta x} + \text{Lim} \, \frac{\Delta w}{\Delta x};$$

that is, by the definition of a derivative,

$$\frac{dy}{dx} = \frac{du}{dx} + \frac{dv}{dx} + \frac{dw}{dx}.$$

The proof is evidently applicable to any finite number of functions.

Example 2. $y = x^4 - 3\,x^3 + 2\,x^2 - 7\,x.$

$$\frac{dy}{dx} = 4\,x^3 - 9\,x^2 + 4\,x - 7.$$

4. *The derivative of the product of a finite number of functions is equal to the sum of the products obtained by multiplying the derivative of each factor by all the other factors.*

Let u and v be two functions of x which can be differentiated, and let

$$y = uv.$$

Give x an increment Δx, and let the corresponding increments of u, v, and y be Δu, Δv, and Δy.

Then $\quad \Delta y = (u + \Delta u)(v + \Delta v) - uv$
$$= u\,\Delta v + v\,\Delta u + \Delta u \cdot \Delta v$$

and $\quad \dfrac{\Delta y}{\Delta x} = u\,\dfrac{\Delta v}{\Delta x} + v\,\dfrac{\Delta u}{\Delta x} + \dfrac{\Delta u}{\Delta x} \cdot \Delta v.$

If, now, $\Delta x \to 0$, we have, by § 34,

$$\text{Lim} \frac{\Delta y}{\Delta x} = u \text{ Lim} \frac{\Delta v}{\Delta x} + v \text{ Lim} \frac{\Delta u}{\Delta x} + \text{Lim} \frac{\Delta u}{\Delta x} \cdot \text{Lim } \Delta v.$$

But $\qquad\qquad \text{Lim } \Delta v = 0,$

and therefore $\qquad\qquad \dfrac{dy}{dx} = u \dfrac{dv}{dx} + v \dfrac{du}{dx}.$

Again, let $\qquad\qquad y = uvw.$

Regarding uv as one function and applying the result already obtained, we have

$$\frac{dy}{dx} = uv \frac{dw}{dx} + w \frac{d(uv)}{dx}$$

$$= uv \frac{dw}{dx} + w \left[u \frac{dv}{dx} + v \frac{du}{dx} \right]$$

$$= uv \frac{dw}{dx} + uw \frac{dv}{dx} + vw \frac{du}{dx}.$$

The proof is clearly applicable to any finite number of factors.

Example 3. $y = (3x - 5)(x^2 + 1)x^3.$

$$\frac{dy}{dx} = (3x - 5)(x^2 + 1) \frac{d(x^3)}{dx} + (3x - 5)x^3 \frac{d(x^2 + 1)}{dx}$$

$$+ (x^2 + 1)x^3 \frac{d(3x - 5)}{dx}$$

$$= (3x - 5)(x^2 + 1)(3x^2) + (3x - 5)x^3(2x) + (x^2 + 1)x^3(3)$$

$$= (18x^3 - 25x^2 + 12x - 15)x^2.$$

5. *The derivative of a fraction is equal to the denominator times the derivative of the numerator minus the numerator times the derivative of the denominator, all divided by the square of the denominator.*

Let $y = \dfrac{u}{v}$, where u and v are two functions of x which can be differentiated. Give x an increment Δx, and let Δu, Δv, and Δy be the corresponding increments of u, v, and y. Then

$$\Delta y = \frac{u + \Delta u}{v + \Delta v} - \frac{u}{v} = \frac{v \Delta u - u \Delta v}{v^2 + v \Delta v}$$

and $\qquad\qquad \dfrac{\Delta y}{\Delta x} = \dfrac{v \dfrac{\Delta u}{\Delta x} - u \dfrac{\Delta v}{\Delta x}}{v^2 + v \Delta v}.$

Now let $\Delta x \to 0$. By § 34,

$$\operatorname{Lim} \frac{\Delta y}{\Delta x} = \frac{v \operatorname{Lim} \dfrac{\Delta u}{\Delta x} - u \operatorname{Lim} \dfrac{\Delta v}{\Delta x}}{v^2 + v \operatorname{Lim} \Delta v};$$

whence
$$\frac{dy}{dx} = \frac{v \dfrac{du}{dx} - u \dfrac{dv}{dx}}{v^2}.$$

Example 4. $y = \dfrac{x^2 - 1}{x^2 + 1}$.

$$\frac{dy}{dx} = \frac{(x^2 + 1)(2\,x) - (x^2 - 1)2\,x}{(x^2 + 1)^2} = \frac{4\,x}{(x^2 + 1)^2}.$$

6. *The derivative of the nth power of a function is obtained by multiplying n times the (n − 1)th power of the function by the derivative of the function.*

Let $y = u^n$, where u is any function of x which can be differentiated and n is a constant. We need to distinguish four cases:

CASE I. When n is a positive integer.

Give x an increment Δx, and let Δu and Δy be the corresponding increments of u and y. Then

$$\Delta y = (u + \Delta u)^n - u^n;$$

whence, by the binomial theorem,

$$\Delta y = n u^{n-1}\, \Delta u + \frac{n(n-1)}{2}\, u^{n-2}(\Delta u)^2 + \cdots + (\Delta u)^n.$$

$$\frac{\Delta y}{\Delta x} = n u^{n-1}\, \frac{\Delta u}{\Delta x} + \frac{n(n-1)}{2}\, u^{n-2}\, \Delta u\, \frac{\Delta u}{\Delta x} + \cdots + (\Delta u)^{n-1}\, \frac{\Delta u}{\Delta x}.$$

Now let $\Delta x,\ \Delta u,\ \Delta y \to$ zero, and apply theorems 1 and 2, § 34. The limit of $\dfrac{\Delta y}{\Delta x}$ is $\dfrac{dy}{dx}$, the limit of $\dfrac{\Delta u}{\Delta x}$ is $\dfrac{du}{dx}$, and the limit of all terms except the first on the right-hand side of the last equation is zero, since each contains the factor Δu. Therefore

$$\frac{dy}{dx} = n u^{n-1}\, \frac{du}{dx}.$$

CASE II. When n is a positive rational fraction.

Let $n = \dfrac{p}{q}$, where p and q are positive integers, and place

$$y = u^{\frac{p}{q}}.$$

By raising both sides of this equation to the qth power, we have

$$y^q = u^p.$$

Here we have two functions of x which are equal for all values of x.

Taking the derivative of both sides of the last equation, we have, by Case I, since p and q are positive integers,

$$qy^{q-1} \frac{dy}{dx} = pu^{p-1} \frac{du}{dx}.$$

Substituting the value of y and dividing, we have

$$\frac{dy}{dx} = \frac{p}{q} u^{\frac{p}{q}-1} \frac{du}{dx}.$$

Hence, in this case also, $\dfrac{dy}{dx} = nu^{n-1} \dfrac{du}{dx}.$

CASE III. When n is a negative rational number.

Let $n = -m$, where m is a positive number, either integral or fractional, and place

$$y = u^{-m} = \frac{1}{u^m}.$$

Then
$$\frac{dy}{dx} = \frac{-\dfrac{d(u^m)}{dx}}{u^{2m}} \qquad \text{[By 5]}$$

$$= -\frac{mu^{m-1} \dfrac{du}{dx}}{u^{2m}} \qquad \text{[By Cases I and II]}$$

$$= -mu^{-m-1} \frac{du}{dx}.$$

Hence, in this case also,

$$\frac{dy}{dx} = nu^{n-1} \frac{du}{dx}.$$

CASE IV. When n is an irrational number.

The formula is true in this case also, but the proof will not be given.

It appears that the theorem is true for all real values of n. It may be restated as a working rule in the following words:

To differentiate a power of any quantity, bring down the exponent as a coefficient, write the quantity with an exponent 1 less, and multiply by the derivative of the quantity.

Example 5. $y = (x^3 + 4\,x^2 - 5\,x + 7)^3.$

$$\frac{dy}{dx} = 3(x^3 + 4\,x^2 - 5\,x + 7)^2 \frac{d}{dx}(x^3 + 4\,x^2 - 5\,x + 7)$$

$$= 3(x^3 + 4\,x^2 - 5\,x + 7)^2(3\,x^2 + 8\,x - 5).$$

Example 6. $y = \sqrt[3]{x^2} + \dfrac{1}{x^3} = x^{\frac{2}{3}} + x^{-3}.$

$$\frac{dy}{dx} = \frac{2}{3}x^{-\frac{1}{3}} - 3\,x^{-4}$$

$$= \frac{2}{3\sqrt[3]{x}} - \frac{3}{x^4}.$$

Example 7. $y = (x + 1)\sqrt{x^2 + 1}.$

$$\frac{dy}{dx} = (x + 1)\,\frac{d(x^2 + 1)^{\frac{1}{2}}}{dx} + (x^2 + 1)^{\frac{1}{2}}\frac{d(x + 1)}{dx}$$

$$= (x + 1)\,[\tfrac{1}{2}\,(x^2 + 1)^{-\frac{1}{2}} \cdot 2\,x] + (x^2 + 1)^{\frac{1}{2}}$$

$$= \frac{x\,(x + 1)}{(x^2 + 1)^{\frac{1}{2}}} + (x^2 + 1)^{\frac{1}{2}}$$

$$= \frac{2\,x^2 + x + 1}{\sqrt{x^2 + 1}}.$$

Example 8. $y = \sqrt[3]{\dfrac{x}{x^3 + 1}} = \left(\dfrac{x}{x^3 + 1}\right)^{\frac{1}{3}}.$

$$\frac{dy}{dx} = \frac{1}{3}\left(\frac{x}{x^3 + 1}\right)^{-\frac{2}{3}}\frac{d}{dx}\left(\frac{x}{x^3 + 1}\right)$$

$$= \frac{1}{3}\left(\frac{x^3 + 1}{x}\right)^{\frac{2}{3}}\frac{1 - 2\,x^3}{(x^3 + 1)^2}$$

$$= \frac{1 - 2\,x^3}{3\,x^{\frac{2}{3}}(x^3 + 1)^{\frac{4}{3}}}.$$

7. *If y is a function of x, then x is a function of y, and the derivative of x with respect to y is the reciprocal of the derivative of y with respect to x.*

Let Δx and Δy be corresponding increments of x and y. It is immaterial whether Δx is assumed and Δy determined, or Δy is assumed and Δx determined. In either case $\Delta x \to 0$ and $\Delta y \to 0$ together. But

$$\frac{\Delta x}{\Delta y} = \frac{1}{\dfrac{\Delta y}{\Delta x}},$$

whence

$$\operatorname{Lim} \frac{\Delta x}{\Delta y} = \frac{1}{\operatorname{Lim} \dfrac{\Delta y}{\Delta x}};$$

that is,

$$\frac{dx}{dy} = \frac{1}{\dfrac{dy}{dx}}.$$

8. *If y is a function of u and u is a function of x, then y is a function of x, and the derivative of y with respect to x is equal to the product of the derivative of y with respect to u and the derivative of u with respect to x.*

An increment Δx determines an increment Δu, since u is a function of x, and this in turn determines an increment Δy, since y is a function of u. Then as $\Delta x \to 0$, $\Delta u \to 0$ and $\Delta y \to 0$. But

$$\frac{\Delta y}{\Delta x} = \frac{\Delta y}{\Delta u} \cdot \frac{\Delta u}{\Delta x},$$

whence

$$\operatorname{Lim} \frac{\Delta y}{\Delta x} = \operatorname{Lim} \frac{\Delta y}{\Delta u} \cdot \operatorname{Lim} \frac{\Delta u}{\Delta x};$$

that is,

$$\frac{dy}{dx} = \frac{dy}{du} \cdot \frac{du}{dx}.$$

Example 9. $y = u^2 + 3\,u + 1$, where $u = \dfrac{1}{x^2}$.

$$\frac{dy}{dx} = (2\,u + 3)\left(-\frac{2}{x^3}\right) = -\frac{2 + 3\,x^2}{x^2} \cdot \frac{2}{x^3} = -\frac{4 + 6\,x^2}{x^5}.$$

The same result is obtained by substituting in the expression for y the value of u in terms of x and then differentiating.

36. Formulas. We may now collect our formulas of differentiation in the following table:

$$\frac{dc}{dx} = 0, \tag{1}$$

$$\frac{d(cu)}{dx} = c\frac{du}{dx}, \tag{2}$$

$$\frac{d(u+v)}{dx} = \frac{du}{dx} + \frac{dv}{dx}, \tag{3}$$

$$\frac{d(uv)}{dx} = u\frac{dv}{dx} + v\frac{du}{dx}, \tag{4}$$

$$\frac{d\left(\dfrac{u}{v}\right)}{dx} = \frac{v\dfrac{du}{dx} - u\dfrac{dv}{dx}}{v^2}, \tag{5}$$

$$\frac{d(u^n)}{dx} = nu^{n-1}\frac{du}{dx}, \tag{6}$$

$$\frac{dx}{dy} = \frac{1}{\dfrac{dy}{dx}}, \tag{7}$$

$$\frac{dy}{dx} = \frac{dy}{du} \cdot \frac{du}{dx}, \tag{8}$$

$$\frac{dy}{dx} = \frac{\dfrac{dy}{du}}{\dfrac{dx}{du}}. \tag{9}$$

Formula (9) is a combination of (7) and (8).

The first six formulas may be changed to corresponding formulas for differentials by multiplying both sides of each equation by dx. They are

$$dc = 0, \tag{10}$$

$$d(cu) = c\,du, \tag{11}$$

$$d(u+v) = du + dv, \tag{12}$$

$$d(uv) = u\,dv + v\,du, \tag{13}$$

$$d\left(\frac{u}{v}\right) = \frac{v\,du - u\,dv}{v^2}, \tag{14}$$

$$d(u^n) = nu^{n-1}du. \tag{15}$$

EXERCISES

Find $\dfrac{dy}{dx}$ in each of the following cases:

1. $y = (2x + 3)(3x^2 + 2x - 3)$.

2. $y = (2x^2 + 1)(x^3 + 3x)$.

3. $y = (x^2 - 1)^2(x + 2)^3$.

4. $y = (x - 1)(x + 2)(x - 3)^2$.

5. $y = \dfrac{x^2 - 4}{x^2 + 4}$.

6. $y = \dfrac{(3x + 1)^2}{(2x - 1)^3}$.

7. $y = \sqrt[5]{x^3} + \dfrac{1}{\sqrt[5]{x^3}}$.

8. $y = (3x^2 - 6x + 1)^{\frac{2}{3}}$.

9. $y = \dfrac{\sqrt{x^2 - 1}}{x + 1}$.

10. $y = \dfrac{x + 1}{\sqrt[3]{x^3 + 2}}$.

11. $y = (x + 1)\sqrt{x^2 - 2x}$.

12. $y = \dfrac{3x + 2}{\sqrt{9x^2 + 4}}$.

13. $y = \dfrac{x^2}{\sqrt[3]{(1 + x^3)^2}}$.

14. $y = (x^2 + 2)^{\frac{1}{2}}(x^3 - 2)^{\frac{1}{3}}$.

15. $y = \dfrac{x^2 + 1}{\sqrt{2x^3 + x}}$.

16. $y = x^2\sqrt{4 - x^2}$.

17. $y = x(x^2 + 4x + 1)^{\frac{5}{2}}$.

18. $y = \dfrac{\sqrt[3]{x^3 + 3x^2}}{x}$.

19. $y = \sqrt{\dfrac{x + 2}{x - 2}}$.

20. $y = \sqrt[3]{\dfrac{x^3 - 3}{x^3 + 3}}$.

21. $y = (3x^2 + 4x + 8)\sqrt{x - 1}$.

22. $y = \dfrac{\sqrt[3]{x + 4x^6}}{x^2}$.

37. Differentiation of implicit functions. Consider any equation containing two variables x and y. If one of them, as x, is chosen as the independent variable and a value is assigned to it, the values of y are determined. Hence the given equation defines y as a function of x. If the equation is solved for y in terms of x, y is called an *explicit* function of x. If the equation is not solved for y, y is called an *implicit* function of x. For example,

$$y^2 + 3x^2 + 4xy + 4x + 2y + 4 = 0,$$

which may be written

$$y^2 + (4x + 2)y + (3x^2 + 4x + 4) = 0,$$

defines y as an implicit function of x.

If the equation is solved for y, the result

$$y = -2x - 1 \pm \sqrt{x^2 - 3}$$

expresses y as an explicit function of x.

If it is required to find the derivative of an implicit function, the equation may be differentiated as given, the result being an equation which may be solved algebraically for the derivative. This method of finding both first and second derivatives is illustrated in the following examples:

Example 1. $x^2 + y^2 = 5$.

If x is the independent variable,

$$\frac{d}{dx}(x^2 + y^2) = \frac{d}{dx}(5) = 0;$$

that is,

$$2\,x + 2\,y\,\frac{dy}{dx} = 0,$$

whence

$$\frac{dy}{dx} = -\frac{x}{y}.$$

Or the derivative may be found by taking the differential of both sides, as follows:

$$d(x^2 + y^2) = d(5) = 0;$$

that is,

$$2\,x\,dx + 2\,y\,dy = 0,$$

whence

$$\frac{dy}{dx} = -\frac{x}{y}.$$

It is also possible first to solve the given equation for y, thus:

$$y = \pm\sqrt{5 - x^2};$$

whence

$$\frac{dy}{dx} = \pm\frac{-x}{\sqrt{5 - x^2}},$$

a result evidently equivalent to the result previously found.

Example 2. Find $\frac{d^2y}{dx^2}$ if $x^2 + y^2 = 5$.

We know from Example 1 that $\dfrac{dy}{dx} = -\dfrac{x}{y}$.

Therefore

$$\frac{d^2y}{dx^2} = -\frac{d}{dx}\left(\frac{x}{y}\right)$$

$$= -\frac{y - x\left(\dfrac{dy}{dx}\right)}{y^2}$$

$$= -\frac{y - x\left(-\dfrac{x}{y}\right)}{y^2}$$

$$= -\frac{y^2 + x^2}{y^3} = -\frac{5}{y^3},$$

since $y^2 + x^2 = 5$, from the given equation.

EXERCISES

Find $\dfrac{dy}{dx}$ from each of the following equations:

1. $y^2(x-y) + x + y = 0.$

2. $\sqrt{y+x} + \sqrt{y-x} = a.$

3. $(x-y)^2(x+y) = a^3.$

4. $y^2 = x + \sqrt{x^2 + y^2}.$

5. $\dfrac{x^3}{y^3} + \dfrac{y}{x} = \dfrac{a}{b}.$

Find $\dfrac{dy}{dx}$ and $\dfrac{d^2y}{dx^2}$ from each of the following equations:

6. $xy + 2x + 3y = 6.$

7. $y = \sqrt{x+y}.$

8. $x^2 + xy - y^2 = 0.$

9. $x^5 + y^5 = a^5.$

10. $x^{\frac{1}{2}} + y^{\frac{1}{2}} = a^{\frac{1}{2}}.$

11. $x^2 + y^2 - 2ax - 2by = 0.$

38. Tangent line. In § 15 we derived the equation of the tangent line to any curve at the point $P_1(x_1, y_1)$ in the form

$$y - y_1 = \left(\frac{dy}{dx}\right)_1 (x - x_1), \tag{1}$$

where $\left(\dfrac{dy}{dx}\right)_1$ is the value of $\dfrac{dy}{dx}$ when $x = x_1$ and $y = y_1$; that is, it is the slope of the curve, and hence of the tangent line, at P_1. The use of (1) in deriving a general equation of the tangent line to any given curve at a chosen point $P_1 (x_1, y_1)$ is illustrated in Example 1.

The angle of intersection of two curves is the angle between their respective tangents at the point of intersection. The method of finding the angle of intersection is illustrated in Example 2.

Example 1. Find the equation of the tangent line to the ellipse $\dfrac{x^2}{a^2} + \dfrac{y^2}{b^2} = 1$ at $P_1(x_1, y_1)$.

By differentiation we have

$$\frac{2x}{a^2} + \frac{2y}{b^2}\frac{dy}{dx} = 0, \tag{1}$$

whence

$$\frac{dy}{dx} = -\frac{b^2x}{a^2y}. \tag{2}$$

Placing $x = x_1$ and $y = y_1$ in (2), we have

$$\left(\frac{dy}{dx}\right)_1 = -\frac{b^2x_1}{a^2y_1}, \tag{3}$$

and the equation of the required tangent line is

$$y - y_1 = -\frac{b^2x_1}{a^2y_1}(x - x_1). \tag{4}$$

It is desirable to put this equation into a simpler form.

Since P_1 is a point of the ellipse, its coördinates satisfy the equation of the ellipse, and hence

$$\frac{x_1{}^2}{a^2} + \frac{y_1{}^2}{b^2} = 1, \tag{5}$$

an equation which enables us to simplify (4).

For, multiplying (4) by $\frac{y_1}{b^2}$, we have

$$\frac{y_1}{b^2}(y - y_1) = -\frac{x_1}{a^2}(x - x_1),$$

which may be written in the form

$$\frac{x_1 x}{a^2} + \frac{y_1 y}{b^2} = \frac{x_1{}^2}{a^2} + \frac{y_1{}^2}{b^2}. \tag{6}$$

But, by virtue of (5) the right-hand member of (6) is 1, and (6) reduces to

$$\frac{x_1 x}{a^2} + \frac{y_1 y}{b^2} = 1, \tag{7}$$

the equation of the required tangent line in simple form.

The obvious similarity between this equation and that of the ellipse makes it easy to remember, if necessary.

Example 2. Find the angle of intersection of the circle $x^2 + y^2 = 8$ and of the parabola $x^2 = 2\,y$.

The points of intersection are $P_1(2, 2)$ and $P_2(-2, 2)$ (Fig. 52), and from the symmetry of the diagram it is evident that the angles of intersection at P_1 and P_2 are the same.

Differentiating the equation of the circle, we have $2\,x + 2\,y\,\dfrac{dy}{dx} = 0$, whence $\dfrac{dy}{dx} = -\dfrac{x}{y}$; and differentiating the equation of the parabola, we find $\dfrac{dy}{dx} = x$.

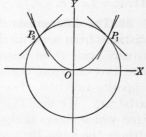

FIG. 52

Hence at P_1 the slope of the tangent to the circle is -1, and the slope of the tangent to the parabola is 2.

Accordingly, if β denotes the angle of intersection, by § 14,

$$\tan \beta = \frac{-1 - 2}{1 - 2} = 3,$$

or

$$\beta = \tan^{-1} 3.$$

EXERCISES

1. Find the equation of the tangent line drawn to the circle $x^2 + y^2 - 4x + 6y = 12$ at the point $(5, 1)$.

2. Find the equation of the tangent line drawn to the curve $y^3 = 4x^2 - yx^2$ at the point $(-2, 2)$.

3. Find the angle of intersection of the tangents to the curve $y^2 = 2x^3$ at the points for which $x = 2$.

4. Show that the equation of the tangent to the hyperbola $\dfrac{x^2}{a^2} - \dfrac{y^2}{b^2} = 1$ at the point (x_1, y_1) is $\dfrac{x_1 x}{a^2} - \dfrac{y_1 y}{b^2} = 1$.

5. Show that the equation of the tangent to the parabola $y^2 = kx$ at the point (x_1, y_1) is $y_1 y = \dfrac{k}{2}(x + x_1)$.

6. Show that the equation of the tangent drawn to the parabola $y^2 = 4ax + 4a^2$ at the point (x_1, y_1) is $y_1 y = 2a(x + x_1) + 4a^2$.

7. Find the point at which the tangent to the curve $y^2(2 + x) = 2 - x$ at the point $(-\frac{6}{5}, 2)$ intersects the curve again.

Draw each pair of the following curves in one diagram and determine the angles at which they intersect:

8. $xy + 6 = 0, 2x + 3y = 0.$ **12.** $xy = 2, x^2 - y^2 = 3.$

9. $3y^2 = 16x, 4x^2 = 9y.$ **13.** $x^2 + y^2 = 5, x^2 + y^2 - 5x + 5y = 0.$

10. $2y^2 = 9x, y^2 = 3(5 - x).$ **14.** $y^2 = 8x, x^2 + y^2 - 5y = 0.$

11. $y^2 = 4x - 8, y = 2x - 8.$ **15.** $y^2 = 4x + 4, y^2 = 64 - 16x.$

39. The differentials dx, dy, ds. On any given curve let the distance from some fixed initial point measured along the curve to any point P be denoted by s, where s is positive if P lies in one direction from the initial point and negative if P lies in the opposite direction. The choice of the positive direction is purely arbitrary. We shall take as the positive direction of the tangent that which shows the positive direction of the curve, and shall denote the angle between the positive direction of OX and the positive direction of the tangent by ϕ.

Now for a fixed curve and a fixed initial point the position of a point P is determined if s is given. Hence x and y, the coördinates of P, are functions of s which in general are continuous and may be differentiated. We shall now show that

$$\frac{dx}{ds} = \cos \phi, \qquad \frac{dy}{ds} = \sin \phi.$$

Let arc $PQ = \Delta s$ (Fig. 53), where P and Q are so chosen that Δs is positive. Then $PR = \Delta x$ and $RQ = \Delta y$, and

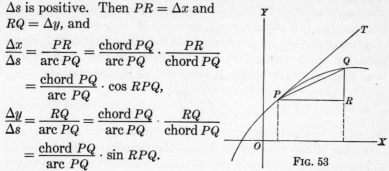

$$\frac{\Delta x}{\Delta s} = \frac{PR}{\text{arc } PQ} = \frac{\text{chord } PQ}{\text{arc } PQ} \cdot \frac{PR}{\text{chord } PQ}$$

$$= \frac{\text{chord } PQ}{\text{arc } PQ} \cdot \cos RPQ,$$

$$\frac{\Delta y}{\Delta s} = \frac{RQ}{\text{arc } PQ} = \frac{\text{chord } PQ}{\text{arc } PQ} \cdot \frac{RQ}{\text{chord } PQ}$$

$$= \frac{\text{chord } PQ}{\text{arc } PQ} \cdot \sin RPQ.$$

FIG. 53

We shall assume without proof that the ratio of a small chord to its arc is very nearly equal to unity, and that the limit of $\dfrac{\text{chord } PQ}{\text{arc } PQ} = 1$ as the point Q approaches the point P along the curve. At the same time the limit of $RPQ = \phi$. Hence, taking limits, we have

$$\frac{dx}{ds} = \cos \phi, \qquad \frac{dy}{ds} = \sin \phi. \tag{1}$$

If the notation of differentials is used, equations (1) become

$$dx = ds \cdot \cos \phi, \qquad dy = ds \cdot \sin \phi;$$

whence, by squaring and adding, we obtain the equation

$$ds^2 = dx^2 + dy^2. \tag{2}$$

This relation between the differentials of x, y, and s is often represented by the triangle of Fig. 54. This figure is convenient as a device for memorizing formulas (1) and (2), but it should be borne in mind that RQ is not rigorously equal to dy (§ 18), nor is PQ rigorously equal to ds. In fact, $RQ = \Delta y$, and $PQ = \Delta s$; but if this triangle is regarded as a plane right triangle, we recall immediately the values of $\sin \phi$, $\cos \phi$, and $\tan \phi$ which have been previously proved.

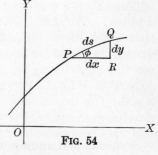

FIG. 54

40. Motion in a curve. When a body moves in a curve, the discussion of velocity and acceleration becomes somewhat complicated, as the directions as well as the magnitudes of these quantities need to be considered. We shall not discuss acceleration, but shall notice that the definition for the magnitude of the velocity, or the speed, is the same as before (namely,

$$v = \frac{ds}{dt},$$

where s is distance measured on the curved path) and that the direction of the velocity is that of the tangent to the curve.

Moreover, as the body moves along a curved path through a distance $PQ = \Delta s$ (Fig. 55), x changes by an amount $PR = \Delta x$, and y changes by an amount $RQ = \Delta y$. We have then

$$\text{Lim} \frac{\Delta s}{\Delta t} = \frac{ds}{dt} = v = \text{velocity}$$

of the body in its path,

$$\text{Lim} \frac{\Delta x}{\Delta t} = \frac{dx}{dt} = v_x = \text{component}$$

of velocity parallel to OX,

$$\text{Lim} \frac{\Delta y}{\Delta t} = \frac{dy}{dt} = v_y = \text{component}$$

of velocity parallel to OY.

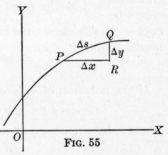

FIG. 55

Otherwise expressed, v represents the velocity of P, v_x the velocity of the projection of P upon OX, and v_y the velocity of the projection of P on OY.

Now, by (8), § 36, and by § 39,

$$v_x = \frac{dx}{dt} = \frac{dx}{ds} \cdot \frac{ds}{dt}$$

$$= v \cos \phi, \tag{1}$$

and
$$v_y = \frac{dy}{dt} = \frac{dy}{ds} \cdot \frac{ds}{dt}$$

$$= v \sin \phi. \tag{2}$$

Squaring and adding, we have

$$v^2 = v_x^2 + v_y^2. \tag{3}$$

Formulas (1), (2), and (3) are of especial value when a particle moves in the plane XOY and the coördinates x and y of its position at any time t are each given as a function of t. The path of the moving particle may then be determined as follows:

Assign any value to t and locate the point corresponding to the values of x and y thus determined. This will evidently be the position of the moving particle at that instant of time. In this way, by assigning successive values to t we can locate other points through which the particle is moving at the corresponding instants of time. The locus of the points thus determined is a curve which is evidently the *path* of the particle.

The two equations accordingly represent the curve and are called its *parametric representation*, the variable t being called a *parameter*.* In case t can be eliminated from the two given equations, the result is the (x, y) equation of the curve, sometimes called the *Cartesian* equation; but such elimination is not essential, and often is not desirable, particularly if the velocity of the particle in its path is to be determined. By (9), § 36, the slope of the curve is given by the formula

$$\frac{dy}{dx} = \frac{\dfrac{dy}{dt}}{\dfrac{dx}{dt}}. \tag{4}$$

Example 1. A particle moves in the plane XOY so that at any time t,
$$x = at, \quad y = bt^2,$$
where a and b are any real constants. Determine its path and its velocity in its path.

Eliminating t from the two equations, we have
$$bx^2 = a^2 y$$
as the Cartesian equation of the path. This equation may be written in the form
$$x^2 = \frac{a^2}{b} y,$$
whence it is immediately evident that the path is a parabola.

---

* It may be noted in passing that the parameter in the parametric representation of a curve is not necessarily time, but may be any third variable in terms of which x and y can be expressed.

To determine the velocity of the particle in its path, we find, by differentiating the given equations,

$$v_x = \frac{dx}{dt} = a, \quad v_y = \frac{dy}{dt} = 2\,bt,$$

whence, by (3), $\qquad\qquad v = \sqrt{a^2 + 4\,b^2 t^2}.$

Example 2. If a projectile starts with an initial velocity v_0 in an initial direction which makes an angle α with the axis of x taken as horizontal, its position at any time t is given by the parametric equations $\qquad x = v_0 t \cos \alpha, \quad y = v_0 t \sin \alpha - \frac{1}{2}\,gt^2.$

Find its velocity in its path.

We have $\qquad\qquad v_x = \dfrac{dx}{dt} = v_0 \cos \alpha,$

$$v_y = \frac{dy}{dt} = v_0 \sin \alpha - gt.$$

Hence $\qquad\qquad v = \sqrt{v_0{}^2 - 2\,gv_0 t \sin \alpha + g^2 t^2}.$

EXERCISES

1. The coördinates of the position of a moving particle at any time t are given by the equations $x = 2\,t^2$, $y = t^3$. Determine the path of the particle and its speed in its path.

2. The coördinates of the position of a moving particle at any time t are given by the equations $x = t^2$, $y = t + 2$. Determine the path of the particle and its speed in its path.

3. The coördinates of the position of a moving particle at any time t are given by the equations $x = 5\,t$, $y = 6\,t - 10\,t^2$. Determine the path of the particle, its speed in its path, and the point in the path at which the speed is the least.

4. The coördinates of the position of a moving particle at any time t are given by the equations $x = t^2$, $y = 2\,t^2 - 25\,t$. Find the path of the particle, its speed in its path, and the point in the path at which the speed is least.

5. The coördinates of the position of a moving particle at any time t are given by the equations $x = t^2 - 3$, $y = t^3 + 2$. Determine the path of the particle, its speed in its path, and the point in the path at which the speed is the least.

6. The coördinates of the position of a moving particle at any time t are given by the equations $x = 4\,t^2$, $y = 4(1 - t)^2$. Determine the path of the particle, its speed in its path, and the point in the path at which the speed is the least.

7. Show that the speed of a projectile is least when the projectile is at its highest point.

8. Find the range of a projectile (that is, the distance to the point at which the projectile will fall on OX), the speed at that point, and the angle at which the projectile will meet OX.

9. Show that in general the same range may be produced by two different values of α, and find the value of α which produces the greatest range.

10. Find the (x, y) equation of the path of a projectile, and plot.

41. Related rates. If we have any variable x expressed in terms of the time t, we may, by differentiating with respect to t, find $\dfrac{dx}{dt}$, which, according to § 6, is *the rate of change of x with respect to the time t*. In the particular case in which x is a distance traveled by a moving body we have called $\dfrac{dx}{dt}$ the velocity of the moving body. It follows that velocity is a special case of a rate with respect to the time t.

More generally, if we have any two variables x and y connected by a single equation, we may regard one of them as the independent variable and the other as a function of it. Suppose we take x as the independent variable; then y is a function of x. Differentiating with respect to x, we find $\dfrac{dy}{dx}$, *the rate of change of y with respect to x*. This type of problem was discussed in § 6.

Suppose, however, that the two variables x and y each vary with respect to the time t. We are now able to differentiate the equation with respect to t. The resulting equation will contain $\dfrac{dx}{dt}$ and $\dfrac{dy}{dt}$, the respective rates of change of x and y with respect to t; and if either rate is known, the other may be readily computed. In fact, by (8), § 36,

$$\frac{dy}{dt} = \frac{dy}{dx} \cdot \frac{dx}{dt}.$$

Hence the two important steps in comparing the rates of two variables with respect to the time t are first, the formation of a general equation containing the two variables; second, the differentiation of that equation with respect to t. These steps appear in the solution of the following illustrative examples:

Example 1. The radius of a circle is increasing at the uniform rate of 2 ft. per second. How fast is the area of the circle increasing when its radius is 4 ft.?

Denoting the area of the circle by A and its radius by r, we have the equation
$$A = \pi r^2.$$

Since A and r are both functions of t, we may differentiate with respect to t, obtaining the result
$$\frac{dA}{dt} = 2\,\pi r\,\frac{dr}{dt}.$$

But $\dfrac{dr}{dt} = 2$, and hence, by substitution,
$$\frac{dA}{dt} = 4\,\pi r,$$

a general formula for the rate of change of A with respect to t, for any value of r.

If $r = 4$, $\dfrac{dA}{dt} = 16\,\pi$, and A is increasing at the rate of 16 π sq. ft. per second.

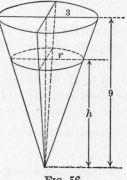

FIG. 56

Example 2. Suppose we have a vessel in the shape of a right circular cone (Fig. 56) of radius 3 in. and altitude 9 in. into which water is being poured at the uniform rate of 100 cu. in. per second. Required the rate at which the depth is increasing when the water is 6 in. deep.

From similar triangles in the figure, if h is the depth of the water and r the radius of its surface, $r = \dfrac{h}{3}$. If V is the volume of the water,
$$V = \tfrac{1}{3}\,\pi r^2 h = \tfrac{1}{27}\,\pi h^3.$$

Since h and V are both functions of t, we may differentiate with respect to t, the result being
$$\frac{dV}{dt} = \frac{1}{9}\,\pi h^2\,\frac{dh}{dt}.$$

We have given $\dfrac{dV}{dt} = 100$ and $h = 6$; from which we compute
$$\frac{dh}{dt} = \frac{25}{\pi} = 7.96.$$

Hence the depth is increasing at the rate of 7.96 in. per second when $h = 6$ in.

As a variation of this problem, suppose the water is leaking out of the same vessel at the uniform rate of 50 cu. in. per second, and it is required to find the rate of change of the depth when the water is 6 in. deep.

Using the same notation as before, we have

$$V = \tfrac{1}{27}\,\pi h^3,$$

whence
$$\frac{dV}{dt} = \frac{1}{9}\,\pi h^2\,\frac{dh}{dt}.$$

In this case, however, V is decreasing and hence $\dfrac{dV}{dt} = -50$. Substituting this value for $\dfrac{dV}{dt}$ and placing $h = 6$, we find, by computation, that $\dfrac{dh}{dt} = -\dfrac{25}{2\,\pi} = -3.98$.

Since $\dfrac{dh}{dt}$ is negative, it follows that the depth is decreasing, as was known to be the case, and at the rate 3.98 in. per second.

Example 3. A lamp is 60 ft. above the ground. A stone is dropped from a point on the same level as the lamp and 20 ft. away from it. Find the speed of the stone's shadow on the ground at the end of 1 sec., assuming that the distance traversed by a falling body in the time t is $16\,t^2$.

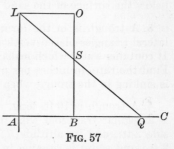

Let AC (Fig. 57) be the surface of the ground, which is assumed to be a horizontal plane, L the position of the lamp, O the point from which the stone was dropped, and S the position of the stone at any time t. Then Q is the position of the shadow of S on the ground, LSQ being a straight line. Let $OS = x$ and $BQ = y$. Then $LO = 20$, $BO = 60$, and $BS = 60 - x$. In the similar triangles LOS and SBQ,

$$\frac{x}{20} = \frac{60 - x}{y}; \qquad (1)$$

whence
$$y = \frac{1200}{x} - 20. \qquad (2)$$

We know $x = 16\,t^2$, whence $\dfrac{dx}{dt} = 32\,t$; and wish to find $\dfrac{dy}{dt}$, the velocity of Q.

FIG. 57

Differentiating (2) with respect to t, we have

$$\frac{dy}{dt} = -\frac{1200}{x^2} \cdot \frac{dx}{dt}.$$

When $t = 1$ sec., $x = 16$, and $\frac{dx}{dt} = 32$; whence, by substitution, we find

$$\frac{dy}{dt} = -150 \text{ ft. per second.}$$

The result is negative because y is decreasing as time goes on.

EXERCISES

1. A solution is being poured into a conical filter at the rate of 5 cc. per second and is running out at the rate of 1 cc. per second. The radius of the top of the filter is 10 cm. and the depth of the filter is 30 cm. Find the rate at which the level of the solution is rising in the filter when it is one fourth of the way to the top.

2. A peg in the form of a right circular cone of which the vertical angle is 60° is being driven into the sand at the rate of 1 in. per second, the axis of the cone being perpendicular to the surface of the sand, which is a plane. How fast is the lateral surface of the peg disappearing in the sand when the vertex of the peg is 5 in. below the surface of the sand?

3. A trough is in the form of a right prism with its ends equilateral triangles placed vertically. The length of the trough is 10 ft. It contains water which leaks out at the rate of $\frac{1}{2}$ cu. ft. per minute. Find the rate, in inches per minute, at which the level of the water is sinking in the trough when the depth is 2 ft.

4. A trough is 10 ft. long, and its cross section, which is vertical, is a regular trapezoid with its top side 4 ft. in length, its bottom side 2 ft., and its altitude 5 ft. It contains water to the depth of 3 ft., and water is running in so that the depth is increasing at the rate of 2 ft. per second. How fast is the water running in?

5. A point is moving on the curve $y^2 = x^3$. The velocity along OX is 2 ft. per second. What is the velocity along OY when $x = 2$?

6. A ball is swung in a circle at the end of a cord 2 ft. long so as to make 20 revolutions per minute. If the cord breaks, allowing the ball to fly off at a tangent, at what rate will it be receding from the center of its previous path 2 sec. after the cord breaks, if no allowance is made for the action of any new force?

X**7.** The inside of a vessel is in the form of an inverted regular quadrangular pyramid, 4 ft. square at the top and 2 ft. deep. The vessel is originally filled with water, which leaks out at the bottom at the rate of 10 cu. in. per minute. How fast is the level of the water falling when the water is 10 in. deep?

8. The top of a ladder 20 ft. long slides down the side of a vertical wall at a speed of 3 ft. per second. The foot of the ladder slides on horizontal land. Find the path described by the middle point of the ladder, and its speed in its path.

X**9.** A boat with the anchor fast on the bottom at a depth of 40 ft. is drifting at the rate of 3 mi. per hour, the cable attached to the anchor slipping over the end of the boat. At what rate is the cable leaving the boat when 50 ft. of cable are out, assuming it forms a straight line from the boat to the anchor?

10. The angle between the straight lines AB and BC is 60°, and AB is 40 ft. long. A particle at A begins to move along AB toward B at the rate of 5 ft. per second, and at the same time a particle at B begins to move along BC toward C at the rate of 4 ft. per second. At what rate are the two particles approaching each other at the end of 1 sec.?

11. The foot of a ladder 50 ft. long rests on horizontal ground, and the top of the ladder rests against the side of a pyramid which makes an angle of 120° with the ground. If the foot of the ladder is drawn directly away from the base of the pyramid at the uniform rate of 2 ft. per second, how fast will the top of the ladder slide down the side of the pyramid?

42. Integration. We know that if n has any value, positive or negative, integral or fractional, we have

$$\frac{d(x^{n+1})}{dx} = (n+1)x^n. \tag{1}$$

Now if $n+1$ is not equal to zero, we may divide equation (1) by $n+1$ and have

$$x^n = \frac{1}{n+1}\frac{d(x^{n+1})}{dx} = \frac{d}{dx}\left(\frac{x^{n+1}}{n+1}\right). \tag{2}$$

Hence by reversing the process of differentiation we have

$$\int x^n dx = \frac{x^{n+1}}{n+1} + C. \tag{3}$$

This is the same formula obtained in § 20, but it is there limited to positive integral values of n, while here it is applicable to any value of n except $n = -1$. For example,

$$\int \sqrt{x}\, dx = \int x^{\frac{1}{2}} dx = \tfrac{2}{3}\, x^{\frac{3}{2}} + C;$$

$$\int \frac{dx}{\sqrt{x}} = \int x^{-\frac{1}{2}} dx = 2\, x^{\frac{1}{2}} + C = 2\, \sqrt{x} + C;$$

$$\int \frac{dx}{x^2} = \int x^{-2}\, dx = -\, x^{-1} + C = -\frac{1}{x} + C.$$

The value of $\int x^{-1} dx = \int \frac{dx}{x}$ cannot be obtained by formula (3), however, and will be found later (see § 57).

We may apply formula (3) to problems of the types discussed in §§ 20–25.

Example 1. The slope of a curve at any point is always equal to the square of the slope of the line joining the point to the origin, and the curve passes through the point (2, 1). Find its equation.

The slope of any curve at any point is $\frac{dy}{dx}$. The slope of the line joining the point to the origin is $\frac{y}{x}$. By the statement of the problem we have

$$\frac{dy}{dx} = \frac{y^2}{x^2},$$

which we may write as

$$\frac{dy}{y^2} = \frac{dx}{x^2}.$$

Integrating by (3), we have

$$-\frac{1}{y} = -\frac{1}{x} + C.$$

Since the curve passes through (2, 1), we have

$$-1 = -\tfrac{1}{2} + C,$$

whence

$$C = -\tfrac{1}{2}.$$

The required equation is therefore

$$\frac{1}{y} = \frac{1}{x} + \frac{1}{2},$$

or

$$xy - 2\, x + 2\, y = 0.$$

Example 2. Find the pressure on a parabolic segment, with base b and altitude a, submerged so that its base is in the surface of the liquid and its axis is vertical.

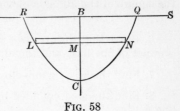

Let RQC (Fig. 58) be the parabolic segment, and let CB be drawn through the vertex C of the segment perpendicular to RQ in the surface of the liquid. According to the data, $RQ = b$, $CB = a$.

FIG. 58

Draw LN parallel to TS, and on LN as a base construct an element of area, dA. Let

$$CM = x.$$

Then

$$dA = (LN)dx.$$

But, from § 30,

$$\frac{\overline{LN}^2}{\overline{RQ}^2} = \frac{CM}{CB} ;$$

whence

$$\overline{LN}^2 = \frac{b^2 x}{a},$$

and therefore

$$dA = \frac{b}{a^{\frac{1}{2}}} x^{\frac{1}{2}} dx.$$

The depth of the line LN below the surface of the liquid is $CB - CM = a - x$; hence, if w is the weight of a unit volume of the liquid,

$$dP = \frac{b}{a^{\frac{1}{2}}} x^{\frac{1}{2}}(a - x)wdx,$$

and

$$P = \int_0^a \frac{bw}{a^{\frac{1}{2}}} x^{\frac{1}{2}}(a - x)dx$$

$$= \tfrac{4}{15} wba^2.$$

WAS DUE March 24 **EXERCISES**

1. The velocity in feet per second of a moving body is equal to $\sqrt{t}$. Find the distance traveled in the time from $t = 2$ to $t = 4$.

2. The velocity in feet per second of a moving body is equal to $\sqrt{s}$, and when $t = 0$, $s = 4$. Find s when $t = 3$.

3. The slope of a curve at any point is always equal to the square root of the abscissa of the point, and the curve passes through the point $(4, 2)$. Find its equation.

4. A curve always cuts at right angles the line joining any point on it to the origin, and the curve passes through the point $(3, -2)$. Find its equation.

5. The slope of a curve at any point is equal to the reciprocal of the square of the abscissa of the point, and the curve passes through the point (1, 1). Find its equation.

6. Prove that the area of a parabolic segment is two thirds of the product of the base and the altitude.

7. Find the area bounded by OX, OY, and the curve $x^{\frac{1}{2}} + y^{\frac{1}{2}} = a^{\frac{1}{2}}$.

8. Find the area bounded by the curve $y^2 = x^3$ and the straight line $y = x$.

9. Find the volume of the solid generated by revolving about OX the triangular area bounded by OX, OY, and the curve $x^{\frac{1}{2}} + y^{\frac{1}{2}} = a^{\frac{1}{2}}$.

10. Find the volume of the solid formed by revolving about the line $x = a$ the area bounded by that line and the curve $ay^2 = x^3$.

11. A parabolic segment with base 18 and altitude 6 is submerged so that its base is horizontal, its axis vertical, and its vertex in the surface of the liquid. Find the total pressure on the segment.

12. A pond 15 ft. in depth is crossed by a roadway with vertical sides. A culvert, whose cross section is in the form of a parabolic segment with horizontal base on a level with the bottom of the pond, runs under the road. Assuming that the base of the parabolic segment is 4 ft. and its altitude is 3 ft., find the total pressure on the bulkhead which temporarily closes the culvert.

GENERAL EXERCISES

Find $\dfrac{dy}{dx}$ in each of the following cases:

1. $y = \dfrac{a}{x - \sqrt{x^2 - a^2}}.$

2. $y = \dfrac{x}{x + \sqrt{x^2 + a^2}}.$

3. $y = x\sqrt{x^2 - a^2} - \dfrac{a^2 x}{\sqrt{x^2 - a^2}}.$

4. $y = (3\,x^2 - 2\,a^2)\sqrt{(x^2 + a^2)^3}.$

5. $y = \dfrac{x - \sqrt{a^2 - x^2}}{x}.$

6. $y = (a^2 - x^2)^{\frac{1}{2}} + \dfrac{a^2}{(a^2 - x^2)^{\frac{1}{2}}}.$

Find $\dfrac{dy}{dx}$ and $\dfrac{d^2y}{dx^2}$ in each of the following cases:

7. $y^3 = a^2(x + y).$

8. $x^{\frac{2}{3}} + y^{\frac{2}{3}} = a^{\frac{2}{3}}.$

9. $x^n + y^n = a^n.$

10. $b^2 x^2 + a^2 y^2 = a^2 b^2.$

11. $x^3 + y^3 - 3\,axy = 0.$

12. $xy^2 = x + y.$

Plot the following curves:

13. $y^2 - 4y = x^3 + 3x^2 - 4$.

14. $(x - 1)^2 - y(y - 2)^2 = 0$.

15. $y = \dfrac{9}{x^2 - 9}$.

16. $y = \dfrac{(x + 2)^2}{x + 1}$.

17. $y = \dfrac{(x - 2)^2}{x + 2}$.

18. $(y - 2)^2(x + 4) = 4$.

19. $y^2(4 + x^2) = x^2(4 - x^2)$.

20. $y^2(4 - x^2) = x^2(4 + x^2)$.

21. $x^2(y^2 - 4) = 4$.

22. $(y - x)^2 = 16 - x^2$.

23. $(y - x)^2 = y^2(3 - y)$.

24. $a^4 y^2 + b^2 x^4 = a^2 b^2 x^2$.

25. $y^2(x^2 + a^2) = a^2 x^2$.

26. $x^2 y^2 + a^2 b^2 = b^2 y^2$.

27. Plot the curve $y = \dfrac{8a^3}{x^2 + 4a^2}$. This curve is called the *witch*.

28. Plot the curve $y^2 = x^2 \dfrac{a - x}{a + x}$. This curve is called the *strophoid*.

29. Plot the curve $x^{\frac{2}{3}} + y^{\frac{2}{3}} = a^{\frac{2}{3}}$. This curve is the *four-cusped hypocycloid*, and is the curve described by any point of a circle of radius $\dfrac{a}{4}$ as the circle rolls on the inside of a circle of radius a.

30. Plot the curve $x^{\frac{1}{2}} + y^{\frac{1}{2}} = a^{\frac{1}{2}}$. This curve is the *parabola*, the axes of x and y being the tangents to the parabola at the ends of the chord drawn through the focus of the parabola perpendicular to the axis of the parabola.

Sketch the following conics:

31. $3x^2 + y^2 - 6x - 6y + 9 = 0$.

32. $9x^2 + 25y^2 - 36x + 50y - 164 = 0$.

33. $36x^2 - 18y^2 + 36x + 24y - 35 = 0$.

34. $12x^2 - 18y^2 - 36x - 12y + 31 = 0$.

35. $x^2 - 4x - 11y - 7 = 0$.

36. $4y^2 - 4y + 6x + 3 = 0$.

37. Find the locus of a point the square of whose distance from a fixed point is always k times its distance from a fixed straight line.

38. Find the equation of the locus of a point whose distance from the fixed point $(c, 0)$ is always e times its distance from the axis of y. Show that the locus is an ellipse if $e < 1$, a hyperbola if $e > 1$, and a parabola if $e = 1$.

39. Find the equation of the locus of a point whose distance from one fixed point is always k times its distance from a second fixed point. Show that the locus is a circle unless $k = 1$, and find its center and radius.

40. Show that the locus of a point which moves so that the sum of the squares of its distances from any number of fixed points is constant is a circle.

41. A point moves so that the length of the tangent from it to the circle $x^2 + y^2 = a^2$ is always equal to the length of the tangent from it to the circle $(x - b)^2 + y^2 = c^2$. Find its locus.

42. A point moves so that the length of the tangent from it to the circle $x^2 + y^2 = 1$ is equal to its distance from the line $x = 3$. Show that the locus is a parabola.

43. Find the general expression for the length of the tangent from any point (x_1, y_1) to any circle $A(x^2 + y^2) + 2\,Gx + 2\,Fy + C = 0$.

44. Find the equation of an ellipse with foci $(3, 0)$ and $(0, 3)$ and major axis equal to 6.

45. Find the equation of an ellipse which passes through the origin and has the foci at $(4, 0)$ and $(0, 4)$.

46. Find the equation of the tangent to the strophoid $y^2 = x^2 \dfrac{a - x}{a + x}$ at the point $\left(-\dfrac{4\,a}{5}, -\dfrac{12\,a}{5}\right)$.

47. Prove that the tangents to the cissoid $y^2 = \dfrac{x^3}{2\,a - x}$ at the points for which $x = a$ make supplementary angles with OX.

48. A chord is drawn through the focus of the parabola $y^2 = kx$ perpendicular to the axis of the parabola. Show that the tangents to the parabola at the ends of the above chord intersect at right angles on the axis of the parabola.

49. Find the equation of the tangent to the curve $x^{\frac{2}{3}} + y^{\frac{2}{3}} = a^{\frac{2}{3}}$ at the point (x_1, y_1).

50. Derive the equation of the tangent to the curve $x^n + y^n = a^n$ at the point (x_1, y_1).

51. Show that the equation of the tangent to the conic
$$Ax^2 + By^2 + 2\,Gx + 2\,Fy + C = 0$$
at the point (x_1, y_1) is
$$Ax_1x + By_1y + G(x + x_1) + F(y + y_1) + C = 0.$$

52. Prove that if a tangent to a parabola $y^2 = kx$ has the slope m, its point of contact is $\left(\dfrac{k}{4\,m^2},\ \dfrac{k}{2\,m}\right)$ and that its equation is $y = mx + \dfrac{k}{4\,m}$.

53. Prove that if a tangent to an ellipse $\dfrac{x^2}{a^2} + \dfrac{y^2}{b^2} = 1$ has the slope m, its point of contact is $\left(\pm\,\dfrac{a^2m}{\sqrt{a^2m^2 + b^2}},\ \mp\,\dfrac{b^2}{\sqrt{a^2m^2 + b^2}}\right)$ and that its equation is $y = mx \pm \sqrt{a^2m^2 + b^2}$.

54. Show that a tangent to a parabola makes equal angles with the axis and a line from the focus to the point of contact.

55. Show that a tangent to an ellipse makes equal angles with the two lines drawn to the foci from the point of contact.

Find the angles of intersection of the following pairs of curves:

56. $x^2 + y^2 - 10\,x = 0,\ y^2 = 4\,x - 16$.

57. $y^2 = x^3,\ y^2 = (2 - x)^3$.

58. $y = (x - 2)^2,\ y = 2 - (x - 2)^2$.

59. $3\,y = (x - 2)^2,\ 9\,y^2 = 8(x - 2)$.

60. $x^2 = 2(y + 1),\ y = \dfrac{8}{x^2 + 4}$.

61. $x^2 - 4\,x + 3\,y = 0,\ x^2 - 4\,x + 4 - y^3 = 0$.

62. $4\,y^2 - 3\,x^2 = 4,\ y^2 = \dfrac{x^3}{4 - x}$.

63. $y^2 = 4 - 2\,x,\ y^2 = \dfrac{8}{2 - x}$.

64. A particle moves so that its coördinates at the time t are $x = 2\,t,\ y = 8\,t^2$. Find its path and its velocity in its path.

65. A particle is moving in the plane XOY so that at the time t its coördinates are $x = 2\sqrt{3\,t - t^2},\ y = 2\,t$. Show that the motion is defined only when $0 < t < 3$, and that the path is a semicircle. Determine the velocity of the particle in its path when $t = 1$.

66. A particle moves so that its coördinates at the time t are $y = t,\ x = \sqrt{t^2 + 9}$. Find its path and its velocity in its path when $t = 4$.

67. A particle moves so that its coördinates at the time t are $x = t + 1,\ y = 2\sqrt{t} + 1$. Find its path and its velocity in its path.

68. A particle moves so that its coördinates at the time t are $x = 3 + 3\sqrt{t},\ y = 2 + 3\,t$. Find its path and its velocity in its path when $t = 4$.

69. A particle moves so that its coördinates at the time t are $x = 2\,t$, $y = 2\sqrt{-t^2 + 4\,t - 3}$. For what interval of time is the motion defined? Find its path and its velocity in its path.

70. The coördinates of a moving particle are given by the equations $x = t^3$, $y = (1 - t^2)^{\frac{3}{2}}$. Find its path and its velocity in its path.

71. A particle moves so that its coördinates at the time t are $x = 2\,t$, $y = \dfrac{2}{t^2 + 1}$. Find its path and its velocity in its path.

72. A body moves so that $x = -2 + t^{\frac{3}{2}}$, $y = 1 + t$. Find its path and its velocity in its path.

73. A man standing on a wharf 20 ft. above the water pulls in a rope, attached to a boat, at the uniform rate of 3 ft. per second. Find the velocity with which the boat approaches the wharf.

74. At 12 o'clock a vessel is sailing due north at the uniform rate of 20 mi. an hour. Another vessel, 40 mi. north of the first, is sailing at the uniform rate of 15 mi. an hour on a course 30° north of east. At what rate is the distance between the two vessels diminishing at the end of one hour? What is the shortest distance between the two vessels?

75. At a certain time two ships, A and B, are 20 mi. apart, and the ship B is due east from the ship A. The ship B is sailing north at the uniform rate of 6 mi. an hour and the ship A is sailing south at the uniform rate of 8 mi. an hour. How fast will the distance between the ships be increasing at the end of 2 hr.?

76. The top of a ladder 32 ft. long rests against a vertical wall, and the foot is drawn at the rate of 4 ft. per second along a straight line at right angles to the wall. Find the path of a point on the ladder one third of the distance from the foot of the ladder, and its velocity in its path.

77. The top of a ladder rests against a vertical wall, and the foot is drawn at a uniform rate along a straight line at right angles to the wall. Prove that any point on the ladder describes an ellipse except the center, which describes a circle.

78. One side of a right triangle, 24 in. long, is increasing at the rate of 3 in. per second and the other side, 10 in. long, is decreasing at the rate of 2 in. per second. At what rate is the hypotenuse changing?

79. The volume and the radius of a cylindrical boiler are expanding at the rate of .8 cu. ft. and .002 ft. per minute, respectively. How fast is the length of the boiler changing when the boiler contains 40 cu. ft. and has a radius of 2 ft.?

80. Sand is being poured on the ground from the end of an elevated pipe and forms a pile which has always the shape of a right circular cone, whose height and the radius of whose base are equal. If the sand is falling at the rate of 6 cu. ft. per second, how fast is the height of the pile increasing when the height is 5 ft.?

81. The inside of a cistern is in the form of a frustum of a right circular cone of vertical angle 90°. The cistern is smallest at the base, which is 4 ft. in diameter. Water is being poured in at the rate of 5 cu. ft. per minute. How fast is the water rising in the cistern when it is $2\frac{1}{2}$ ft. deep?

82. The inside of a bowl is in the form of a hemispherical surface of radius 10 in. If water is running out of it at the rate of 2 cu. in. per minute, how fast is the depth of the water decreasing when the water is 3 in. deep?

83. How fast is the surface of the bowl in Ex. 82 being exposed?

84. The inside of a certain vessel is in the form of a surface of revolution formed by revolving $x^2 = 4\,y$ around OY. If the vessel contains water which leaks out at the uniform rate of $2\,\pi$ cu. in. per second, how fast is the depth of the water falling when the depth is 4 in.?

85. A man walks at the uniform rate of 4 ft. per second directly across a street from a point B which is 40 ft. from a lamp-post. How fast does his shadow move along the wall which is on the opposite side of the street, the width of the street from lamp-post to wall being 80 ft.?

86. The hypotenuse of a right triangle is given. Find the other sides if the area is a maximum.

87. A wire 10 ft. long is to be bent into the form of an isosceles triangle, and the triangle is to be revolved about its altitude to form a cone of revolution. What will be the length of the base and the sides of the triangle when the volume of the cone is the greatest?

88. The stiffness of a rectangular beam varies as the product of the breadth and the cube of the depth. Find the dimensions of the stiffest beam which can be cut from a circular cylindrical log of diameter 18 in.

89. A rectangular box with a square base and open at the top is to be made out of a given amount of material. If no allowance is made for thickness of material or for waste in construction, what are the proportions of the largest box which can be made?

90. A rectangular box open at the top is to have a square base. The capacity of the box is to be 27 cu. ft. The box is to be lined, the cost of the lining for the bottom being twice as much per square foot as the cost of the lining for the sides. Find the inside dimensions of the least expensive box that may be constructed.

91. A metal box open at the top is to be cast in the form of a right circular cylinder, the bottom to be 2 in. thick and the side 1 in. thick. The box is to have a capacity of 16 π cu. in. What should be its dimensions that the least amount of material may be required?

92. A covered tin can is to be made in the form of a right circular cylinder of capacity 54 π cu. in. What must be its radius and height to have the can as light as possible?

93. A horizontal gasoline tank in the form of a right circular cylinder is to be made of iron plates. The plates for the upper half of the tank cost 50 cents per square foot; those for the lower half, 60 cents. The tank is to contain 60 π cu. ft. Find the dimensions of the tank that will make the cost a minimum.

94. The outside and the inside surfaces of a metal vessel are each to be in the form of a right circular cone, vertex at the bottom, and the radius and the altitude of the inner surface are each one inch less than the corresponding dimensions of the outer surface. The vessel is open at the top and has a capacity of 9 π cu. in. What are the dimensions of the inner surface when the vessel is of the least possible weight?

95. A volume of metal is cast in the form of a right circular cylinder and the ends are hollowed out in the form of hemispheres, the radii of the hemispheres and the cylinder being equal. If the volume of the solid is $\frac{5}{6}$ π cu. in., what is the radius of the cylinder when the cost of finishing the total surface is as small as possible?

96. A tent is to be constructed in the form of a regular quadrangular pyramid. Find the ratio of its height to a side of its base when the air space inside the tent is as great as possible for a given wall surface.

97. It is required to construct from two equal circular plates of radius a a buoy composed of two equal cones having a common base. Find the radius of the base when the volume is the greatest.

98. A vessel is anchored 4 mi. offshore. Opposite a point 5 mi. farther along the shore another vessel is anchored 8 mi. offshore. A boat from the first vessel is to land a passenger on the shore and proceed to the other vessel. If the shore is a straight line, determine the shortest course of the boat.

99. Two towns, A and B, are situated respectively 12 mi. and 18 mi. back from a straight river from which they are to get their water supply by means of the same pumping station. At what point on the bank of the river should the station be placed so that the least amount of piping may be required, if the nearest points on the river from A and B respectively are 20 mi. apart and if the piping goes directly from the pumping station to each of the towns?

100. A man on one side of a river, the banks of which are assumed to be parallel straight lines $\frac{1}{4}$ mi. apart, wishes to reach a point on the opposite side of the river and 5 mi. farther along the bank. If he can row 3 mi. an hour and travel on land 5 mi. an hour, find the route he should take to make the trip in the least time.

101. A power house stands upon one side of a river of width b miles, and a manufacturing plant stands upon the opposite side, a miles downstream. Find the most economical way to construct the connecting cable if it costs m dollars per mile on land and n dollars a mile through water, assuming the banks of the river to be parallel straight lines.

102. A vessel A is sailing due east at the uniform rate of 8 mi. per hour when she sights another vessel B directly ahead and 20 mi. away. B is sailing in a straight course S. 30° W. at the uniform rate of 6 mi. per hour. When will the two vessels be nearest to each other?

103. The number of tons of coal consumed per hour by a certain ship is $0.2 + 0.001\, v^3$, where v is the speed in miles per hour. Find an expression for the amount of coal consumed on a voyage of 1000 mi. and the most economical speed at which to make the voyage.

104. The fuel consumed by a certain steamship in an hour is proportional to the cube of the velocity which would be given to the steamship in still water. If it is required to steam a certain distance against a current flowing a miles an hour, find the most economical speed.

105. An isosceles triangle is inscribed in the ellipse $\dfrac{x^2}{a^2} + \dfrac{y^2}{b^2} = 1$, $(a > b)$, with its vertex in the upper end of the minor axis of the ellipse and its base parallel to the major axis. Determine the length of the base and the altitude of the triangle of greatest area which can be so inscribed.

106. In the ellipse $\dfrac{x^2}{16} + \dfrac{y^2}{9} = 1$ is inscribed an isosceles triangle, its vertex being at one end of the minor axis and its base being parallel to the major axis of the ellipse. What will be the altitude of the triangle when the volume of the cone formed by revolving the triangle about its altitude is a maximum?

107. Light emanating from a point A is reflected from a plane surface to a point B. Assuming that light travels in the shortest possible time between the two points, prove that the angle of incidence is equal to the angle of reflection.

108. Light emanating from a point A in a medium in which the velocity of light is v_1 reaches a point B in a medium in which the velocity of light is v_2. The two media are separated by a plane surface. Assuming that light travels in the shortest possible time from A to B, prove that the sine of the angle of incidence is to the sine of the angle of refraction as v_1 is to v_2.

109. Prove that any curve the slope of which at any point is proportional to the abscissa of the point is a parabola.

110. Find the curve the slope of which at any point is proportional to the square of the ordinate of the point and which passes through $(1, 1)$.

111. A point moves in a plane curve such that the tangent to the curve at any point and the straight line from the same point to the origin of coördinates make complementary angles with the axis of x. What is the equation of the curve?

112. Show that if the normal to a curve always passes through a fixed point the curve is a circle.

113. If water is running out of an orifice near the bottom of a cylindrical tank, the rate at which the level of the water is sinking is proportional to the square root of the depth of water. If the level of the water sinks halfway to the orifice in 20 min., how long will it be before it sinks to the orifice?

114. A bullet is fired into a sand bank in which the retardation is equal to the square root of the velocity. When will it come to rest if its velocity on entering is 100 ft. per second?

115. Find the area bounded by the curve $y^2 = 4\,x^3$ and the straight line $y = 2\,x$.

116. Find the area bounded by the curve $(y - 1)^2 = 4\,x$ and the straight line $x = 4$.

117. Find the volume of the solid generated by revolving about OY the surface bounded by OY and the curve $x^{\frac{2}{3}} + y^{\frac{2}{3}} = a^{\frac{2}{3}}$.

CHAPTER V

TRIGONOMETRIC FUNCTIONS

43. Formulas. The following formulas of trigonometry, which are sufficient for the purposes of this book, are collected here for convenient reference:

$$\tan A = \frac{\sin A}{\cos A}, \ \operatorname{ctn} A = \frac{1}{\tan A}, \ \sec A = \frac{1}{\cos A}, \ \csc A = \frac{1}{\sin A}. \quad (1)$$

$$\sin^2 A + \cos^2 A = 1, \ \sec^2 A = 1 + \tan^2 A, \ \csc^2 A = 1 + \operatorname{ctn}^2 A. \quad (2)$$

$$\sin (A \pm B) = \sin A \cos B \pm \cos A \sin B. \quad (3)$$

$$\cos (A \pm B) = \cos A \cos B \mp \sin A \sin B. \quad (4)$$

$$\tan (A \pm B) = \frac{\tan A \pm \tan B}{1 \mp \tan A \tan B}. \quad (5)$$

$$\sin 2A = 2 \sin A \cos A. \quad (6)$$

$$\begin{aligned} \cos 2A &= \cos^2 A - \sin^2 A \\ &= 2 \cos^2 A - 1 \\ &= 1 - 2 \sin^2 A. \end{aligned} \quad (7)$$

$$\sin^2 A = \frac{1 - \cos 2A}{2}, \quad \cos^2 A = \frac{1 + \cos 2A}{2}. \quad (8)$$

$$\sin \tfrac{1}{2} A = \sqrt{\frac{1 - \cos A}{2}}, \quad \cos \tfrac{1}{2} A = \sqrt{\frac{1 + \cos A}{2}}. \quad (9)$$

$$\sin (- A) = - \sin A, \ \cos (- A) = \cos A, \ \tan (- A) = - \tan A. \quad (10)$$

$$\begin{aligned} \sin (90° - A) &= \cos A, \qquad \cos (90° - A) = \sin A, \\ \tan (90° - A) &= \operatorname{ctn} A. \end{aligned} \quad (11)$$

$$\begin{aligned} \sin (90° + A) &= \cos A, \qquad \cos (90° + A) = - \sin A, \\ \tan (90° + A) &= - \operatorname{ctn} A. \end{aligned} \quad (12)$$

$$\begin{aligned} \sin (180° - A) &= \sin A, \qquad \cos (180° - A) = - \cos A, \\ \tan (180° - A) &= - \tan A. \end{aligned} \quad (13)$$

137

$$\sin(180° + A) = -\sin A, \quad \cos(180° + A) = -\cos A,$$
$$\tan(180° + A) = \tan A. \tag{14}$$

$$\sin(270° - A) = -\cos A, \quad \cos(270° - A) = -\sin A,$$
$$\tan(270° - A) = \operatorname{ctn} A. \tag{15}$$

$$\sin(270° + A) = -\cos A, \quad \cos(270° + A) = \sin A,$$
$$\tan(270° + A) = -\operatorname{ctn} A. \tag{16}$$

$$\sin(360° - A) = -\sin A, \quad \cos(360° - A) = \cos A,$$
$$\tan(360° - A) = -\tan A. \tag{17}$$

The following table gives the values of sine, cosine, and tangent at each of the quadrant points and their algebraic signs in each of the quadrants marked I, II, III, IV.

	0°	I	90°	II	180°	III	270°	IV	360°
sin	0	+	1	+	0	−	− 1	−	0
cos	1	+	0	−	− 1	−	0	+	1
tan	0	+	∞	−	0	+	∞	−	0

44. Circular measure. The *circular measure* of an angle is the quotient of the length of an arc of a circle, with its center at the vertex of the angle and included between its sides, divided by the radius of the arc. Thus, if θ is the angle, a the length of the arc, and r the radius, we have

$$\theta = \frac{a}{r}. \tag{1}$$

The unit of angle in this measurement is the *radian*, which is the angle for which $a = r$ in (1), and any angle may be said to contain a certain number of radians. But the quotient $\frac{a}{r}$ in formula (1) is an abstract number, and it is also customary to speak of the angle θ as having the magnitude $\frac{a}{r}$ without using the word "radian." Thus, we speak of the angle 1, the angle $\frac{2}{3}$, the angle $\frac{\pi}{4}$, etc.

In all work involving calculus, and in most theoretical work of any kind, all angles which occur are understood to be expressed in radians. In fact, many of the calculus formulas would be false unless the angles involved were so expressed. The student should carefully note this fact, although the reason for it is not yet apparent.

From this point of view such a trigonometric equation as

$$y = \sin x \tag{2}$$

may be considered as defining a functional relation between two quantities exactly as does the simpler equation $y = x^2$. For we may, in (2), assign any arbitrary value to x and determine the corresponding value of y. This may be done by a direct computation (as will be shown in Chapter VIII), or it may be done by means of a table of trigonometric functions, in which case we must interpret the value of x as denoting so many radians.

One of the reasons for expressing an angle in circular measure is that it makes true the formula

$$\operatorname*{Lim}_{h \to 0} \frac{\sin h}{h} = 1. \tag{3}$$

To prove this theorem we proceed as follows:

Let h be the angle AOB (Fig. 59), and r the radius of the arc AB described from O as a center. BC is a line drawn from B perpendicular to OA, and BD is a line tangent to the arc AB at B and meeting OA produced in D.

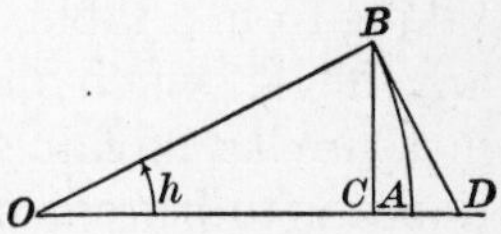

We thus form two triangles, COB and DOB.

FIG. 59

In the triangle COB, $OC = r \cos h$, $BC = r \sin h$, and hence the area of the triangle is $\frac{1}{2} r^2 \sin h \cos h$.

In the triangle DOB, $BD = r \tan h$, $OB = r$, and hence the area of the triangle is $\frac{1}{2} r^2 \tan h$.

The area of the sector AOB is $\frac{1}{2} r^2 h$, since, by hypothesis, the angle h is in circular measure.

Since the triangle DOB entirely includes the sector AOB and the sector AOB entirely includes the triangle COB, it follows that

$$\text{area } DOB > \text{area } AOB > \text{area } COB,$$

that is, $\qquad \frac{1}{2} r^2 \tan h > \frac{1}{2} r^2 h > \frac{1}{2} r^2 \sin h \cos h.$

Dividing by $\frac{1}{2}\,r^2 \sin h$, we have

$$\frac{1}{\cos h} > \frac{h}{\sin h} > \cos h,$$

or, by inverting, $\qquad \cos h < \dfrac{\sin h}{h} < \dfrac{1}{\cos h}.$

Now as $h \to 0$, $\cos h \to 1$, and $\dfrac{1}{\cos h} \to 1$. Hence $\dfrac{\sin h}{h}$, which lies between $\cos h$ and $\dfrac{1}{\cos h}$, must also approach 1; that is,

$$\operatorname*{Lim}_{h \to 0} \frac{\sin h}{h} = 1.$$

This result may be used to find the limit of $\dfrac{1 - \cos h}{h}$ as h approaches zero as a limit. For we have

$$\frac{1 - \cos h}{h} = \frac{2 \sin^2 \dfrac{h}{2}}{h} = \frac{\sin^2 \dfrac{h}{2}}{\dfrac{h}{2}} = \sin \frac{h}{2} \left(\frac{\sin \dfrac{h}{2}}{\dfrac{h}{2}} \right).$$

Now as $h \to 0$, $\dfrac{\sin \dfrac{h}{2}}{\dfrac{h}{2}} \to 1$ by (3). Therefore

$$\operatorname*{Lim}_{h \to 0} \frac{1 - \cos h}{h} = 0. \tag{4}$$

45. Graphs of trigonometric functions. We may plot a trigonometric function by assigning values to x and computing, or taking from a table, the corresponding values of y. In so doing, any angle which may occur should be expressed in circular measure, as explained in the preceding section. In this connection it is to be remembered that π is simply the number 3.1416, and that the angle π means an angle with that number of radians and is therefore the angle whose degree measure is 180°.

The manner of plotting can best be explained by examples.

Example 1. $y = a \sin bx.$

It is convenient first to fix the values of x which make y equal to zero. Now the sine is zero when the angle is 0, π, $2\,\pi$, $3\,\pi$, $-\,\pi$, $-\,2\,\pi$, or, in general, $k\pi$, where k is any positive or negative integer. To make $y = 0$, therefore, we have to place

$$bx = \cdots, \quad -2\,\pi, \quad -\,\pi, \quad 0, \quad \pi, \quad 2\,\pi, \quad 3\,\pi, \quad \cdots;$$

whence $\quad x = \cdots, \quad -\dfrac{2\,\pi}{b}, \quad -\dfrac{\pi}{b}, \quad 0, \quad \dfrac{\pi}{b}, \quad \dfrac{2\,\pi}{b}, \quad \dfrac{3\,\pi}{b}, \quad \cdots.$

The sine takes its maximum value $+1$ when

$$bx = \cdots, \quad -\frac{7\,\pi}{2}, \quad -\frac{3\,\pi}{2}, \quad \frac{\pi}{2}, \quad \frac{5\,\pi}{2}, \quad \cdots;$$

whence $\quad x = \cdots, \quad -\frac{7\,\pi}{2\,b}, \quad -\frac{3\,\pi}{2\,b}, \quad \frac{\pi}{2\,b}, \quad \frac{5\,\pi}{2\,b}, \quad \cdots.$

For these values $y = a$.

The sine takes its minimum value -1 when

$$bx = \cdots, \quad -\frac{5\,\pi}{2}, \quad -\frac{\pi}{2}, \quad \frac{3\,\pi}{2}, \quad \frac{7\,\pi}{2}, \quad \cdots,$$

whence $\quad x = \cdots, \quad -\frac{5\,\pi}{2\,b}, \quad -\frac{\pi}{2\,b}, \quad \frac{3\,\pi}{2\,b}, \quad \frac{7\,\pi}{2\,b}, \quad \cdots.$

For these values of x, $y = -a$.

These values of x for which the sine is ± 1 lie halfway between the values of x for which the sine is 0.

These points on the graph are enough to determine its general shape. Other values of x may be used to fix the shape more exactly.

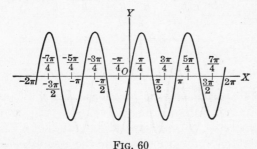

FIG. 60

The graph is shown in Fig. 60, with $a = 3$ and $b = 2$. The curve may be said to represent a wave. The distance from peak to peak, $\frac{2\,\pi}{b}$, is the wave length, and the height a above OX is the amplitude.

Example 2. $y = a \cos bx.$

As in Example 1, we fix first the points for which $y = 0$. Now the cosine of an angle is zero when the angle is $\frac{\pi}{2}, \frac{3\,\pi}{2}, \frac{5\,\pi}{2}, -\frac{\pi}{2}, -\frac{3\,\pi}{2},$ etc.; that is, any odd multiple of $\frac{\pi}{2}$. We have, therefore, $y = 0$ when

$$bx = \cdots, \quad -\frac{3\,\pi}{2}, \quad -\frac{\pi}{2}, \quad \frac{\pi}{2}, \quad \frac{3\,\pi}{2}, \quad \frac{5\,\pi}{2}, \quad \cdots;$$

whence $\quad x = \cdots, \quad -\frac{3\,\pi}{2\,b}, \quad -\frac{\pi}{2\,b}, \quad \frac{\pi}{2\,b}, \quad \frac{3\,\pi}{2\,b}, \quad \frac{5\,\pi}{2\,b}, \quad \cdots.$

Halfway between these points the cosine has its maximum value $+1$ or its minimum value -1 alternately, and $y = \pm a$. The graph is shown in Fig. 61, with $a = 3$ and $b = 2$.

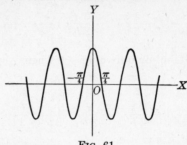

FIG. 61

Example 3. $y = a \sin (bx + c)$.

We have $y = 0$ when $bx + c = 0$, π, 2π, 3π, etc.; that is, when

$$x = \cdots, \quad -\frac{c}{b}, \quad -\frac{c}{b} + \frac{\pi}{b}, \quad -\frac{c}{b} + \frac{2\pi}{b}, \quad \cdots.$$

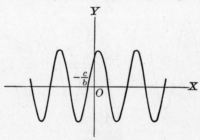

FIG. 62

Halfway between these values of x, $y = \pm a$. The curve is the same as in Example 1, but is shifted $\frac{c}{b}$ units to the left (Fig. 62).

Example 4. $y = \sin x + \frac{1}{2} \sin 2x$.

The graph is found by adding the ordinates of the two curves $y = \sin x$ and $y = \frac{1}{2} \sin 2x$, as shown in Fig. 63.

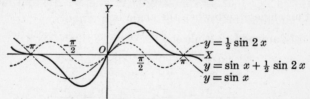

FIG. 63

EXERCISES

Plot the graphs of the following equations:

1. $y = 4 \sin 3x$.

2. $y = 2 \sin \dfrac{x}{2}$.

3. $y = 2 \cos 3x$.

4. $y = 3 \cos \tfrac{2}{3} x$.

5. $y = 2 \sin \left(x - \dfrac{\pi}{3}\right)$.

6. $y = \tfrac{1}{2} \cos \left(x + \dfrac{\pi}{4}\right)$.

7. $y = 2 \sin (3x - 2)$.

8. $y = 3 \cos (2x - 3)$.

9. $y = \tan x$.

10. $y = \tan 2x$.

11. $y = \operatorname{ctn} x$.

12. $y = 2 \operatorname{ctn} \dfrac{x}{2}$.

13. $y = \sec 2x$.

14. $y = \csc 3x$.

15. $y = \operatorname{vers} x$.

16. $y = 2 + \sin 3x$.

17. $y = \cos x - \sin x$.

18. $y = 2 \cos x + \sin 2x$.

46. Differentiation of trigonometric functions. The formulas for the differentiation of trigonometric functions are as follows, where u represents any function of x which can be differentiated:

$$\frac{d}{dx} \sin u = \cos u \, \frac{du}{dx}, \tag{1}$$

$$\frac{d}{dx} \cos u = - \sin u \, \frac{du}{dx}, \tag{2}$$

$$\frac{d}{dx} \tan u = \sec^2 u \, \frac{du}{dx}, \tag{3}$$

$$\frac{d}{dx} \operatorname{ctn} u = - \csc^2 u \, \frac{du}{dx}, \tag{4}$$

$$\frac{d}{dx} \sec u = \sec u \tan u \, \frac{du}{dx}, \tag{5}$$

$$\frac{d}{dx} \csc u = - \csc u \operatorname{ctn} u \, \frac{du}{dx}. \tag{6}$$

These formulas are proved as follows:

1. Let $y = \sin u$, where u is any function of x which may be differentiated. Give x an increment Δx and let Δu and Δy be the corresponding increments of u and y. Then

$$\Delta y = \sin (u + \Delta u) - \sin u$$
$$= \sin u \cos \Delta u + \cos u \sin \Delta u - \sin u$$
$$= \cos u \sin \Delta u - (1 - \cos \Delta u) \sin u;$$

whence $\quad \dfrac{\Delta y}{\Delta u} = \cos u \, \dfrac{\sin \Delta u}{\Delta u} - \dfrac{1 - \cos \Delta u}{\Delta u} \sin u.$

Now let Δx and therefore Δu approach zero. By (3), § 44, $\text{Lim} \dfrac{\sin \Delta u}{\Delta u} = 1$, and, by (4), § 44, $\text{Lim} \dfrac{1 - \cos \Delta u}{\Delta u} = 0$. Therefore

$$\frac{dy}{du} = \cos u.$$

But by (8), § 36, $\qquad \dfrac{dy}{dx} = \dfrac{dy}{du}\dfrac{du}{dx},$

and therefore $\qquad \dfrac{d}{dx} \sin u = \cos u \dfrac{du}{dx}.$

2. To find $\dfrac{d}{dx} \cos u$, we write

$$\cos u = \sin\left(\frac{\pi}{2} - u\right).$$

Then $\qquad \dfrac{d}{dx} \cos u = \dfrac{d}{dx} \sin\left(\dfrac{\pi}{2} - u\right)$

$$= \cos\left(\frac{\pi}{2} - u\right)\frac{d}{dx}\left(\frac{\pi}{2} - u\right) \qquad \text{[By (1)]}$$

$$= -\cos\left(\frac{\pi}{2} - u\right)\frac{du}{dx}$$

$$= -\sin u \frac{du}{dx}.$$

3. To find $\dfrac{d}{dx} \tan u$, we write

$$\tan u = \frac{\sin u}{\cos u}.$$

Then $\dfrac{d}{dx} \tan u = \dfrac{d}{dx} \dfrac{\sin u}{\cos u}$

$$= \frac{\cos u \dfrac{d}{dx} \sin u - \sin u \dfrac{d}{dx} \cos u}{\cos^2 u} \qquad \text{[By (5), § 36]}$$

$$= \frac{(\cos^2 u + \sin^2 u)\dfrac{du}{dx}}{\cos^2 u} \qquad \text{[By (1) and (2)]}$$

$$= \sec^2 u \frac{du}{dx}.$$

4. To find $\dfrac{d}{dx} \text{ctn } u$, we write

$$\text{ctn } u = \frac{\cos u}{\sin u}.$$

Then $\dfrac{d}{dx}$ ctn $u = \dfrac{d}{dx}\dfrac{\cos u}{\sin u}$

$$= \frac{\sin u \dfrac{d}{dx}\cos u - \cos u \dfrac{d}{dx}\sin u}{\sin^2 u} \qquad \text{[By (5), § 36]}$$

$$= \frac{-\sin^2 u - \cos^2 u}{\sin^2 u}\frac{du}{dx} \qquad \text{[By (1) and (2)]}$$

$$= - \csc^2 u \frac{du}{dx}.$$

5. To find $\dfrac{d}{dx}$ sec u, we write

$$\sec u = \frac{1}{\cos u} = (\cos u)^{-1}.$$

Then $\qquad \dfrac{d}{dx}$ sec $u = - (\cos u)^{-2}\dfrac{d}{dx}\cos u \qquad$ [By (6), § 36]

$$= \frac{\sin u}{\cos^2 u}\frac{du}{dx} \qquad\qquad \text{[By (2)]}$$

$$= \sec u \tan u \frac{du}{dx}.$$

6. To find $\dfrac{d}{dx}$ csc u, we write

$$\csc u = \frac{1}{\sin u} = (\sin u)^{-1}.$$

Then $\qquad \dfrac{d}{dx}$ csc $u = - (\sin u)^{-2}\dfrac{d}{dx}\sin u \qquad$ [By (6), § 36]

$$= - \csc u \,\text{ctn}\, u \frac{du}{dx}. \qquad\qquad \text{[By (1)]}$$

Example 1. $y = \tan 2x - \tan^2 x = \tan 2x - (\tan x)^2.$

$$\frac{dy}{dx} = \sec^2 2x \frac{d}{dx}(2x) - 2(\tan x)\frac{d}{dx}\tan x$$

$$= 2 \sec^2 2x - 2 \tan x \sec^2 x.$$

Example 2. $y = (2 \sec^4 x + 3 \sec^2 x) \sin x.$

$$\frac{dy}{dx} = \sin x \left[8 \sec^3 x \frac{d}{dx}(\sec x) + 6 \sec x \frac{d}{dx}(\sec x) \right]$$

$$+ (2 \sec^4 x + 3 \sec^2 x)\frac{d}{dx}(\sin x)$$

$$= \sin x \,(8 \sec^4 x \tan x + 6 \sec^2 x \tan x) + (2 \sec^4 x + 3 \sec^2 x) \cos x$$

$$= (1 - \cos^2 x)(8 \sec^5 x + 6 \sec^3 x) + (2 \sec^3 x + 3 \sec x)$$

$$= 8 \sec^5 x - 3 \sec x.$$

EXERCISES

Find $\dfrac{dy}{dx}$ in each of the following cases:

1. $y = 4 \sin 2\,x.$

2. $y = 3 \tan \dfrac{x}{3}.$

3. $y = \sin^2 3\,x.$

4. $y = \frac{1}{4} \tan^2 2\,x.$

5. $y = \dfrac{x}{2} + \dfrac{1}{20} \sin 10\,x.$

6. $y = \frac{1}{5} \cos^5 3\,x - \frac{1}{3} \cos^3 3\,x.$

7. $y = \sec^5 \dfrac{3\,x}{5}.$

8. $y = \frac{1}{2} \csc^2 4\,x.$

9. $y = \sin \dfrac{x}{4} - \dfrac{1}{3} \sin^3 \dfrac{x}{4}.$

10. $y = \dfrac{3}{5} \tan^5 \dfrac{x}{3} + \tan^3 \dfrac{x}{3}.$

11. $y = 3 \cos \dfrac{2\,x}{3} + 2\,x \sin \dfrac{2\,x}{3}.$

12. $y = \dfrac{\csc 2\,x - \operatorname{ctn} 2\,x}{\csc 2\,x + \operatorname{ctn} 2\,x}.$

13. $y = \sin\,(3\,x + 2) \cos\,(3\,x - 2).$

14. $y = \tan^3 \dfrac{x}{3} - 3 \tan \dfrac{x}{3} + x.$

15. $y = \frac{1}{2} \sec 2\,x + \frac{1}{6} \tan^3 2\,x.$

16. $y = \sec^3 2\,x - 3 \sec 2\,x.$

17. $\cos 3\,x + \sec 2\,y = 0.$

18. $xy + \operatorname{ctn} xy = 0.$

19. $\tan\,(x + y) + \tan\,(x - y) = 1.$

20. $\sin \dfrac{x}{y} + \cos \dfrac{y}{x} = 0.$

47. Graphs of inverse trigonometric functions. The equation

$$x = \sin y \tag{1}$$

defines a relation between the quantities x and y which may be stated by saying either that x is the sine of the angle y or that the angle y has the sine x. When we wish to use the latter form of expressing the relation, we write in place of equation (1) the equation

$$y = \sin^{-1} x, \tag{2}$$

where -1 is not to be understood as a negative exponent but as part of a new symbol $\sin^{-1}$. To avoid the possible ambiguity, formula (2) is sometimes written

$$y = \operatorname{arc} \sin x.$$

Equations (1) and (2) have exactly the same meaning, and the student should accustom himself to pass from one to the other without difficulty. In equation (1) y is considered the independent variable, while in (2) x is considered the independent variable. Equation (2) then defines a function of x which is called the *anti-sine* of x or the *inverse sine* of x. It will add to the clearness of the student's thinking, however, if he will read equation (2) as "y is the angle whose sine is x."

Similarly, if $x = \cos y$, then $y = \cos^{-1} x$; if $x = \tan y$, then $y = \tan^{-1} x$; and so on for the other trigonometric functions. We get in this way the whole class of *inverse trigonometric functions*.

It is to be noticed that, from equation (2), y is not completely determined when x is given, since there is an infinite number of angles with the same sine. For example, if $x = \frac{1}{2}$, $y = \frac{\pi}{6}$, $\frac{5\pi}{6}$, $\frac{13\pi}{6}$, etc. This causes a certain amount of ambiguity in using inverse trigonometric functions. We have the same sort of ambiguity when we pass from the equation $x = y^2$ to the equation $y = \pm \sqrt{x}$, for if x is given, there are two values of y.

To obtain the graph of the function expressed in (2) we may change (2) into the equivalent form (1) and proceed as in § 45. In this way it is evident that the graphs of the inverse trigonometric functions are the same as those of the direct functions but differently placed with reference to the coördinate axes. It is to be noticed particularly that to any value of x corresponds an infinite number of values of y.

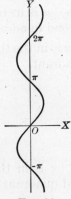
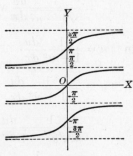

FIG. 64   FIG. 65

Example 1. $y = \sin^{-1} x$.

From this, $x = \sin y$, and we may plot the graph by assuming values of y and computing those of x (Fig. 64).

Example 2. $y = \tan^{-1} x$.

Then $x = \tan y$, and the graph is as in Fig. 65.

EXERCISES

Plot the graphs of the following equations:

1. $y = \sin^{-1}\dfrac{x}{2}$.

2. $y = 2\cos^{-1}3x$.

3. $y = \frac{1}{2}\sin^{-1}(2x - 1)$.

4. $y = \frac{1}{3}\cos^{-1}(2x - 3)$.

5. $y = \tan^{-1}2x$.

6. $y = 2\operatorname{ctn}^{-1}\dfrac{x}{3}$.

7. $y + \dfrac{\pi}{2} = \sin^{-1}(2x + 3)$.

8. $y + \sin^{-1}(x + 2) = \dfrac{\pi}{2}$.

9. $y + 2\cos^{-1}(x - 2) = \pi$.

10. $\pi - 2y - 2\sin^{-1}(2x - 1) = 0$.

48. Differentiation of inverse trigonometric functions. The formulas for the differentiation of the inverse trigonometric functions are as follows:

1. $\dfrac{d}{dx}\sin^{-1}u = \dfrac{1}{\sqrt{1 - u^2}}\dfrac{du}{dx}$ when $\sin^{-1}u$ is in the first or the fourth quadrant;

$\qquad = -\dfrac{1}{\sqrt{1 - u^2}}\dfrac{du}{dx}$ when $\sin^{-1}u$ is in the second or the third quadrant.

2. $\dfrac{d}{dx}\cos^{-1}u = -\dfrac{1}{\sqrt{1 - u^2}}\dfrac{du}{dx}$ when $\cos^{-1}u$ is in the first or the second quadrant;

$\qquad = \dfrac{1}{\sqrt{1 - u^2}}\dfrac{du}{dx}$ when $\cos^{-1}u$ is in the third or the fourth quadrant.

3. $\dfrac{d}{dx}\tan^{-1}u = \dfrac{1}{1 + u^2}\dfrac{du}{dx}$.

4. $\dfrac{d}{dx}\operatorname{ctn}^{-1}u = -\dfrac{1}{1 + u^2}\dfrac{du}{dx}$.

5. $\dfrac{d}{dx}\sec^{-1}u = \dfrac{1}{u\sqrt{u^2 - 1}}\dfrac{du}{dx}$ when $\sec^{-1}u$ is in the first or the third quadrant;

$\qquad = -\dfrac{1}{u\sqrt{u^2 - 1}}\dfrac{du}{dx}$ when $\sec^{-1}u$ is in the second or the fourth quadrant.

6. $\dfrac{d}{dx}\csc^{-1}u = -\dfrac{1}{u\sqrt{u^2 - 1}}\dfrac{du}{dx}$ when $\csc^{-1}u$ is in the first or the third quadrant;

$\qquad = \dfrac{1}{u\sqrt{u^2 - 1}}\dfrac{du}{dx}$ when $\csc^{-1}u$ is in the second or the fourth quadrant.

The proofs of these formulas are as follows:

1. If
$$y = \sin^{-1} u,$$
then
$$\sin y = u.$$

Hence, by § 46,
$$\cos y \frac{dy}{dx} = \frac{du}{dx};$$

whence
$$\frac{dy}{dx} = \frac{1}{\cos y} \frac{du}{dx}.$$

But $\cos y = \sqrt{1 - u^2}$ when y is in the first or the fourth quadrant, and $\cos y = -\sqrt{1 - u^2}$ when y is in the second or the third quadrant.

2. If
$$y = \cos^{-1} u,$$
then
$$\cos y = u.$$

Hence
$$-\sin y \frac{dy}{dx} = \frac{du}{dx};$$

whence
$$\frac{dy}{dx} = -\frac{1}{\sin y} \frac{du}{dx}.$$

But $\sin y = \sqrt{1 - u^2}$ when y is in the first or the second quadrant, and $\sin y = -\sqrt{1 - u^2}$ when y is in the third or the fourth quadrant.

3. If
$$y = \tan^{-1} u,$$
then
$$\tan y = u.$$

Hence
$$\sec^2 y \frac{dy}{dx} = \frac{du}{dx};$$

whence
$$\frac{dy}{dx} = \frac{1}{1 + u^2} \frac{du}{dx}.$$

4. If
$$y = \operatorname{ctn}^{-1} u,$$
then
$$\operatorname{ctn} y = u.$$

Hence
$$-\csc^2 y \frac{dy}{dx} = \frac{du}{dx};$$

whence
$$\frac{dy}{dx} = -\frac{1}{1 + u^2} \frac{du}{dx}.$$

5. If $\qquad\qquad y = \sec^{-1} u,$

then $\qquad\qquad\qquad \sec y = u.$

Hence $\qquad\qquad \sec y \tan y \dfrac{dy}{dx} = \dfrac{du}{dx};$

whence $\qquad\qquad\qquad \dfrac{dy}{dx} = \cdot\dfrac{1}{\sec y \tan y}\dfrac{du}{dx}.$

But $\sec y = u$, and $\tan y = \sqrt{u^2 - 1}$ when y is in the first or the third quadrant, and $\tan y = -\sqrt{u^2 - 1}$ when y is in the second or the fourth quadrant.

6. If $\qquad\qquad y = \csc^{-1} u,$

then $\qquad\qquad\qquad \csc y = u.$

Hence $\qquad -\csc y \operatorname{ctn} y \dfrac{dy}{dx} = \dfrac{du}{dx};$

whence $\qquad\qquad\qquad \dfrac{dy}{dx} = -\dfrac{1}{\csc y \operatorname{ctn} y}\dfrac{du}{dx}.$

But $\csc y = u$, and $\operatorname{ctn} y = \sqrt{u^2 - 1}$ when y is in the first or the third quadrant, and $\operatorname{ctn} y = -\sqrt{u^2 - 1}$ when y is in the second or the fourth quadrant.

If the quadrant in which an angle lies is not material in a problem, it will be assumed to be in the first quadrant. This applies particularly to formal exercises in differentiation.

Example 1. $y = \sin^{-1}\sqrt{1 - x^2}$, where y is an acute angle.

$$\frac{dy}{dx} = \frac{1}{\sqrt{1 - (1 - x^2)}} \cdot \frac{d}{dx}(1 - x^2)^{\frac{1}{2}} = -\frac{1}{\sqrt{1 - x^2}}.$$

This result may also be obtained by placing $\sin^{-1}\sqrt{1-x^2} = \cos^{-1}x$.

Example 2. $y = \sec^{-1}\sqrt{4\,x^2 + 4\,x + 2}.$

$$\frac{dy}{dx} = \frac{\dfrac{d}{dx}\sqrt{4\,x^2 + 4\,x + 2}}{\sqrt{4\,x^2 + 4\,x + 2}\,\sqrt{(4\,x^2 + 4\,x + 2) - 1}}$$

$$= \frac{4\,x + 2}{(4\,x^2 + 4\,x + 2)(2\,x + 1)} = \frac{1}{2\,x^2 + 2\,x + 1}.$$

EXERCISES

Find $\dfrac{dy}{dx}$ in each of the following cases:

1. $y = \sin^{-1} 2x.$

2. $y = \cos^{-1} \dfrac{2}{3x}.$

3. $y = \tan^{-1}(2x - 1).$

4. $y = \operatorname{ctn}^{-1} \sqrt{x^2 + 2x}.$

5. $y = \sec^{-1} 3x.$

6. $y = \csc^{-1}(2x + 1).$

7. $y = \sin^{-1} \dfrac{x - 2}{2}.$

8. $y = \tan^{-1} \dfrac{x + 2}{2}.$

9. $y = \cos^{-1} \dfrac{x^2}{x^2 + 2}.$

10. $y = \tan^{-1} \dfrac{x + 6}{3x - 2}.$

11. $y = \operatorname{ctn}^{-1} \dfrac{1}{2}\left(\dfrac{2}{x} - \dfrac{x}{2}\right).$

12. $y = \sec^{-1} \dfrac{\sqrt{2 + 2x^2}}{1 + x}.$

13. $y = \dfrac{3x}{x^2 + 9} + \operatorname{ctn}^{-1} \dfrac{3}{x}.$

14. $y = \sec^{-1} \dfrac{x}{\sqrt{x^2 - 4}}.$

15. $y = \csc^{-1} \dfrac{1 + x}{1 - x}.$

16. $y = 3\sqrt{9 - x^2} + 2\sin^{-1} \dfrac{x}{3}.$

17. $y = \tan^{-1}(2x + 1) + \operatorname{ctn}^{-1} \dfrac{1 + x}{x}.$

18. $y = x^2\sqrt{1 - x^4} + \sin^{-1} x^2.$

19. $y = \dfrac{x}{\sqrt{4x - x^2}} - \cos^{-1} \dfrac{x - 2}{2}.$

20. $y = \csc^{-1} \dfrac{x - 2}{2}.$

49. Angular velocity. If a line OP (Fig. 66) is revolving in a plane about O, and in a time t has moved from OM to OP, the angle $MOP = \theta$ denotes the amount of rotation. The rate of change of θ with respect to t is called the *angular velocity* of OP, and is commonly denoted by the Greek letter ω. Hence we have the formula

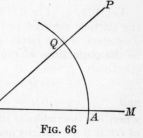

$$\omega = \frac{d\theta}{dt}. \qquad (1)$$

If θ is in radians and t is in seconds, the angular velocity is in radians per second. By dividing by 2π, the angular velocity may be reduced to revolutions per second, since one revolution is equivalent to 2π radians.

FIG. 66

A point Q on the line OP at a distance r from O describes a circle of radius r which intersects OM at A. If s is the length of the arc of the circle AQ measured from A, then, by § 44,

$$s = r\theta. \qquad (2)$$

Now $\dfrac{ds}{dt}$ is called the *linear velocity* v of the point Q, since it measures the rate at which s is described; and, from (2) and, (1),

$$v = \frac{ds}{dt} = r\,\frac{d\theta}{dt} = r\omega, \tag{3}$$

showing that the farther the point Q is from O the greater is its linear velocity.

Similarly, the angular acceleration, which is denoted by α, is defined by the relation

$$\alpha = \frac{d\omega}{dt} = \frac{d^2\theta}{dt^2}. \tag{4}$$

Example 1. If a wheel revolves so that the angular velocity is given by the formula $\omega = 8\,t$, how many revolutions will it make in the time from $t = 2$ to $t = 5$?

We take a spoke of the wheel as the line OP. Then we have

$$d\theta = 8\,t\,dt.$$

Hence the angle through which the wheel revolves in the given time is

$$\theta = \int_2^5 8\,t\,dt = [4\,t^2]_2^5 = 100 - 16 = 84.$$

The result is in radians. It may be reduced to revolutions by dividing by $2\,\pi$. The answer is 13.4 revolutions.

Example 2. A particle traverses a circle at a uniform rate of n revolutions per second. Determine the motion of the projection of the particle on a diameter of the circle.

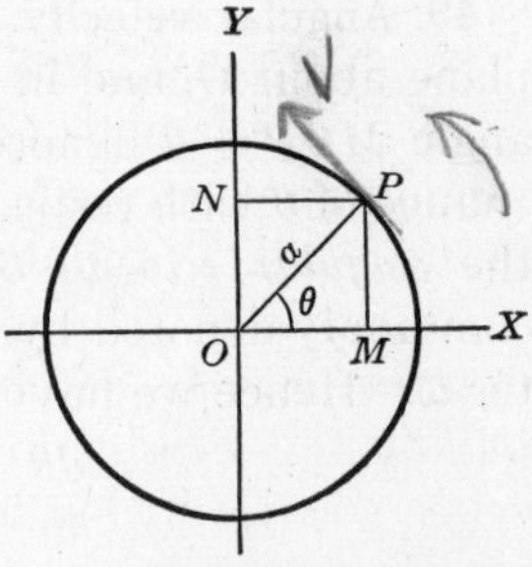

Let $P(x, y)$ (Fig. 67) be the position of the particle referred to two perpendicular diameters of the circle, and let M and N be the projections of P on OX and OY respectively. Then

$$x = OM = a \cos \theta,$$

and

$$y = ON = a \sin \theta,$$

FIG. 67

where a is the radius of the circle. By hypothesis the angular velocity of OP is $2\,n\pi$ radians per second. Therefore

$$\omega = \frac{d\theta}{dt} = 2\,n\pi;$$

whence

$$\theta = 2\,n\pi t + C.$$

If we consider that when $t = 0$, the particle is on OX, then $C = 0$. Therefore

$$x = a \cos \theta = a \cos 2\,n\pi t = a \cos \omega t,$$

$$y = a \sin \theta = a \sin 2\,n\pi t = a \sin \omega t.$$

EXERCISES

1. A flywheel 4 ft. in diameter makes 4 revolutions per second. Find the components of velocity in feet per second of a point on the rim when it is 1 ft. above the level of the center of the wheel.

2. A point on the rim of a flywheel of radius 5 ft. which is 4 ft. above the level of the center of the wheel has a horizontal component of velocity of 120 ft. per second. Find the number of revolutions of the wheel per second.

3. The coördinates of a moving particle at a time t are $x = 10 \cos 4\, t$, $y = 10 \sin 4\, t$. Prove that the particle moves in a circle, and find the angular velocity of the radius drawn from the particle to the center.

4. Find the angular velocity of OP joining the origin O to the point (x, y) when the point moves so that x and y increase at a uniform rate of 4 ft. per second.

5. A particle moves around a circle of radius 100 ft. in such a manner that at any time t (in seconds) its distance s from a fixed point on the circumference is $s = 10\, t^2$ ft. Find a general expression for the angular velocity of the radius joining the point to the center of the circle.

50. Simple harmonic motion. In many natural phenomena we have to consider the motion of a point, or a particle, which is vibrating in a straight line. An example is the motion of a point in the bob of a pendulum when the arc of swing of the pendulum is so small that it may be considered a straight line. Another example may be had by attaching a weight to an elastic string, pulling the weight down a little, and letting go. Other cases occur when we consider the motion of a particle of a medium which is transmitting a wave of sound, light, or an electric impulse.

In all such cases theory teaches us that, if we neglect the forces which may tend to stop such a motion, the relation between the distance s from a fixed point in the line of motion and the time t is expressed by either of the equations

$$s = c \sin bt, \qquad\qquad (1)$$

or
$$s = c \cos bt, \qquad\qquad (2)$$

according as the time is measured from the instant when the

particle is at the middle or the end of its swing. A motion that can be so expressed is called *simple harmonic motion*. A geometric construction of such a motion is found in the motion of either M or N of Example 2, § 49.

It is easy to see that equations (1) and (2) represent a vibratory motion. Take, for example, (1). When $t = 0$, $s = 0$ and the particle is at O (Fig. 68). When $t = \dfrac{\pi}{2\,b}$, $s = c$, which is the largest value s can have, and the particle is at A, where $OA = c$. As t continues to increase, s becomes smaller until when $t = \dfrac{\pi}{b}$, $s = 0$ and the particle is back at O. As time

FIG. 68

continues to increase, s becomes negative, until when $t = \dfrac{3\,\pi}{2\,b}$, $s = -c$, which is the least value s can have, and the particle is at B, where $OB = -c$. Finally, when $t = \dfrac{2\,\pi}{b}$, $s = 0$ and the particle is back at O. The motion is then repeated.

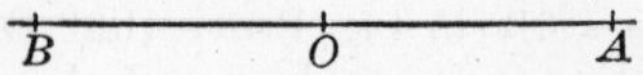

Similarly for equation (2). When $t = 0$, $s = c$ and the particle is at A. When $t = \dfrac{\pi}{2\,b}$, $s = 0$ and the particle is at O. When $t = \dfrac{\pi}{b}$, $s = -c$ and the particle is at B. When $t = \dfrac{3\,\pi}{2\,b}$, $s = 0$ and the particle is at O. When $t = \dfrac{2\,\pi}{b}$, $s = c$ and the particle is back at A. The motion then repeats.

In each case the particle oscillates between B and A, the time required for a complete oscillation being, as we have seen, $\dfrac{2\,\pi}{b}$. The quantity c is called the *amplitude*, and the interval $\dfrac{2\,\pi}{b}$, after which the motion repeats itself, is the *period*.

If instead of equations (1) and (2) we write the equations

$$s = c \sin b(t - t_0), \tag{3}$$

and

$$s = c \cos b(t - t_0), \tag{4}$$

the change amounts simply to altering the instant from which the time is measured. For the value of s which corresponds to $t = t_1$ in (1) and (2) equals the value of s which corresponds to $t = t_1 + t_0$ in (3) and (4). Hence either (3) or (4) represents simple harmonic motion of amplitude c and period $\dfrac{2\,\pi}{b}$.

But (3) and (4) may be written respectively as

$$s = c \cos bt_0 \sin bt - c \sin bt_0 \cos bt \qquad (5)$$

and
$$s = c \cos bt_0 \cos bt + c \sin bt_0 \sin bt \qquad (6)$$

either of which is the same as

$$s = A \sin bt + B \cos bt, \qquad (7)$$

where A and B are constants.

Conversely, any equation (7) may be reduced to either (3) or (4). If we wish to reduce (7) to (3), we place

$$A = c \cos bt_0, \qquad B = -c \sin bt_0;$$

whence
$$c = \sqrt{A^2 + B^2}, \qquad t_0 = -\frac{1}{b} \tan^{-1} \frac{B}{A}.$$

If we wish to reduce (7) to (4), we place

$$A = c \sin bt_0, \qquad B = c \cos bt_0,$$

whence
$$c = \sqrt{A^2 + B^2}, \qquad t_0 = \frac{1}{b} \tan^{-1} \frac{A}{B}.$$

Therefore equation (7) always represents simple harmonic motion, with amplitude $\sqrt{A^2 + B^2}$ and period $\frac{2\pi}{b}$.

From (1) we have, for the velocity v and the acceleration a,

$$v = cb \cos bt, \qquad (8)$$

$$a = -cb^2 \sin bt. \qquad (9)$$

Since force is proportional to the mass times the acceleration, the force F acting on the particle is given by the formula
$$F = kma = -kmcb^2 \sin bt = -kmb^2 s.$$

This shows that the force is proportional to the distance s from the point O. The negative sign shows that the force produces acceleration with a sign opposite to that of s, and therefore slows up the particle when it is moving away from O and increases its speed when it moves toward O. The force is therefore always directed toward O and is an attracting force.

EXERCISES

1. A point moves with simple harmonic motion of period 6 sec. and amplitude 4 ft. Find the equation of its motion.

2. Given the equation $s = 10 \cos 3\,t$. Find the time of a complete oscillation and the amplitude of the swing.

3. A particle moves around a circle of radius 5, center at O, so that its projection on OX describes the simple harmonic motion defined by the equation $x = 5 \cos 4\,t$. Determine the velocity of the particle and the angular velocity of the radius joining the particle to the center of the circle.

4. Discuss the changes in the velocity of a particle describing simple harmonic motion.

5. Discuss the changes in the acceleration of a particle describing simple harmonic motion.

6. The motion of a particle in a straight line is expressed by the equation $s = 8 - 4 \sin^2 2\,t$. Express the velocity and the acceleration in terms of s, and show that the motion is simple harmonic.

7. A particle moving with a simple harmonic motion of amplitude 4 ft. has a velocity of 6 ft. per second when at a distance of 3 ft. from its mean position. Find its period.

8. A particle moving with simple harmonic motion has a velocity of 3 ft. per second when at a distance of 4 ft. from its mean position, and a velocity of 4 ft. per second when at a distance of 3 ft. from its mean position. Find its amplitude and its period.

9. A particle is moving in a straight line so that $s = 4 \sin \dfrac{t}{3} - 3 \cos \dfrac{t}{3}$. Show that its motion is simple harmonic, and find the speed at which it passes through the middle point of its path.

10. A particle moving in simple harmonic motion with a period of 3 sec. has a velocity of $\dfrac{8\,\pi}{3}$ ft. per second when it is a distance of 4 ft. from its mean position. Find the amplitude of the motion.

11. The amplitude of a certain simple harmonic motion is 4 ft. When the particle is halfway from its mean position to its extreme position, its velocity is 2 ft. per second. Find the period of the motion.

51. Cycloid. If a wheel rolls upon a straight line, each point of the rim describes a curve called a *cycloid*.

Let a wheel of radius a roll upon the axis of x, and let C

(Fig. 69) be its center at any time of its motion, N its point of contact with OX, and P the point which describes the cycloid.

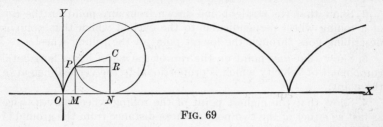

FIG. 69

Take as the origin of coördinates, O, the point found by rolling the wheel to the left until P meets OX.

Then $$ON = \text{arc } PN.$$

Draw MP and CN, each perpendicular to OX, PR parallel to OX, and connect C and P. Let

$$\text{Angle } NCP = \phi.$$

Then
$$
\begin{aligned}
x = OM &= ON - MN \\
&= \text{arc } PN - PR \\
&= a\phi - a \sin \phi. \\
y = MP &= NC - RC \\
&= a - a \cos \phi.
\end{aligned}
$$

Hence the parametric representation (§ 40) of the cycloid is
$$x = a(\phi - \sin \phi),$$
$$y = a(1 - \cos \phi).$$

If the wheel revolves with a constant angular velocity $\omega = \dfrac{d\phi}{dt}$, we have, by § 40,

$$v_x = a(1 - \cos \phi)\,\frac{d\phi}{dt} = a\omega(1 - \cos \phi),$$

$$v_y = a \sin \phi \frac{d\phi}{dt} = a\omega \sin \phi;$$

whence $$v^2 = a^2\omega^2(2 - 2\cos \phi) = 4\,a^2\omega^2 \sin^2 \frac{\phi}{2},$$

and $$v = 2\,a\omega \sin \frac{\phi}{2},$$

as an expression for the velocity in its path of a point on the rim of the wheel.

EXERCISES

1. Prove that the slope of the cycloid at any point is ctn $\frac{\phi}{2}$.

2. Show that the straight line drawn from any point on the rim of a rolling wheel perpendicular to the cycloid which that point is describing goes through the lowest point of the rolling wheel.

3. Show that any point on the rim of the wheel has a horizontal component of velocity which is proportional to the vertical height of the point.

4. Show that the highest point of the rolling wheel moves twice as fast as either of the two points whose distance from the ground is half the radius of the wheel.

5. Show that the vertical component of velocity is a maximum when the point which describes the cycloid is on the level of the center of the rolling wheel.

6. Show that a point on the spoke of a rolling wheel of radius a at a distance b from the center describes a curve given by the equations

$$x = a\phi - b \sin \phi, \quad y = a - b \cos \phi,$$

and find the velocity of the point in its path. The curve is called a *trochoid*.

7. Find the slope of the trochoid and find the point at which the curve is steepest.

8. Show that when a point on a spoke of a wheel describes a trochoid, the average of the velocities of the point when in its highest and lowest positions is equal to the linear velocity of the wheel.

9. Show that the Cartesian equation of the cycloid is

$$x = a \cos^{-1} \frac{a - y}{a} - \sqrt{2\,ay - y^2}.$$

52. Curvature. If a point describes a curve, the change of direction of its motion may be measured by the change of the angle ϕ (§ 15).

For example, in the curve of Fig. 70, if $AP_1 = s$ and $P_1P_2 = \Delta s$, and if ϕ_1 and ϕ_2 are the values of ϕ for the points P_1 and P_2 respectively, then $\phi_2 - \phi_1$ is the total change of direction of the curve between

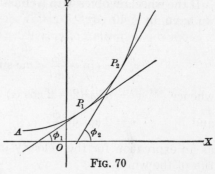

FIG. 70

P_1 and P_2. If $\phi_2 - \phi_1 = \Delta\phi$, expressed in circular measure, the ratio $\dfrac{\Delta\phi}{\Delta s}$ is the average change of direction per linear unit of the arc P_1P_2. Regarding ϕ as a function of s, and taking the limit of $\dfrac{\Delta\phi}{\Delta s}$ as Δs approaches zero as a limit, we have $\dfrac{d\phi}{ds}$, which is called the *curvature* of the curve at the point P. Hence the curvature of a curve is the rate of change of the direction of the curve with respect to the length of the arc.

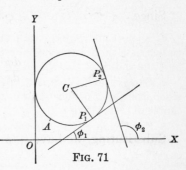

FIG. 71

If $\dfrac{d\phi}{ds}$ is constant, the curvature is constant or *uniform*; otherwise the curvature is variable. Applying this definition to the circle of Fig. 71, of which the center is C and the radius is a, we have $\Delta\phi = P_1CP_2$, and hence $\Delta s = a\,\Delta\phi$. Therefore $\dfrac{\Delta\phi}{\Delta s} = \dfrac{1}{a}$. Hence $\dfrac{d\phi}{ds} = \dfrac{1}{a}$, and *the circle is a curve of constant curvature equal to the reciprocal of its radius.*

The reciprocal of the curvature is called the *radius of curvature* and will be denoted by ρ. Through every point of a curve we may pass a circle with its radius equal to ρ, which shall have the same tangent as the curve at the point and shall lie on the same side of the tangent. Then the curvatures of the curve and of the circle are the same, and the circle shows the curvature of the curve in a manner similar to that in which the tangent shows the direction of the curve. The circle is called the *circle of curvature*.

From the definition of curvature it follows that

$$\rho = \frac{ds}{d\phi}.$$

If the equation of the curve is in rectangular coördinates,

$$\rho = \frac{\dfrac{ds}{dx}}{\dfrac{d\phi}{dx}}. \qquad \text{[By (9), § 36]}$$

To transform this expression further, we note that

$$ds^2 = dx^2 + dy^2 \, ;$$

whence, dividing by dx^2 and taking the square root, we have

$$\frac{ds}{dx} = \sqrt{1 + \left(\frac{dy}{dx}\right)^2}.$$

Since
$$\phi = \tan^{-1}\left(\frac{dy}{dx}\right), \qquad \text{[By § 15]}$$

$$\frac{d\phi}{dx} = \frac{\dfrac{d^2y}{dx^2}}{1 + \left(\dfrac{dy}{dx}\right)^2}.$$

Substituting, we have
$$\rho = \frac{\left[1 + \left(\dfrac{dy}{dx}\right)^2\right]^{\frac{3}{2}}}{\dfrac{d^2y}{dx^2}}.$$

In the above expression for ρ there is an apparent ambiguity of sign, on account of the radical sign. If only the numerical value of ρ is required, a negative sign may be disregarded.

Example 1. Find the radius of curvature of the ellipse $\dfrac{x^2}{a^2} + \dfrac{y^2}{b^2} = 1$.

Here
$$\frac{dy}{dx} = -\frac{b^2x}{a^2y}$$

and
$$\frac{d^2y}{dx^2} = -\frac{b^4}{a^2y^3}.$$

Therefore
$$\rho = \frac{(a^4y^2 + b^4x^2)^{\frac{3}{2}}}{a^4b^4}.$$

Example 2. Find the radius of curvature of the cycloid (§ 51).

We have
$$\frac{dx}{d\phi} = a(1 - \cos \phi) = 2\,a \sin^2 \frac{\phi}{2},$$

$$\frac{dy}{d\phi} = a \sin \phi = 2\,a \sin \frac{\phi}{2} \cos \frac{\phi}{2}.$$

Therefore, by (9), § 36,

$$\frac{dy}{dx} = \operatorname{ctn} \frac{\phi}{2}.$$

Hence
$$\frac{d^2y}{dx^2} = -\frac{1}{2} \csc^2 \frac{\phi}{2} \frac{d\phi}{dx} = -\frac{1}{4a} \csc^4 \frac{\phi}{2},$$

and
$$\rho = \frac{\left(1 + \text{ctn}^2 \frac{\phi}{2}\right)^{\frac{3}{2}}}{\frac{1}{4a} \csc^4 \frac{\phi}{2}} = 4a \sin \frac{\phi}{2}.$$

EXERCISES

1. Find the radius of curvature of the curve $y = \dfrac{8a^3}{x^2 + 4a^2}$ at the point $(2a, a)$.

2. Find the radius of curvature of the curve $y = \sin^{-1}\sqrt{2x - x^2}$ at a point for which $x = \frac{1}{2}$.

3. Find the radius of curvature of the curve $y^2 = \frac{4}{27} x^3$.

4. Find the radius of curvature of the curve $x^{\frac{2}{3}} + y^{\frac{2}{3}} = a^{\frac{2}{3}}$.

5. Show that the circle $\left(x - \dfrac{\pi}{2}\right)^2 + y^2 = 1$ is tangent to the curve $y = \sin x$ at the point for which $x = \dfrac{\pi}{2}$, and has the same radius of curvature at that point.

6. Find the radius of curvature of the curve $x = \sin t$, $y = \cos 2t$, at the point for which $t = \dfrac{\pi}{2}$.

7. Find the radius of curvature of the curve whose parametric equations are $x = a \cos \phi + a\phi \sin \phi$, $y = a \sin \phi - a\phi \cos \phi$.

8. Find the radius of curvature at the point for which $x = \dfrac{a}{2}$ of the curve $y = a \cos^{-1} \dfrac{a - x}{a} - \sqrt{2ax - x^2}$.

9. Find the radius of curvature of the curve $y = x \sin x$ at the point for which $x = \dfrac{\pi}{2}$.

53. Integration. Since, by § 46, $\dfrac{d}{dx}\left(\dfrac{1}{a} \sin ax\right) = \cos ax$ and $\dfrac{d}{dx}\left(\dfrac{1}{a} \cos ax\right) = -\sin ax$, we have immediately

$$\int \sin ax \, dx = -\frac{1}{a} \cos ax + C, \qquad (1)$$

$$\int \cos ax \, dx = \frac{1}{a} \sin ax + C. \qquad (2)$$

Also, by aid of (8), § 43, we have

$$\int \sin^2 ax \, dx = \int \frac{1 - \cos 2\,ax}{2} \, dx = \frac{x}{2} - \frac{\sin 2\,ax}{4\,a} + C, \quad (3)$$

$$\int \cos^2 ax \, dx = \int \frac{1 + \cos 2\,ax}{2} \, dx = \frac{x}{2} + \frac{\sin 2\,ax}{4\,a} + C. \quad (4)$$

By a similar inversion of formulas for the differentiation of inverse trigonometric functions we have

$$\int \frac{dx}{\sqrt{a^2 - x^2}} = \sin^{-1} \frac{x}{a} + C, \quad (5)$$

$$\int \frac{dx}{a^2 + x^2} = \frac{1}{a} \tan^{-1} \frac{x}{a} + C. \quad (6)$$

These formulas may be applied to the solution of the following exercises:

EXERCISES

1. Find the area bounded by the axis of x and one arch of the curve $y = \sin x$.

2. Find the area bounded by the axis of x, the witch $y = \dfrac{8\,a^3}{x^2 + 4\,a^2}$, and the two ordinates $x = -2\,a$ and $x = 2\,a$.

3. Find the area bounded by the axis of x and one arch of the curve $y = 5 \sin^2 3\,x$.

4. Find the triangular area bounded on the left by the axis of y and on the other two sides by the curves $y = \sin x$ and $y = \cos x$.

5. Find the area bounded by a portion of the first arch of each of the curves $y = \sin x$ and $y = \sin 2\,x$.

6. A line is drawn from the origin to the point $\left(\dfrac{3\,\pi}{4}, \dfrac{\sqrt{2}}{2}\right)$ on the curve $y = \sin x$. Find the area bounded by this line and the curve.

7. Find the area bounded by the axis of x, the axis of y, the curve $y = \dfrac{1}{\sqrt{a^2 - x^2}}$, and the ordinate $x = \dfrac{a}{2}$.

8. Find the volume of the solid formed by revolving about the line $2\,y + a = 0$ the area bounded by the first arch of the curve $y = \sin x$ and the axis of x.

9. Find the volume of the solid generated by revolving about the line $y = 1$ the area bounded by one arch of the curve $y = \cos x$ and the axis of x.

10. By use of Ex. 26, p. 77, find the pressure on a board bounded by an arch of a sine curve and its base line, if it is submerged vertically with the base line in the surface of the water.

GENERAL EXERCISES

Find $\dfrac{dy}{dx}$ in each of the following cases:

1. $y = \cos(2x + 3)\cos(2x - 3)$.

2. $y = 15\tan\dfrac{x}{2} + 10\tan^3\dfrac{x}{2} + 3\tan^5\dfrac{x}{2}$.

3. $y = \cos^3 3x \tan 3x$.

4. $y = \sin^2 4x \cos^4 2x$.

5. $y = x + 2\left(\operatorname{ctn}\dfrac{x}{2} - \csc\dfrac{x}{2}\right)$.

6. $y = (2x^2 - 1)\sin 2x + 2x\cos 2x$.

7. $y = (3a^2x^2 - 6)\sin ax - (a^3x^3 - 6ax)\cos ax$.

8. $\cos(x + y)\sin(x - y) = a$.

9. $y = x\sec\dfrac{y}{x}$.

15. $y = \operatorname{ctn}^{-1}\dfrac{\sqrt{x^2 + 4x}}{2}$.

10. $y = \sin^{-1}\dfrac{x - 2}{x + 2}$.

16. $y = (8x^2 - 1)\sin^{-1} 2x + 2x\sqrt{1 - 4x^2}$.

11. $y = \cos^{-1}\dfrac{x^2 - 1}{x^2 + 1}$.

17. $y = \tan^{-1} x + \frac{1}{3}\tan^{-1} x^3$.

12. $y = \sin^{-1}\dfrac{\sqrt{9x^2 - 4}}{3x}$.

18. $y = \dfrac{x}{\sqrt{4 - x^2}} + \cos^{-1}\dfrac{x}{2}$.

13. $y = \tan^{-1} x\sqrt{x^2 - 2}$.

19. $xy + \tan^{-1}\dfrac{y}{x} = 0$.

14. $y = \sec^{-1}\dfrac{x + 1}{\sqrt{x^2 + 2x}}$.

20. $\sqrt{y^2 - x^2} + \csc^{-1}\dfrac{y}{x} = 0$.

Plot the graphs of the following equations:

21. $y = 5\sin\left(2x + \dfrac{3\pi}{4}\right)$.

22. $y = 2\sin 2\left(x + \dfrac{\pi}{3}\right)$.

23. $y = 3\sin\dfrac{x + 2}{3}$.

24. $y = 2\cos\left(x - \dfrac{3\pi}{4}\right)$.

25. $y = 2\cos(3x - 2)$.

26. $y = 2\cos 2(x - 2)$.

27. $y^2 = \tan 2x$.

28. $y = \operatorname{ctn}^2\dfrac{x}{2}$.

29. $y = \sin x + \sin 2x$.

30. $y = 2\sin 2x + 3\sin 3x$.

31. $y = 2 + \sin^{-1}(2x - 3)$.

32. $2y + \sin^{-1}(2x - 3) = \pi$.

33. $2y = 1 - \cos^{-1}(2x + 1)$.

34. $3y + \cos^{-1} 2x = \pi$.

35. A particle moves on the ellipse $\frac{x^2}{a^2} + \frac{y^2}{b^2} = 1$ so that its projection upon OX describes simple harmonic motion given by $x = a \cos kt$. Show that its projection upon OY also describes simple harmonic motion, and find the velocity of the particle in its path.

36. A particle moving with simple harmonic motion of period $\frac{\pi}{2}$ has a velocity of 6 ft. per second when at a distance of 2 ft. from its mean position. Find the amplitude of the motion.

37. A particle moves in a straight line according to the equation $s = 5 \sin \frac{2}{3} t + 3 \cos \frac{2}{3} t$. Show that the motion is simple harmonic, and find the amplitude of the swing and a time at which the particle passes through its mean position.

38. A particle moves in a straight line so that at the time t, $s = 12 - 6 \cos^2 \frac{\pi t}{2}$. Prove that the motion is simple harmonic, and determine its amplitude and period.

39. The amplitude of a given simple harmonic motion is 20 ft. When midway between the mean and the extreme points of its path the speed of the particle is $4\sqrt{3}$ ft. per second. What is the period of the motion?

40. A particle is moving in simple harmonic motion. The period of the motion is 4 sec., and when the particle is midway between its mean and extreme positions its speed is $10\,\pi\,\sqrt{3}$ ft. per second. Find the amplitude of the motion.

41. The amplitude of a certain simple harmonic motion is 10 ft. and its period is $\frac{\pi}{2}$ seconds. Find the velocity when the particle is 5 ft. from its mean position.

42. Time is measured from 12 o'clock noon. At 12.15 P.M. a particle moving with simple harmonic motion passes through its mean position with a speed of $2\,\pi$ ft. per minute. At 12.20 P.M. the particle is 30 ft. from its mean position and moving with a speed of $\pi\sqrt{3}$ ft. per minute. Determine the amplitude and the period of the motion.

43. Find the radius of curvature of the curve $y = x \sin \frac{1}{x}$ at the point for which $x = \frac{2}{\pi}$.

44. Find the radius of curvature of the curve $y = \frac{\sin x}{x}$ at the point for which $x = \pi$.

45. Find the radius of curvature at the point for which $x = \frac{a}{2}$ of the curve $y = a \sin^{-1} \frac{x}{a} - \sqrt{a^2 - x^2}$.

46. Find the radius of curvature of the curve $x = a \cos \phi$, $y = b \sin \phi$ at the point for which $\phi = \dfrac{\pi}{4}$.

47. Find the radius of curvature of the curve $x = 2 \cos \phi$, $y = \sin^2 \phi$. Find the Cartesian equation of the curve, and sketch.

48. Find the radius of curvature of the curve $x = 2 \cos^2 \phi$, $y = 2 \sin^3 \phi$ at the point for which $\phi = \dfrac{\pi}{2}$.

49. Find the radius of curvature of the curve $x = a \sin^4 \phi$, $y = a \cos^4 \phi$ at the point for which $\phi = \dfrac{\pi}{4}$.

50. Prove that the radius of curvature of the curve $x = a \cos^3 \phi$, $y = a \sin^3 \phi$ has its greatest value when $\phi = \dfrac{\pi}{4}$.

51. A revolving light in a lighthouse $\frac{1}{4}$ mi. offshore makes one revolution a minute. If the line of the shore is a straight line, how fast is the ray of light moving along the shore when it passes a point one mile from the point nearest to the lighthouse?

52. BC is a rod a feet long, connected with a piston rod at C, and at B with a crank AB, b feet long, revolving about A. Find C's velocity in terms of AB's angular velocity.

53. At any time t the coördinates of a point moving in the xy-plane are $x = 2 - 3 \cos t$, $y = 3 + 2 \sin t$. Find its path and its velocity in its path. At what points will it have a maximum speed?

54. At any time t the coördinates of a moving point are $x = 2 \sec 3\,t$, $y = 4 \tan 3\,t$. Find the equation of its path and its velocity in its path.

55. The parametric equations of the path of a moving particle are $x = 2 \cos^3 \phi$, $y = 2 \sin^3 \phi$. If the angle ϕ increases at the rate of 2 radians per second, find the velocity of the particle in its path.

56. A particle moves along the curve $x = a(\cos \phi + \phi \sin \phi)$, $y = a(\sin \phi - \phi \cos \phi)$, ϕ increasing uniformly b radians per second. Find the velocity of the particle along the curve.

57. At any time t the coördinates of a point moving in the xy-plane are $x = 2 \tan 3\,t$, $y = 2 \operatorname{ctn} 3\,t$. Find the path, and the velocity in the path at the point for which $x = y$.

58. At any time t the coördinates of a point moving in the xy-plane are $x = 2 \cos^2 2\,t$, $y = 2 \sin^3 2\,t$. Find the path, and the velocity in the path when $t = \dfrac{\pi}{8}$.

59. At any time t the coördinates of a point moving in the xy-plane are $x = 2 \cos 3\, t$, $y = 2 \sin^2 3\, t$. Find the path, and the velocity in the path when $t = \dfrac{\pi}{6}$.

60. Two men, A and B, starting at the same point on the circumference of a circle one mile in radius walk each at the rate of one mile an hour, A going straight toward the center, and B going around the circumference. At what rate is the distance between them changing when B has walked a quarter of the way around the circle?

61. The equal sides of an isosceles triangle are always 6 ft. long, and the vertical angle θ is increasing at the uniform rate of $\dfrac{\pi}{180}$ radians per second. How fast is the area of the triangle changing? When will the area be increasing and when decreasing?

62. If a ball is fired from a gun with the initial velocity v_0, it describes a path the equation of which is $y = x \tan \alpha - \dfrac{gx^2}{2\, v_0{}^2 \cos^2 \alpha}$, where α is the angle of elevation of the gun and OX is horizontal. What is the value of α when the horizontal range is greatest?

63. In measuring an electric current by means of a tangent galvanometer, the percentage of error due to a small error in reading is proportional to $\tan x + \text{ctn}\, x$. For what value of x will this percentage of error be least?

64. A tablet 10 ft. high is placed on a wall so that the bottom of the tablet is 20 ft. from the ground. How far from the wall should a person stand in order that he may see the tablet to best advantage (that is, so that the angle between the lines from his eye to the top and to the bottom of the tablet should be the greatest), assuming that his eye is 5 ft. from the ground?

65. One side and the opposite angle of a triangle are given. Prove that the triangle having the greatest area is isosceles.

66. Above the center of a round table of radius 2 ft. is a hanging lamp. How far should the lamp be above the table in order that the edge of the table may be most brilliantly lighted, given that the illumination varies inversely as the square of the distance and directly as the cosine of the angle of incidence?

67. A weight P is dragged along the ground by a force F. If the coefficient of friction is k, in what direction should the force be applied to produce the best result?

68. An open gutter is to be constructed of boards in such a way that the bottom and sides, measured on the inside, are to be each 8 in. wide and both sides are to have the same slope. How wide should the gutter be across the top in order that its capacity may be as great as possible?

69. A steel girder 27 ft. long is to be moved on rollers along a passageway and into a corridor 8 ft. in width at right angles to the passageway. If the horizontal width of the girder is neglected, how wide must the passageway be in order that the girder may go around the corner?

70. Two particles are moving in the same straight line so that their distances from a fixed point O are, respectively, $x = a \cos kt$ and $x' = a \cos \left(kt + \dfrac{\pi}{4}\right)$, k and a being constants. Find the greatest distance between them.

71. The top of a wall on the edge of an ice pond is 8 ft. above the level of the water. An ice house stands back 27 ft. horizontally from the wall. A runway just resting on the wall extends from the water to an opening in the ice house. What is the minimum length of the runway?

72. Find the angle of intersection of the curves $y = \sin x$ and $y = \cos x$.

73. Find the angle of intersection of the curves $y = \sin x$ and $y = \sin \left(x + \dfrac{\pi}{3}\right)$.

74. Find the angle of intersection of the curves $y = \cos x$ and $y = \cos 2x$ at the points of intersection between the lines $x = 0$ and $x = 2\pi$.

75. Find the points of intersection of the curves $y = \sin x$ and $y = \sin 3x$ between the lines $x = 0$ and $x = \pi$. Determine the angles at the points of intersection.

76. Find the angle of intersection of the curves $y = 2 \sin 2x$ and $y = \tan 2x$ at their common points which are between the lines $x = -\dfrac{\pi}{4}$ and $x = \dfrac{\pi}{4}$.

77. Prove that the curves $y = 2 \tan \dfrac{x}{2}$ and $y = 4 \sin \dfrac{x}{3}$ intersect at the point $\left(\dfrac{\pi}{2}, 2\right)$, and determine their angle of intersection at that point.

78. Prove that the curves $y = 2 \cos x$ and $9 x^2 = \pi^2 y$ intersect at the point $\left(\dfrac{\pi}{3}, 1\right)$, and determine their angle of intersection at that point.

CHAPTER VI

EXPONENTIAL AND LOGARITHMIC FUNCTIONS

54. The exponential function. The equation
$$y = a^x,$$
where a is any constant, defines y as a function of x called the *exponential function*.

If $x = n$, an integer, y is determined by raising a to the nth power by multiplication.

If $x = \dfrac{p}{q}$, a positive fraction, y is the qth root of the pth power of a.

If x is a positive irrational number, the approximate value of y may be obtained by expressing x approximately as a fraction.

If $x = 0$, $y = a^0 = 1$. If $x = -m$, $y = a^{-m} = \dfrac{1}{a^m}$.
The graph of the function is readily found.

Example. Find the graph of $y = (1.5)^x$. By giving convenient values to x we obtain the curve shown in Fig. 72. To determine the shape of the curve at the extreme left, we place x equal to a large negative number, say $x = -100$. Then $y = (1.5)^{-100} = \dfrac{1}{(1.5)^{100}}$, which is very small. It is obvious that the larger numerically the negative value of x becomes, the smaller y becomes, so that the curve approaches asymptotically the negative portion of the x-axis.

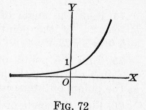

Fig. 72

On the other hand, if x is a large positive number, y is also large.

55. The logarithm. If a number N may be obtained by placing an exponent L on another number a and computing the result, then L is said to be the logarithm of N to the base a. That is, if

$$N = a^L, \tag{1}$$
then
$$L = \log_a N. \tag{2}$$

Formulas (1) and (2) are simply two different ways of expressing the same fact as to the relation of N and L, and the

168

student should accustom himself to pass from one to the other as convenience may demand.

From these formulas follow easily the fundamental properties of logarithms; namely,

$$\log_a N + \log_a M = \log_a MN,$$

$$\log_a N - \log_a M = \log_a \frac{N}{M},$$

$$n \log_a N = \log_a N^n,$$ (3)

$$\log_a 1 = 0,$$

$$\log_a \frac{1}{N} = - \log_a N.$$

Theoretically any number, except 0 or 1, may be used as the base of a system of logarithms. Practically there are only two numbers so used. The first is the number 10, the use of which as a base gives the common system of logarithms, which are the most convenient for calculations and are used almost exclusively in trigonometry.

Another number, however, is more convenient in theoretical discussions, since it gives simpler formulas. This number is denoted by the letter e and is expressed by the infinite series

$$e = 1 + \frac{1}{1} + \frac{1}{2!} + \frac{1}{3!} + \frac{1}{4!} + \cdots,$$

where $2! = 1 \times 2,\ 3! = 1 \times 2 \times 3,\ 4! = 1 \times 2 \times 3 \times 4,$ etc.

Computing the above series to seven decimal places, we have

$$e = 2.7182818 \cdots.$$

An important theorem, which is used in finding the derivative of a logarithm, is that

$$\underset{h \to 0}{\text{Lim}}\ (1 + h)^{\frac{1}{h}} = e.$$ (4)

To check this arithmetically we may take successive small values of h and make the following computation:

When $h = .1$, $\quad (1 + h)^{\frac{1}{h}} = (1.1)^{10} = 2.59374.$

When $h = .01$, $\quad (1 + h)^{\frac{1}{h}} = (1.01)^{100} = 2.70481.$

When $h = .001$, $\quad (1 + h)^{\frac{1}{h}} = (1.001)^{1000} = 2.71692.$

When $h = .0001$, $\quad (1 + h)^{\frac{1}{h}} = (1.0001)^{10000} = 2.71815.$

Working algebraically, we expand $(1 + h)^{\frac{1}{h}}$ by the binomial theorem, obtaining

$$(1 + h)^{\frac{1}{h}} = 1 + \frac{1}{h} h + \frac{\frac{1}{h}\left(\frac{1}{h} - 1\right)}{2!} h^2 + \frac{\frac{1}{h}\left(\frac{1}{h} - 1\right)\left(\frac{1}{h} - 2\right)}{3!} h^3 + \ldots$$

$$= 1 + \frac{1}{1} + \frac{(1 - h)}{2!} + \frac{(1 - h)(1 - 2h)}{3!} + \ldots$$

$$= 1 + \frac{1}{1} + \frac{1}{2!} + \frac{1}{3!} + \ldots + R,$$

where R represents the sum of all terms involving h, h^2, h^3, etc. Now it may be shown by advanced methods that as h approaches zero, R also approaches zero; so that

$$\operatorname*{Lim}_{h \to 0} (1 + h)^{\frac{1}{h}} = 1 + \frac{1}{1} + \frac{1}{2!} + \frac{1}{3!} + \ldots = e.$$

When the number e is used as the base of a system of logarithms, the logarithms are called *natural logarithms*. We shall denote a natural logarithm by the symbol ln*; thus,

if $\qquad\qquad\qquad N = e^L,$

then $\qquad\qquad\qquad L = \ln N.$ $\qquad\qquad\qquad\qquad$ (5)

Tables of natural logarithms exist, and should be used if possible. In case such a table is not available, the student may find the natural logarithm by use of a table of common logarithms, as follows:

Let it be required to find $\ln N$.

If $\qquad\qquad\qquad x = \ln N,$

then, by (5), $\qquad\qquad\qquad N = e^x;$

whence, by (3), $\log N = x \log e = \ln N \log e,$

or $\qquad\qquad \ln N = \frac{\log N}{\log e} = \frac{\log N}{0.4343}.$

---

*This notation is generally used by engineers. However, the abbreviation "log" is used by many authors to denote the natural logarithm. In this book "log" is used for the logarithm to the base 10.

Certain graphs involving the number e are important and are shown in the examples.

Example 1. $y = \ln x$.

Giving x positive values and finding y, we obtain Fig. 73.

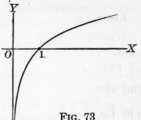

Fig. 73

Example 2. $y = e^{-x^2}$.

The curve (Fig. 74) is symmetrical with respect to OY and is always above OX. When $x = 0$, $y = 1$. As x increases numerically, y decreases, approaching zero. Hence OX is an asymptote.

Example 3. $y = \dfrac{a}{2}\left(e^{\frac{x}{a}} + e^{-\frac{x}{a}}\right)$.

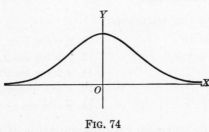

Fig. 74

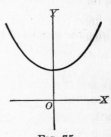

Fig. 75

This is the curve (Fig. 75) made by a cord or a chain held at the ends and allowed to hang freely. It is called the *catenary*.

Example 4. $y = e^{-ax} \sin bx$.

The values of y may be computed by multiplying the ordinates of the curve $y = e^{-ax}$ by the values of $\sin bx$ for the corresponding abscissas. Since the value of $\sin bx$ oscillates between 1 and -1, the values of $e^{-ax} \sin bx$ cannot exceed those of e^{-ax}. Hence the graph lies in the portion of the plane between the curves $y = e^{-ax}$ and $y = -e^{-ax}$. When x is a multiple of $\dfrac{\pi}{b}$, y is zero. The graph therefore

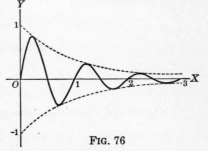

Fig. 76

crosses the axis of x an infinite number of times. Fig. 76 shows the graph when $a = 1$, $b = 2\pi$.

Example 5. $y = e^{\frac{1}{x}}$.

When x approaches zero, being positive, y increases without limit. When x approaches zero, being negative, y approaches zero; for example, when $x = \frac{1}{1000}$, $y = e^{1000}$,

and when $x = -\frac{1}{1000}$, $y = e^{-1000} = \dfrac{1}{e^{1000}}$.

The function is therefore discontinuous for $x = 0$.

The line $y = 1$ is an asymptote (Fig. 77), for as x increases numerically without limit, being positive or negative, $\dfrac{1}{x}$ approaches 0, and y approaches 1.

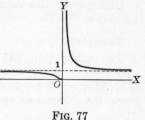

FIG. 77

EXERCISES

Plot the graphs of the following equations:

1. $y = e^x$.

2. $y = (\frac{1}{2})^{\frac{1}{x}}$.

3. $y = e^{1-x}$.

4. $y = e^{-\frac{1}{x}}$.

5. $y = xe^x$.

6. $y = \frac{1}{2}(e^x - e^{-x})$.

7. $y = xe^{-2x}$.

8. $y = \dfrac{e^{2x}}{x}$.

9. $y = \log 3x$.

10. $y = \log \cos x$.

11. $y = \log \csc x$.

12. $y = e^{-3x} \sin 2x$.

13. $y = e^x \sin x$.

56. Differentiation. The formulas for the differentiation of the exponential and the logarithmic functions are as follows, where, as usual, u represents any function which can be differentiated with respect to x, ln means the Napierian logarithm, and a is any constant:

$$\frac{d}{dx} \log_a u = \frac{\log_a e}{u} \frac{du}{dx}, \tag{1}$$

$$\frac{d}{dx} \ln u = \frac{1}{u} \frac{du}{dx}. \tag{2}$$

$$\frac{d}{dx} a^u = a^u \ln a \frac{du}{dx}, \tag{3}$$

$$\frac{d}{dx} e^u = e^u \frac{du}{dx}. \tag{4}$$

The proofs of these formulas are as follows:

1. By (8), § 36, $\dfrac{d}{dx} \log_a u = \dfrac{d}{du} \log_a u \cdot \dfrac{du}{dx}$.

To find $\dfrac{d}{du} \log_a u$, place $y = \log_a u$.

Then, if u is given an increment Δu, y receives an increment Δy, where

$$\Delta y = \log_a (u + \Delta u) - \log_a u$$

$$= \log_a \left(1 + \frac{\Delta u}{u}\right)$$

$$= \frac{\Delta u}{u} \log_a \left(1 + \frac{\Delta u}{u}\right)^{\frac{u}{\Delta u}},$$

the transformations being made by (3), § 55.

Then

$$\frac{\Delta y}{\Delta u} = \frac{1}{u} \log_a \left(1 + \frac{\Delta u}{u}\right)^{\frac{u}{\Delta u}}.$$

Now, as Δu approaches zero the fraction $\frac{\Delta u}{u}$ may be taken as h in (4), § 55.

Hence

$$\mathop{\mathrm{Lim}}_{\Delta u \to 0} \left(1 + \frac{\Delta u}{u}\right)^{\frac{u}{\Delta u}} = e.$$

Therefore

$$\frac{dy}{du} = \frac{1}{u} \log_a e$$

and

$$\frac{dy}{dx} = \frac{\log_a e}{u} \frac{du}{dx}.$$

2. If $y = \ln u$, the base a of the previous formula is e; and since $\log_e e = 1$, we have

$$\frac{dy}{dx} = \frac{1}{u} \frac{du}{dx}.$$

3. If
$$y = a^u,$$
we have
$$\ln y = \ln a^u = u \ln a.$$

Hence, by formula (2),

$$\frac{1}{y} \frac{dy}{dx} = \ln a \frac{du}{dx};$$

whence

$$\frac{dy}{dx} = a^u \ln a \frac{du}{dx}.$$

4. If $y = e^u$ the previous formula becomes

$$\frac{dy}{dx} = e^u \frac{du}{dx}.$$

Example 1. $y = \ln (x^2 - 4x + 5)$.

$$\frac{dy}{dx} = \frac{2x - 4}{x^2 - 4x + 5}.$$

Example 2. $y = e^{-x^2}$. $\dfrac{dy}{dx} = -2xe^{-x^2}$.

Example 3. $y = e^{-ax} \cos bx$.

$$\frac{dy}{dx} = \cos bx \frac{d}{dx} (e^{-ax}) + e^{-ax} \frac{d}{dx} (\cos bx) = -ae^{-ax} \cos bx - be^{-ax} \sin bx$$
$$= -e^{-ax} (a \cos bx + b \sin bx).$$

EXERCISES

Find $\dfrac{dy}{dx}$ in each of the following cases:

1. $y = e^{-\frac{2}{x}}$.

2. $y = \dfrac{a}{2} \left(e^{\frac{x}{a}} + e^{-\frac{x}{a}} \right)$.

3. $y = a^{x^2 - 1}$.

4. $y = a^{\tan^{-1} x}$.

5. $y = \ln (x^2 + 6x - 1)$.

6. $y = \ln \sqrt{2x^2 + 8x + 9}$.

7. $y = \dfrac{1}{8} \ln \dfrac{x - 4}{x + 4}$.

8. $y = \ln (x + \sqrt{x^2 + 9})$.

9. $y = \ln (5x + \sqrt{25 x^2 + 1})$.

10. $y = \ln \dfrac{1 - \cos 2x}{1 + \cos 2x}$.

11. $y = \ln (e^{3x} + e^{-3x})$.

12. $y = e^{-3x} \sin 2x$.

13. $y = \ln \sqrt{1 + x^2} - x \tan^{-1} x$.

14. $y = e^{2x}(2x^2 - 2x + 1)$.

15. $y = e^{3x}(3 \cos x + \sin x)$.

16. $y = \sin^{-1} \dfrac{e^x - e^{-x}}{e^x + e^{-x}}$.

17. $y = \sec x \tan x + \ln (\sec x + \tan x)$.

18. $y = \ln \dfrac{\sqrt{x + 1} - 1}{\sqrt{x + 1} + 1}$.

19. $e^{x+y} = \ln \dfrac{x}{y}$.

20. $xy = \ln (x + y)$.

57. Integration. By reversing the formula for the differentiation of an exponential function, we may write

$$\int e^{ax} \, dx = \frac{1}{a} e^{ax} + C. \tag{1}$$

Similarly, from the formula for the derivative of $\ln x$ we have

$$\int \frac{dx}{x} = \ln x + C. \tag{2}$$

Since $\dfrac{1}{x} = x^{-1}$ this gives us the integral of $x^n \, dx$ when $n = -1$.

All other values of n are taken care of by formula (3), § 42.

EXERCISES

1. The velocity of a particle in feet per second is equal to $\frac{3}{t}$, and when $t = 1$, $s = 0$. Find s when $t = 5$.

2. The slope of a curve at any point is always twice the slope of the line from the point to the origin, and the curve passes through $(4, 2)$. Find its equation.

3. The slope of a curve at any point is always equal to the reciprocal of the abscissa of the point, and the curve passes through $(3, 2)$. Find its equation.

4. Find the area bounded by the curve $y = e^{ax}$, the axis of x, the axis of y, and the ordinate $x = a$.

5. Find the area bounded by the curve $xy = 4$, the axis of x, and the ordinates $x = 2$ and $x = 4$.

6. Find the area bounded by the catenary $y = \frac{a}{2}\left(e^{\frac{x}{a}} + e^{-\frac{x}{a}}\right)$, the axis of x, and the lines $x = \pm h$.

7. Find the area bounded by the curve $xy = 18$ and the straight line $x + y = 9$.

8. Find the volume generated by revolving about OX the area bounded by the catenary $y = \frac{a}{2}\left(e^{\frac{x}{a}} + e^{-\frac{x}{a}}\right)$, the axis of x, and the lines $x = \pm h$.

9. Find the volume generated by revolving about the line $y + 1 = 0$, the area bounded by that line, the curve $xy = 8$, and the lines $x = 2$ and $x = 4$.

58. The compound-interest law. An important use of the exponential function occurs in the problem of determining a function whose rate of change is proportional to the value of the function. If y is such a function of x, it must satisfy the equation

$$\frac{dy}{dx} = ky, \tag{1}$$

where k is a constant called the proportionality factor.

We may write equation (1) in the form

$$\frac{dy}{y} = k\,dx\,;$$

whence
$$\ln y = kx + C.$$

From this, by (1) and (2), § 55,

$$y = e^{kx + C} = e^{kx}e^{C}.$$

Finally we place $e^C = A$, where A may be any constant, since C is any constant, and have as a final result

$$y = Ae^{kx}. \tag{2}$$

The constants A and k must be determined by other conditions of a particular problem, as was done in § 20.

The law of change here discussed is often called the *compound-interest law*, because of its occurrence in the following problem:

Example. Let a sum of money P be put at interest at the rate of r % per annum. The interest gained in a time Δt is $P \dfrac{r}{100} \Delta t$, where Δt is expressed in years. But the interest is an increment of the principal P, so that we have

$$\Delta P = P \frac{r}{100} \Delta t.$$

In ordinary compound interest the interest is computed for a certain interval (usually one half-year), the principal remaining constant during that interval. The interest at the end of the half-year is then added to the principal to make a new principal on which interest is computed for the next half-year. The principal F therefore changes abruptly at the end of each half-year.

Let us now suppose that the principal changes continuously; that is, that any amount of interest theoretically earned, in no matter how small a time, is immediately added to the principal. The average rate of change of the principal in the period Δt is, from § 6,

$$\frac{\Delta P}{\Delta t} = \frac{Pr}{100}. \tag{1}$$

To obtain the rate of change we must let Δt approach zero in equation (1), and have

$$\frac{dP}{dt} = P \frac{r}{100}.$$

From this, as in the text, we have

$$P = Ae^{\frac{r}{100}t}. \tag{2}$$

To make the problem concrete, suppose the original principal were \$100 and the rate 4 %, and we ask what would be the principal at the end of 14 yr. We know that when $t = 0$, $P = 100$. Substituting these values in (2), we have $A = 100$, so that (2) becomes

$$P = 100\, e^{\frac{4}{100}t} = 100\, e^{\frac{t}{25}}.$$

Placing now $t = 14$, we have to compute $P = 100 \, e^{\frac{14}{25}}$. The value of P may be taken from a table if the student has access to tables of powers of e. In case a table of common logarithms is alone available, P may be found by first taking the logarithm of both sides of the last equation. Thus

$$\log P = \log 100 + \tfrac{14}{25} \log e = 2.2432 \, ;$$

whence $\qquad\qquad P = \$175$, approximately.

EXERCISES

1. The rate of change of y with respect to x is always equal to $\tfrac{1}{3} \, y$, and when $x = 0$, $y = 6$. Find the law connecting y and x.

2. The rate of change of y with respect to x is always 0.01 times y, and when $x = 10$, $y = 60$. Find the law connecting y and x.

3. The rate of change of y with respect to x is proportional to y. When $x = 0$, $y = 8$, and when $x = 2$, $y = 16$. Find the law connecting y and x.

4. The sum of \$100 is put at interest at the rate of 5 % per annum under the condition that the interest shall be compounded at each instant of time. How much will it amount to in 30 yr.?

5. At a certain date the population of a town is 10,000. Forty years later it is 35,000. If the population increases at a rate which is always proportional to the population at the time, find a general expression for the population at any time t. $\quad t_0 = 0$

6. In a chemical reaction the rate of change of concentration of a substance is proportional to the concentration at any time. If the concentration is $\frac{1}{100}$ when $t = 0$, and is $\frac{1}{125}$ when $t = 6$, find the law connecting the concentration and the time.

7. A rotating wheel is slowing down in such a manner that the angular acceleration is proportional to the angular velocity. If the angular velocity at the beginning of the slowing down is 200 revolutions per second, and in 1 min. it is cut down to 50 revolutions per second, how long will it take to reduce the velocity to 25 revolutions per second? $\quad \alpha = k\,\omega \qquad \alpha = \dfrac{d\omega}{dt}$

59. Certain empirical equations. If x and y are two related quantities which are connected by a given equation, we may plot the corresponding curve on a system of xy-coördinates, and every point of this curve determines corresponding values of x and y.

Conversely, let x and y be two related quantities of which some corresponding pairs of values have been determined, and let it be desired to find by means of these data an equation connecting x and y in general. On this basis alone the problem cannot be solved exactly. The best we can do is to assume that the desired equation is of a certain form and then endeavor to adjust the constants in the equation in such a way that it fits the data as nearly as possible. We may proceed as follows:

Plot the points corresponding to the known values of x and y. The simplest case is that in which the plotted points appear to lie on a straight line or nearly so. In that case it is assumed that the required relation may be put in the form

$$y = mx + b, \tag{1}$$

where m and b are constants to be determined to fit the data. The next step is to draw a straight line so that the plotted points either lie on it or are close to it and about evenly distributed on both sides of it. The equation of this line may be found by means of two points on it, which may be either two points determined by the original data or any other two points on the line.

The resulting equation is called an *empirical equation* and expresses approximately the general relation between x and y. In fact, more than one such equation may be derived from the same data, and the choice of the best equation depends on the judgment and experience of the worker.

Example 1. Corresponding values of two related quantities x and y are given by the following table:

x	1	2	4	6	10
y	1.3	2.2	2.9	3.9	6.1

Find the empirical equation connecting them.

We plot the points (x, y) and draw the straight line, as shown in Fig. 78. The straight line is seen to pass through the points $(0, 1)$ and $(2, 2)$. Its equation is therefore, by § 14,

$$y = 0.5\, x + 1,$$

which is the required equation.

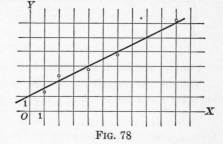

FIG. 78

In many cases, however, the plotted points will not appear to lie on or near a straight line. We shall consider here only two of these cases, which are closely connected with the case just considered. They are the cases in which it may be anticipated from previous experience that the required relation is either of the form

$$y = ab^x, \tag{2}$$

where a and b are constants, or of the form

$$y = ax^n, \tag{3}$$

where a and n are constants.

Both of these cases may be brought directly under the first case by taking the logarithm of the equation as written. Equation (2) then becomes

$$\log y = \log a + x \log b. \tag{4}$$

As $\log a$ and $\log b$ are constants, if we denote $\log y$ by y', (4) assumes the form (1) in x and y', and we have only to plot the points (x, y') on an xy'-system of axes and determine a straight line by means of them. The transformation from (4) back to (2) is easy, as shown in Example 2.

Taking the logarithm of (3), we have

$$\log y = \log a + n \log x. \tag{5}$$

If we denote $\log y$ by y' and $\log x$ by x', (5) assumes the form (1) in x' and y', since $\log a$ and n are constants. Accordingly we plot the points (x', y') on an $x'y'$-system of axes, determine the corresponding straight line, and then transform back to (3), as shown in Example 3.

Example 2. Corresponding values of two related quantities x and y are given by the following table:

x	8	10	12	14	16	18	20
y	3.2	4.6	7.3	9.8	15.2	24.6	36.4

Find an empirical equation of the form $y = ab^x$.

Taking the logarithm of the equation $y = ab^x$, and denoting $\log y$ by y', we have $\quad y' = \log a + x \log b.$

Determining the logarithm of each of the given values of y, we form a table of corresponding values of x and y', as follows:

x	8	10	12	14	16	18	20
$y' = \log y$	0.5051	0.6628	0.8633	0.9912	1.1818	1.3909	1.5611

We choose a large-scale plotting-paper, assume on the y'-axis a scale four times as large as that on the x-axis, plot the points (x, y'), and draw the straight line (Fig. 79) through the first and the sixth point. Its equation is, by § 14,

$$y' = 0.08858\, x - 0.20354.$$

Therefore $\log a = -0.20354$ $= 9.7965 - 10$, whence $a = 0.626$; and $\log b = 0.08858$, whence $b = 1.22$. Substituting these values in the assumed equation, we have

$$y = 0.626\ (1.22)^x$$

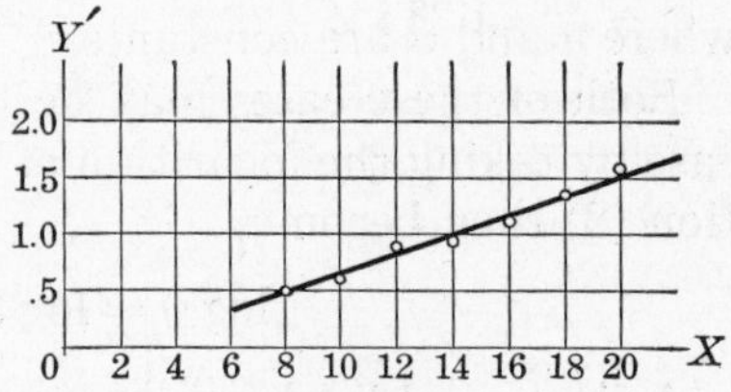

FIG. 79

as the required empirical equation. The result may be tested by substituting the given values of x in the equation. The computed values of y will be found to agree fairly well with the given values.

Example 3. Corresponding values of pressure and volume taken from an indicator card of an air-compressor are as follows:

p	18	21	26.5	33.5	44	62
v	0.635	0.556	0.475	0.397	0.321	0.243

Find the relation between them in the form $pv^n = c$.

Writing the assumed relation in the form $p = cv^{-n}$ and taking the logarithms of both sides of the equation, we have

$$\log p = -n \log v + \log c,$$

or $\qquad\qquad\qquad y = -nx + b,$

where $\qquad\qquad y = \log p,\ x = \log v,\ \text{and}\ b = \log c.$

The corresponding values of x and y are

$x = \log v$	-0.1972	-0.2549	-0.3233	-0.4012	-0.4935	-0.6144
$y = \log p$	1.2553	1.3222	1.4232	1.5250	1.6435	1.7924

We take large-scale plotting-paper assuming on the x-axis a scale twice as large as that on the y-axis, plot the points (x, y), and draw the straight line as shown in Fig. 80. The line is seen to pass through the points $(-0.05, 1.075)$ and $(-0.46, 1.6)$. Its equation is therefore, by § 14,

$$y = -1.28\,x + 1.01.$$

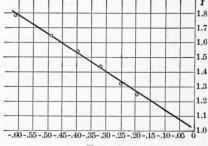

Fig. 80

Hence $n = 1.28$, $\log c = 1.01$, $c = 10.2$, and the required relation between p and v is

$$pv^{1.28} = 10.2.$$

EXERCISES

1. Show that the following points lie approximately on a straight line, and find its equation:

x	4	9	13	20	22	25	30
y	2.1	4.6	7	12	12.9	14.5	18.2

2. For a galvanometer the deflection D, measured in millimeters on a proper scale, and the current I, measured in microamperes, are determined in a series of readings as follows:

D	29.1	48.2	72.7	92.0	118.0	140.0	165.0	199.0
I	0.0493	0.0821	0.123	0.154	0.197	0.234	0.274	0.328

Find an empirical law connecting D and I.

3. Corresponding values of two related quantities x and y are given in the following table:

x	0.1	0.3	0.5	0.7	0.9	1.1	1.3	1.5
y	0.3316	0.4050	0.4946	0.6041	0.7379	0.9013	1.1008	1.3445

Find an empirical equation connecting x and y in the form $y = ab^x$.

4. In a certain chemical reaction the concentration c of sodium acetate produced in a stated number of minutes t is as follows:

t	1	2	3	4	5
c	0.00837	0.00700	0.00586	0.00492	0.00410

Find an empirical equation connecting c and t in the form $c = ab^t$.

5. The deflection a of a loaded beam with a constant load is found for various lengths l as follows:

l	1000	900	800	700	600
a	7.14	5.22	3.64	2.42	1.50

Find an empirical equation connecting a and l in the form $a = nl^m$.

6. The relation between the pressure p and the volume v of a gas is found experimentally as follows:

p	20	23.5	31	42	59	78
v	0.619	0.540	0.442	0.358	0.277	0.219

Find an empirical equation connecting p and v in the form $pv^n = c$.

GENERAL EXERCISES

Find $\dfrac{dy}{dx}$ in each of the following cases:

1. $y = x - \frac{1}{2} \ln (1 + e^{2x})$.

2. $y = \ln \sqrt{\dfrac{1 + x^2}{1 - x^2}}$.

3. $y = \ln \left(4\,x + \sqrt{16\,x^2 + 1}\right)$.

4. $y = \dfrac{1}{14} \ln \dfrac{7\,x - 3}{7\,x + 3}$.

5. $y = \ln \sqrt{\dfrac{1 + e^{-2x}}{1 - e^{-2x}}} - e^{2x}$.

6. $y = x(\ln 2\,x)^2 - 2\,x \ln 2\,x + 2\,x$.

7. $y = 2\,x \tan^{-1} 2\,x - \frac{1}{2} \ln (1 + 4\,x^2)$.

8. $y = \frac{1}{2} \sec^2 ax + \ln \cos ax$.

9. $y = \frac{1}{8} e^{2x}(4\,x^3 - 6\,x^2 + 6\,x - 3)$.

10. $y = 3\,x \sec^{-1} 3\,x - \ln \left(3\,x + \sqrt{9\,x^2 - 1}\right)$.

Find the graphs of the following equations:

11. $y = e^{\frac{x+1}{x}}$.

15. $y = e^{\frac{1}{1-x}}$.

19. $y = x^2 e^{-x}$.

12. $y = xe^{\frac{1-x}{x}}$.

16. $y = \frac{1}{2}(e^x + e^{-x})$.

13. $y = xe^{-x^2}$.

17. $y = \dfrac{e^x - e^{-x}}{e^x + e^{-x}}$.

20. $y = e^{-\frac{x}{2}} \cos x$.

14. $y = \left(\frac{1}{2}\right)^{-x}$.

18. $y = xe^{-x}$.

21. $y = \log \sin 2\,x$.

22. $y = \log \tan 3\,x$.

23. Prove that the curve $y = e^{-2x} \sin 3\,x$ is tangent to the curve $y = e^{-2x}$ at any point common to the two curves.

24. Show that the catenary $y = \dfrac{a}{2}\left(e^{\frac{x}{a}} + e^{-\frac{x}{a}}\right)$ and the parabola $y = a + \dfrac{1}{2\,a}\,x^2$ have the same slope and the same curvature at their common point.

25. Find the radius of curvature of the curve $x = e^t \sin t$, $y = e^t \cos t$.

26. Find the radius of curvature of the curve $y = \ln x$ and its least value.

27. Find the radius of curvature at the point $x = 2\,a$ of the curve $y = \sqrt{x^2 - a^2} - a \ln\left(x + \sqrt{x^2 - a^2}\right)$.

28. Find the radius of curvature of the curve $y = e^{-\frac{x}{2}} \sin 3\,x$ at the origin.

29. Find the radius of curvature of the curve $y = e^{\frac{1+x}{1-x}}$ at the point for which $x = 0$.

30. Show that the radius of curvature of the curve $y = \ln \cos x$ can never be less than unity in numerical value.

31. The slope of a curve at any point is always equal to n times the slope of the line joining the point to the origin, and the curve passes through the point $(1, a)$. Find its equation.

32. Find the curves such that the portion of the tangent between the coördinate axes is bisected by the point of tangency.

33. Find the area in the first quadrant bounded by the hyperbola $xy = 6$ and the parabola $x^2 + 5\,y - 19 = 0$.

34. Find the volume generated by revolving about the line $x = 2$ the triangular area bounded by the curve $xy = 10$ and the lines $x = 2$ and $y = 2$.

35. A substance of amount x is being decomposed at a rate which is proportional to x. If $x = 3.24$ when $t = 0$, and $x = 1.72$ when $t = 40$ min., find the value of x when $t = 1$ hr.

36. A substance is being transformed into another at a rate which is proportional to the amount of the substance still untransformed. If the amount is 50 when $t = 0$, and 16.4 when $t = 4$ hr., find how long it will be before $\frac{1}{100}$ of the original substance will remain.

37. According to Newton's law the rate at which the temperature of a body cools in air is proportional to the difference between the temperature of the body and that of the air. If the temperature of the air is kept at 60°, and the body cools from 130° to 120° in 300 sec., when will its temperature be 100°?

38. Assuming that the rate of change of atmospheric pressure p with respect to the distance h above the surface of the earth is proportional to the pressure, and that the pressure at sea level is 14.7 lb. per square inch and at a distance of 1600 ft. above sea level is 13.8 lb. per square inch, find the law connecting p and h.

39. For a copper-nickel thermocouple the relation between the temperature t in degrees and the thermoelectric power p in microvolts is given by the following table:

t	0	50	100	150	200
p	24	25	26	26.9	27.5

Find an empirical law connecting t and p.

40. The safe loads in thousands of pounds for beams of the same cross section but of various lengths in feet are found as follows:

Length	10	11	12	13	14	15
Load	123.6	121.5	111.8	107.2	101.3	90.4

Find an empirical equation connecting the data.

41. In the following table s denotes the distance of a moving body from a fixed point in its path at time t:

t	1	2	4	6	7	8
s	10	4	0.6400	0.1024	0.0410	0.0164

Find an empirical equation connecting s and t in the form $s = ab^t$.

42. In the following table c denotes the chemical concentration of a substance at the time t:

t	2	4	6	8	10
c	0.0069	0.0048	0.0033	0.0023	0.0016

Find an empirical equation connecting c and t in the form $c = ab^t$.

43. The relation between the length l in millimeters and the time t in seconds of a swinging pendulum is found as follows:

l	63.4	80.5	90.4	101.3	107.3	140.6
t	0.806	0.892	0.960	1.010	1.038	1.198

Find an empirical equation connecting l and t in the form $t = kl^n$.

44. For a dynamometer the relation between the deflection θ, when the unit $\theta = \dfrac{2\,\pi}{400}$, and the current I, measured in amperes, is as follows:

θ	40	86	120	160	201	240	280	320	362
I	0.147	0.215	0.252	0.293	0.329	0.360	0.390	0.417	0.442

Find an empirical equation connecting I and θ in the form $I = k\theta^n$.

45. In a chemical experiment the relation between the concentration y of undissociated hydrochloric acid and the concentration x of hydrogen ions is shown in the table:

x	1.68	1.22	0.784	0.426	0.092	0.047	0.0096	0.0049
y	1.32	0.676	0.216	0.074	0.0085	0.00315	0.00036	0.00014

Find an empirical equation connecting the two quantities in the form $y = kx^n$.

CHAPTER VII

POLAR COÖRDINATES

60. Graphs. So far we have determined the position of a point in the plane by two distances, x and y. We may, however, use a distance and a direction, as follows:

Let O (Fig. 81), called the *origin*, or *pole*, be a fixed point, and let OM, called the *initial line*, be a fixed line. Take P any point in the plane, and draw OP. Denote OP by r, and the angle MOP by θ. Then r and θ are called the *polar coördinates* of the point $P(r, \theta)$, and when given will completely determine P.

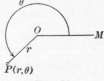

FIG. 81

For example, the point (2, 15°) is plotted by laying off the angle $MOP = 15°$ and measuring $OP = 2$.

OP, or r, is called the *radius vector*, and θ the *vectorial angle*, of P. These quantities may be either positive or negative. A negative value of θ is laid off in the direction of the motion of the hands of a clock, a positive angle in the opposite direction. After the angle θ has been constructed, positive values of r are measured from O along the terminal line of θ, and negative values of r from O along the backward extension of the terminal line. It follows that the same point may have more than one pair of coördinates. Thus (2, 195°), (2, − 165°), (− 2, 15°), and (− 2, − 345°) refer to the same point. In practice it is usually convenient to restrict θ to positive values.

Plotting in polar coördinates is facilitated by using paper ruled as in Figs. 83 and 84. The angle θ is determined from the numbers at the ends of the straight lines, and the value of r is counted off on the concentric circles, either toward or away from the number which indicates θ, according as r is positive or negative.

The relation between (r, θ) and (x, y) is found as follows:

Let the pole O and the initial line OM of a system of polar coördinates be at the same time the origin and the axis of x of a system of rectangular coördinates. Let P (Fig. 82) be any point of the plane, (x, y) its rectangular coördinates, and (r, θ) its polar coördinates. Then, by the definition of the trigonometric functions,

$$\cos \theta = \frac{x}{r},$$

$$\sin \theta = \frac{y}{r}.$$

Whence follows, on the one hand,

$$x = r \cos \theta,$$
$$y = r \sin \theta,$$
(1)

and, on the other hand,

$$r = \sqrt{x^2 + y^2}, \quad \sin \theta = \frac{y}{\sqrt{x^2 + y^2}}, \quad \cos \theta = \frac{x}{\sqrt{x^2 + y^2}}. \quad (2)$$

By means of (1) a transformation can be made from rectangular to polar coördinates, and by means of (2) from polar to rectangular coördinates.

When an equation is given in polar coördinates, the corresponding curve may be plotted by giving to θ convenient values, computing the corresponding values of r, plotting the resulting points, and drawing a curve through them.

Example 1.

$r = 3 + 2 \cos \theta$.

To plot this curve, we assign values to θ, com-

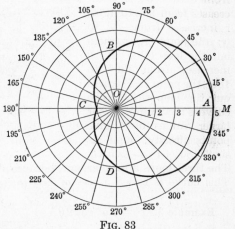

FIG. 83

pute the corresponding values of r with the aid of a table of natural cosines, and plot the points of the curve whose coördinates are thus determined. Proceeding in this manner we see that, as the values assigned to θ increase from 0° to 90°, $\cos \theta$ decreases from 1 to 0; hence r decreases from 5 to 3, and we draw the corresponding arc AB (Fig. 83). As θ increases from 90° to 180°, $\cos \theta$ decreases from 0 to

-1, r decreases from 3 to 1, and we draw the arc BC. As θ increases from $180°$ to $270°$, $\cos \theta$ increases from -1 to 0, r increases from 1 to 3, and we draw the arc CD. As θ increases from $270°$ to $360°$, $\cos \theta$ increases from 0 to 1, r increases from 3 to 5, and we draw the arc DA.

If any more values are assigned to θ, the corresponding points will follow the curve already drawn. Hence the curve in Fig. 83 is the complete curve of the given equation. The curve is one form of *limaçon*.

Example 2. $r = a \sin 3\,\theta$.

As θ increases from $0°$ to $30°$, r increases from 0 to a; as θ increases from $30°$ to $60°$, r decreases from a to 0; the point (r, θ) traces out the loop OAO (Fig. 84), which is evidently symmetrical with respect to the radius OA. As θ increases from $60°$ to $90°$, r is negative and decreases from 0 to $-a$; as θ increases from $90°$ to $120°$, r increases from $-a$ to 0; the point (r, θ) traces out the loop OBO. As θ increases from $120°$ to $180°$, the point (r, θ) traces out the loop OCO. The curve is now complete, for larger values of θ give points already found, as $\sin 3\,(180° + \theta) = -\sin 3\,\theta$.

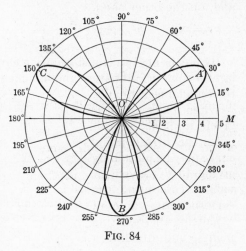

Fig. 84

The three loops are congruent, because $\sin 3\,(60° + \theta) = -\sin 3\,\theta$. This curve is called a *rose of three leaves*.

Example 3. $r^2 = 2\,a^2 \cos 2\,\theta$.

Solving for r, we have $r = \pm\, a\sqrt{2 \cos 2\,\theta}$.

Hence, corresponding to any values of θ which make $\cos 2\,\theta$ positive, there will be two values of r numerically equal and opposite in sign, and two corresponding points of the curve symmetrically situated with respect to the pole. If values are assigned to θ which make $\cos 2\,\theta$ negative, the corresponding values of r will be imaginary and there will be no points on the curve.

Accordingly, as θ increases from $0°$ to $45°$, r decreases numerically from $a\sqrt{2}$ to 0, and the portions of the curve in the first and the third quadrant are constructed (Fig. 85); as θ increases from $45°$ to $135°$, $\cos 2\,\theta$ is negative, and there is no portion of the curve between the lines $\theta = 45°$ and $\theta = 135°$; finally, as θ increases from $135°$ to $180°$, r increases numerically from 0 to $a\sqrt{2}$, and the portions of the curve in the second and the fourth quadrant are constructed. The curve is now complete, as we

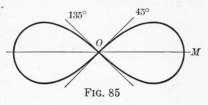

FIG. 85

should only repeat the curve already found if we assigned further values to θ; it is called the *lemniscate*.

Example 4. $r = a\theta$.

In plotting this curve, θ is considered in circular measure. When $\theta = 0$, $r = 0$; and as θ increases, r increases, so that the curve winds an infinite number of times around the origin while receding from it (Fig. 86). In this example, we obtain for negative values of θ points of the curve which cannot be obtained by use of positive values. In the figure the heavy line shows the portion of the spiral corresponding

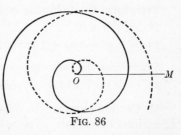

FIG. 86

to positive values of θ, and the dotted line the portion corresponding to negative values of θ. The curve is called the *spiral of Archimedes*.

Example 5. $r = e^{a\theta}$.

When $\theta = 0$, $r = 1$. As θ increases, r increases, and the curve winds around the origin at increasing distances from it (Fig. 87). When θ is negative and increasing numerically without limit, r approaches zero. Hence the curve winds an infinite number of times around the origin, continually approaching it. The dotted line in the figure corresponds to negative values of θ.

The curve is called the *logarithmic spiral*.

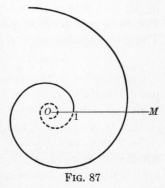

FIG. 87

EXERCISES

Plot the following curves:

1. $r = a \sin 2\,\theta$.

2. $r = a \cos 3\,\theta$.

3. $r = a \sin \dfrac{\theta}{3}$.

4. $r = a \sin \dfrac{\theta}{2}$.

5. $r = 2 + 3 \cos \theta$.

6. $r = a\,(1 + \cos \theta)^*$.

7. $r = a \sin^3 \dfrac{\theta}{3}$.

8. $r^2 = a^2 \sin \theta$.

9. $r^2 = a^2 \sin 3\,\theta$.

10. $r = a\,(1 - \cos 2\,\theta)$.

11. $r = a\,(1 + 2 \cos 2\,\theta)$.

12. $r = a \tan \theta$.

13. $r = a \tan 2\,\theta$.

Plot in one diagram each of the following pairs of curves and find their points of intersection:

14. $r = 3 \cos \theta,\ r = 3\sqrt{3} \sin \theta$.

15. $r^2 = a^2 \sin \theta,\ r^2 = a^2 \sin 2\,\theta$.

16. $r = 1 + \cos \theta,\ r = 2 \cos \theta$.

17. $r^2 = a^2 \sin \theta,\ r^2 = a^2 \sin 3\,\theta$.

Transform the following equations to polar coördinates:

18. $xy + 2 = 0$.

19. $x^2 + y^2 - 2\,ax + 2\,ay = 0$.

20. $x^2 + y^2 + 2\,ax = 0$.

21. $(x^2 + y^2)^2 = a^2(x^2 - y^2)$.

Transform the following equations to rectangular coördinates:

22. $r = a \csc \theta$.   23. $r = 2\,a \sin \theta$.   24. $r = a \tan \theta$.   25. $r = a \sin 2\,\theta$.

61. Certain curves. In this section we shall derive the polar equations of certain curves directly from their definitions or geometrical properties.

1. *The straight line.* Let LK (Fig. 88) be a straight line perpendicular to the initial line OM at A, where $OA = a$. Let $P(r, \theta)$ be any point of LK, and draw OP. Then, by trigonometry, $OP \cos \theta = OA$, or

$$r \cos \theta = a. \qquad (1)$$

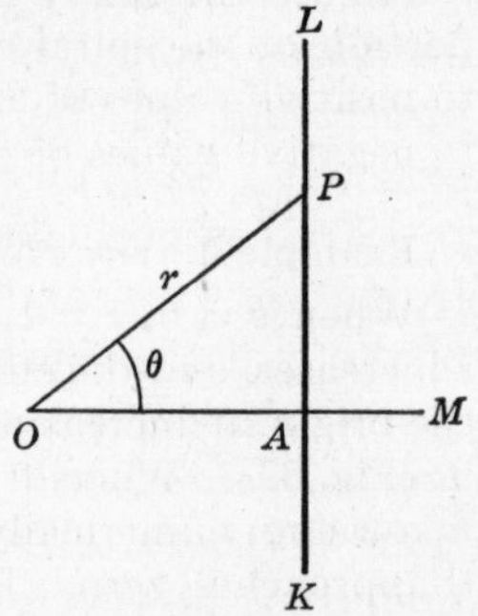

Conversely, if the coördinates of any point P satisfy (1), it can be shown that P is on a straight line perpendicular to OM at

Fig. 88

A, that is, is a point of LK. Hence (1) is the polar equation of LK.

As θ increases from $0°$ to $90°$, $\cos \theta$ decreases from 1 to 0, whence it is evident, if the equation is written in the form

* This curve is called a *cardioid*.

$r = \dfrac{a}{\cos \theta}$, that r increases from a to ∞, and the corresponding part of the line is AL. As θ increases from 90° to 180°, cos θ decreases from 0 to -1, r is negative and decreases in numerical value from ∞ to a, and the corresponding part of the line is KA. If any other values are assigned to θ, no new points can be found. It is to be noted, however, that the part AK of the line may also be found by letting θ vary from 0° to $-90°$.

2. *The circle.* Take any point of the circle as O and the diameter through that point as the initial line for the system of polar coördinates (Fig. 89). Let the radius of the circle be a; then $OA = 2\,a$. Let $P(r, \theta)$ be any point of the circle, and draw OP and PA. Since the triangle OPA is inscribed in a semicircle, it is a right triangle. Therefore, by trigonometry,

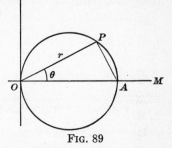

$$OP = OA \cos AOP,$$

or $\qquad r = 2\,a \cos \theta. \qquad (2)$

FIG. 89

Conversely, if the coördinates of any point P satisfy (2), it can be shown that OPA is a right triangle, and hence P is a point of the circle. Hence (2) is the polar equation of the circle.

As θ increases from 0° to 90°, r decreases from $2\,a$ to 0 and the upper half of the circle is constructed. As θ increases from 90° to 180°, r is negative and decreases from 0 to $-2\,a$, and the lower half of the circle is constructed. If any more values are assigned to θ, the points located will be but repetitions of those already located. If preferred, however, the lower half of the circle may be plotted by assigning values of θ from 0° to $-90°$.

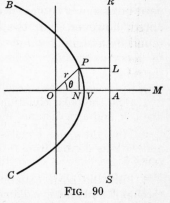

FIG. 90

3. *The parabola.* Let O (Fig. 90) be the focus of a parabola, whose directrix RS is perpendicular to the initial line OM at the point A, where $OA = 2\,c$. Then OM is the axis of the parabola.

Let $P(r, \theta)$ be any point of the parabola and draw OP, PN perpendicular to OM, and PL perpendicular to RS. By the definition of the parabola, $OP = PL$; but $OP = r$, and $PL = NA$ $= OA - ON = 2\,c - r \cos \theta$. Therefore $r = 2\,c - r \cos \theta$, which may be written in the form

$$r = \frac{2\,c}{1 + \cos \theta}. \tag{3}$$

Conversely, if the coördinates of any point P satisfy (3), it may be proved that P is equally distant from O and RS, and hence is a point of the parabola.

Equation (3) is usually written in the form

$$r = \frac{k}{1 + \cos \theta}, \tag{4}$$

where the constant k is the distance from the focus to the directrix.

As θ increases from $0°$ to $180°$, $\cos \theta$ decreases from 1 to -1 and r increases from $\frac{k}{2}$ to ∞, the corresponding part of the parabola being VB. As θ increases from $180°$ to $360°$, $\cos \theta$ increases from -1 to 1 and r decreases from ∞ to $\frac{k}{2}$, the corresponding part of the parabola being CV. No other values need be assigned to θ, as the curve is now complete. It may be noted, however, that the lower part of the parabola may be found by assigning values of θ from $0°$ to $-180°$.

EXERCISES

1. Find the polar equation of a straight line parallel to the initial line OM and at a distance a from O.

2. Find the polar equation of a straight line distant a from O and with its normal from O making an angle α with the initial line OM.

3. Find the polar equation of a circle of diameter $2\,a$ passing through O and having a diameter perpendicular to OM at O.

4. Find the polar equation of a parabola having its focus at O and its directrix perpendicular to the radius vector $\theta = 180°$ at a distance k from O.

5. Find the polar equation of the locus of a point which moves so that its distance from O is always one half its distance from the straight line RS which is perpendicular to the initial line OM at the point A, where $OA = a$.

6. In a parabola prove that the length of a focal chord which makes an angle of 30° with the axis of the curve is four times the length of the focal chord perpendicular to the axis.

7. A comet is moving in a parabolic orbit around the sun at the focus of the parabola. When the comet is 100,000,000 miles from the sun, the radius vector makes an angle of 60° with the axis of the orbit. How near does it come to the sun?

8. A comet moving in a parabolic orbit around the sun is observed at two points of its path, its focal distances being 5 and 15 million miles, and the angle between them being 90°. How near does it come to the sun?

62. The differentials dr, $d\theta$, ds. We have seen, in § 39, that the differential of arc in rectangular coördinates is given by the equation
$$ds^2 = dx^2 + dy^2. \tag{1}$$

If we wish to change this to polar coördinates, we have to place
$$x = r \cos \theta, \quad y = r \sin \theta;$$
whence
$$dx = \cos \theta \, dr - r \sin \theta \, d\theta,$$
$$dy = \sin \theta \, dr + r \cos \theta \, d\theta.$$

Substituting in (1), we have
$$ds^2 = dr^2 + r^2 \, d\theta^2. \tag{2}$$

This formula may be remembered by means of an "elementary triangle" (Fig. 91), constructed as follows:

Let P be a point on a curve $r = f(\theta)$, the coördinates of P being (r, θ), where $OP = r$ and $MOP = \theta$. Let θ be increased by an amount $d\theta$, thus determining another point Q on the curve. From O as a center and with a radius equal to r, describe an arc of a circle intersecting OQ in R so that $OR = OP = r$. Then, by § 44, $PR = r \, d\theta$. Now RQ is equal to Δr, and PQ is equal

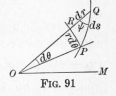

FIG. 91

to Δs. We shall mark them, however, as dr and ds respectively, and the formula (2) is then correctly obtained by treating the triangle PQR as a right triangle with straight-line sides. The fact is that the smaller the triangle becomes as Q approaches P, the more nearly does it behave as a straight-line triangle; and in the limit, formula (2) is exactly true.

Other formulas may be read out of the triangle PQR. Let us denote by ψ the angle PQR, which is the angle made by the curve with any radius vector. Then, if we treat the triangle PQR as a straight-line right-angle triangle, we have the formulas:

$$\sin \psi = \frac{r\,d\theta}{ds}, \quad \cos \psi = \frac{dr}{ds}, \quad \tan \psi = \frac{r\,d\theta}{dr}. \tag{3}$$

The above is not a proof of the formulas. To supply the proof we need to go through a limit process, as follows:

We connect the points P and Q by a straight line (Fig. 92) and draw a straight line from P perpendicular to OQ meeting OQ at S. Then the triangle PQS is a straight-line right-angle triangle, and therefore

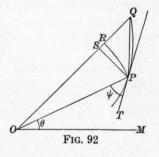

FIG. 92

$$\sin SQP = \frac{SP}{\text{chord } PQ}$$

$$= \frac{SP}{\text{arc } PQ} \cdot \frac{\text{arc } PQ}{\text{chord } PQ}.$$

Now angle $POQ = \Delta\theta$, arc $PQ = \Delta s$, and, from the right triangle OSP, $SP = OP \sin POQ = r \sin \Delta\theta$. Therefore

$$\sin SQP = \frac{r \sin \Delta\theta}{\Delta s} \cdot \frac{\text{arc } PQ}{\text{chord } PQ} = r \frac{\sin \Delta\theta}{\Delta\theta} \cdot \frac{\Delta\theta}{\Delta s} \cdot \frac{\text{arc } PQ}{\text{chord } PQ}. \tag{4}$$

Now let $\Delta\theta$ approach zero as a limit, so that Q approaches P along the curve. The angle SQP approaches the angle OPT, where PT is the tangent at P. At the same time $\frac{\sin \Delta\theta}{\Delta\theta}$ approaches 1, by § 44; $\frac{\Delta\theta}{\Delta s}$ approaches $\frac{d\theta}{ds}$, by definition; and $\frac{\text{arc } PQ}{\text{chord } PQ}$ approaches 1, by § 39. In this figure we denote the angle OPT by ψ and have, from (4),

$$\sin \psi = \frac{r\,d\theta}{ds}, \tag{5}$$

which is the first of formulas (3). It is true that in Fig. 92 we have denoted OPT by ψ and that in Fig. 91 ψ denotes OQP. But if we remember that the angle OQP approaches OPT as a limit when Q approaches P, and that in using Fig. 91 to read off the formulas (3) we are really anticipating this limit process, the difference appears unessential.

The other formulas (3) may be obtained by a limit process similar to the one just used, or they may be obtained more quickly by combining (5) and (2). For, from (2) and (5), we have

$$1 = \left(\frac{dr}{ds}\right)^2 + \left(\frac{r\,d\theta}{ds}\right)^2 = \left(\frac{dr}{ds}\right)^2 + \sin^2 \psi\,;$$

whence

$$\cos \psi = \frac{dr}{ds}. \tag{6}$$

By dividing (5) by (6) we have

$$\tan \psi = \frac{r\,d\theta}{dr}. \tag{7}$$

In using (7) it may be convenient to write it in the form

$$\tan \psi = \frac{r}{\frac{dr}{d\theta}}, \tag{8}$$

since the equation of the curve is usually given in the form $r = f(\theta)$, and $\frac{dr}{d\theta}$ is found by direct differentiation.

Example. Find the angle which the curve $r = a \sin 4\,\theta$ makes with the radius vector $\theta = 30°$.

Here $\frac{dr}{d\theta} = 4\,a \cos 4\,\theta$. Therefore, from (8),

$$\tan \psi = \frac{a \sin 4\,\theta}{4\,a \cos 4\,\theta} = \frac{1}{4} \tan 4\,\theta.$$

Substituting $\theta = 30°$, we have

$$\tan \psi = \tfrac{1}{4} \tan 120° = - \tfrac{1}{4}\sqrt{3} = -.4330.$$

Therefore $\qquad\qquad \psi = 156° \, 35'.$

EXERCISES

1. Find the angle which the curve $r = a \sin 3\theta$ makes with the initial line.

2. Find the angle which the curve $r = 3 + 2 \cos \theta$ makes with the radius vector $\theta = 60°$.

3. Find the angles which the curve $r = a(1 + \sin 2\theta)$ makes with the initial line and with the line $\theta = 45°$.

4. Find the angle which the curve $r = a \cos^2 \dfrac{\theta}{2}$ makes with the initial line at each point where it intersects that line.

5. Find the angle at which the curve $r = 2(1 - 2 \sin \theta)$ crosses the initial line at each point of intersection.

6. Show that for the curve $r = a \sin^3 \dfrac{\theta}{3}$, $\psi = \dfrac{\theta}{3}$.

7. Show that the angle between the cardioid $r = a(1 - \cos \theta)$ and any radius vector is always half the angle between the radius vector and the initial line.

8. Show that the angle between the lemniscate $r^2 = 2\,a^2 \cos 2\theta$ and any radius vector is $\dfrac{\pi}{2}$ plus twice the angle between the radius vector and the initial line, if θ is in the first quadrant.

63. Area. Let O (Fig. 93) be the pole and OM the initial line of a system of polar coördinates (r, θ), OP_1 and OP_2 two fixed radius vectors for which $\theta = \theta_1$, and $\theta = \theta_2$ respectively, and P_1P_2 any curve for which the equation is $r = f(\theta)$. Required the area P_1OP_2.

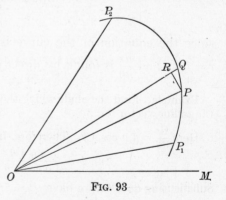

FIG. 93

To construct the differential of area, dA, we divide the angle P_1OP_2 into parts, $d\theta$. Let OP and OQ be any two consecutive radius vectors; then the angle $POQ = d\theta$. With O as a center and OP as a radius, we draw the arc of a circle, intersecting OQ at R. The area of the sector $POR = \frac{1}{2}(OP)^2 \, d\theta = \frac{1}{2} r^2 \, d\theta$.

It is obvious that the required area is the limit of the sum of the sectors as their number is indefinitely increased. Therefore we have

$$dA = \tfrac{1}{2}\, r^2\, d\theta$$

and

$$A = \int_{\theta_1}^{\theta_2} \tfrac{1}{2}\, r^2\, d\theta.$$

This result is unchanged if P_1 coincides with O, but in that case OP_1 must be tangent to the curve. So also P_2 may coincide with O.

Example. Find the area of one loop of the curve $r = a \sin 3\,\theta$ (Fig. 84, § 60).

As the loop is contained between the two tangents $\theta = 0$ and $\theta = \dfrac{\pi}{3}$, the required area is given by the equation

$$A = \int_0^{\frac{\pi}{3}} \tfrac{1}{2}\, a^2 \sin^2 3\,\theta\, d\theta$$

$$= \frac{a^2}{2}\left[\frac{\theta}{2} - \frac{\sin 6\,\theta}{12}\right]_0^{\frac{\pi}{3}} \qquad \text{[By (3), § 53]}$$

$$= \frac{\pi a^2}{12}.$$

EXERCISES

1. Find the total area of the lemniscate $r^2 = 2\,a^2 \cos 2\,\theta$.

2. Find the area of one loop of the curve $r = a \sin n\theta$.

3. Find the total area of the cardioid $r = a(1 + \cos\theta)$.

4. Find the total area bounded by the curve $r = 5 + 3 \cos\theta$.

5. Find the total area bounded by the curve $r = 3 + 2 \sin\theta$.

6. Find the area bounded by the curves $r = a \cos 3\,\theta$ and $r = a$.

7. Find the total area bounded by the curve $r = 3 + 2 \cos 4\,\theta$.

8. Find the area bounded by the curves $r = 6 + 4 \cos\theta$ and $r = 4 \cos\theta$.

9. Find the area which is inside the curve $r = 4 + 2 \cos\theta$ and outside the circle $r = 4$.

10. Find the area of each of the two portions into which the circle $r = 4 \cos\theta$ is divided by the straight line $r = 3 \sec\theta$. *Integrate both*

GENERAL EXERCISES

Plot the following curves:

1. $r^2 = a^2 \sin \dfrac{\theta}{2}$.

2. $r^2 = a^2 \sin 4\,\theta$.

3. $r = a(1 - \sin \theta)$.

4. $r = a(1 + \cos 2\,\theta)$.

5. $r = 2 + 4 \cos \theta$.

6. $r = 1 - 2 \sin 2\,\theta$.

7. $r = 1 - 2\,\theta$.

8. $r^2 = 4 \sec 2\,\theta$.

9. $r^2 = a^2 \tan \theta$.

10. $r^2 = a^2 \tan \dfrac{\theta}{2}$.

11. $r = 1 + \sin \dfrac{\theta}{2}$.

12. $r = 2 + \sin \dfrac{\theta}{2}$.

13. $r = 1 + \sin \dfrac{3\,\theta}{2}$.

14. $r^2 = a^2(1 + 2 \cos 2\,\theta)$.

Plot in one diagram each of the following pairs of curves, and find their points of intersection:

15. $r = 2 + \sin \theta$, $r = 2 + \cos \theta$.

16. $r = a \cos \theta$, $r = a \sin 2\,\theta$.

17. $r = a \sin \theta$, $r^2 = a^2 \cos 2\,\theta$.

18. $r^2 = 3 \cos 2\,\theta$, $r^2 = 2 \cos^2 \theta$.

19. $r = a \sin \theta$, $r^2 = a^2 \sin 2\,\theta$.

20. $r = a(1 + \sin 2\,\theta)$, $r^2 = 4\,a^2 \sin 2\,\theta$.

Transform the following equations to polar coördinates:

21. $y^2 = \dfrac{x^3}{2\,a - x}$.

22. $y^4 + y^2 x^2 - a^2 x^2 = 0$.

Transform the following equations to rectangular coördinates:

23. $r^2 = 2\,a^2 \sin 2\,\theta$.

24. $r = a(1 + \cos \theta)$.

25. Show that the curves $r^2 = a^2 \sin 2\,\theta$ and $r^2 = a^2 \cos 2\,\theta$ intersect at right angles.

26. Find the angle of intersection of the curves $r = 2 \sin \theta$ and $r^2 = 4 \sin 2\,\theta$.

27. Find the angle at which the curve $r = a(1 + 2 \sin \theta)$ cuts the radius vector perpendicular to OM at each point at which it intersects it.

28. Find the angle at which the curve $r = 2 + \cos 2\,\theta$ meets the circle $r = 2$.

29. Find the angle of intersection of the curves $r = a \cos \theta$ and $r = a \sin 2\,\theta$.

30. Find the polar equation of the curve which intersects all the radius vectors at the same angle.

31. Find the polar equation of a curve, passing through the point $(2, 0)$, such that the tangent of the angle between the radius vector and the curve is equal to the square of the radius vector.

32. Find the polar equation of a curve, passing through the point $(1, 2)$, such that the tangent of the angle between the radius vector and the curve is equal to minus the reciprocal of the radius vector.

33. Find the total area bounded by the curve $r^2 = a^2 \sin \theta$.

34. Find the area bounded by the radius vectors $\theta = 0$ and $\theta = \dfrac{\pi}{2}$ and a part of the first turn of the logarithmic spiral $r = e^{a\theta}$.

35. Find the total area bounded by the curve $r^2 = a^2 \sin 3\,\theta$.

36. Find the area which is inside the circle $r = a$ and outside the cardioid $r = a(1 + \cos \theta)$.

CHAPTER VIII

SERIES

64. Power series. The expression

$$a_0 + a_1 x + a_2 x^2 + a_3 x^3 + a_4 x^4 + \cdots, \tag{1}$$

where a_0, a_1, a_2, $\cdots$ are constants, is called a *power series* in x. The terms of the series may be unlimited in number, in which case we have an infinite series, or the series may terminate after a finite number of terms, in which case it reduces to a polynomial.

If the series (1) is an infinite series, it is said to *converge* for a definite value of x when the sum of the first n terms approaches a limit as n increases indefinitely.

Infinite series may arise through the use of elementary operations. Thus, if we divide 1 by $1 - x$ in the ordinary manner, we obtain the quotient $1 + x + x^2 + x^3 + \cdots$, and we may write

$$\frac{1}{1-x} = 1 + x + x^2 + x^3 + x^4 + \cdots. \tag{2}$$

Similarly, if we extract the square root of $1 + x$ by the rule taught in elementary algebra, arranging the work as follows,

$$
\begin{array}{r|l}
1 + x & 1 + \dfrac{x}{2} - \dfrac{x^2}{8} + \cdots \\
1 & \\
\hline
2 + \dfrac{x}{2} & x \\
& x + \dfrac{x^2}{4} \\
\hline
2 + x - \dfrac{x^2}{8} & -\dfrac{x^2}{4} \\
& -\dfrac{x^2}{4} - \dfrac{x^3}{8} + \dfrac{x^4}{64} \\
\hline
\end{array}
$$

the operation may be continued indefinitely. We may write

$$\sqrt{1 + x} = 1 + \frac{x}{2} - \frac{x^2}{8} + \cdots. \tag{3}$$

The results (2) and (3) are useful only for values of x for which the series in each case converges. When that happens the more terms we take of the series, the more nearly is their sum equal to the function on the left of the equation, and in that sense the function is equal to the series. For example, the series (2) is a geometric progression which is known to converge when x is a positive or negative number numerically less than 1. If we place $x = \frac{1}{3}$ in (2), we have

$$\tfrac{3}{2} = 1 + \tfrac{1}{3} + \tfrac{1}{9} + \tfrac{1}{27} + \tfrac{1}{81} + \cdots,$$

which is true in the sense that the limit of the sum of the terms on the right is $\frac{3}{2}$. If, however, we place $x = 3$ in (2), we have

$$-\tfrac{1}{2} = 1 + 3 + 9 + 27 + \cdots,$$

which is false. A reason for this difference may be seen by considering the remainder in the division which produced (2) but which is neglected in writing the series. This remainder is x^n after n terms of the quotient have been obtained. Therefore we have exactly

$$\frac{1}{1 - x} = 1 + x + x^2 + \cdots + x^{n-1} + \frac{x^n}{1 - x}. \qquad (4)$$

If x is numerically less than 1, the last term in (4) becomes smaller and smaller as n increases, while if x is numerically greater than 1, that term becomes larger. Hence in the former case it may be neglected, but not in the latter case.

The calculus offers a general method for finding such series as those obtained by the special methods which led to (2) and (3). This method will be given in the following section.

65. Maclaurin series. We shall assume that a function can usually be expressed by a power series which is valid for appropriate values of x, and that the derivative of the function may be found by differentiating the series term by term. The proof of these assumptions lies outside the scope of this book.

If we wish to find the power series for a given function, we may follow a procedure which we shall now outline in general and afterward carry out in detail in the illustrative examples. We begin by equating the function, whatever it is, to a series of the form

$$A + Bx + Cx^2 + Dx^3 + Ex^4 + Fx^5 + \cdots, \qquad (1)$$

where the coefficients A, B, C, $\cdots$ are unknown constants which are to be determined. They are called *undetermined coefficients*. We next differentiate both terms of the equation thus formed, then differentiate that result, and so on, forming as many new equations as seems desirable.

We have then a set of equations which are to be true for all values of x which make the series convergent. We may consequently place $x = 0$ in each equation, and find that we may usually determine A, B, C, $\cdots$. These values substituted in (1) give the required series. In a few elementary cases (see Example 3) the values of A, B, C, $\cdots$ become infinite. This means the series (1) cannot be found. For a full discussion of this matter the student must consult more advanced texts.

Example 1. Expand $\sin x$ into a power series in x.

Place $\sin x = A + Bx + Cx^2 + Dx^3 + Ex^4 + Fx^5 + \cdots$.

Differentiating successively, we have:

$$\cos x = B + 2\,Cx + 3\,Dx^2 + 4\,Ex^3 + 5\,Fx^4 + \cdots,$$
$$-\sin x = \qquad 2\,C + 6\,Dx + 12\,Ex^2 + 20\,Fx^3 + \cdots,$$
$$-\cos x = \qquad\qquad 6\,D + 24\,Ex + 60\,Fx^2 + \cdots,$$
$$\sin x = \qquad\qquad\qquad 24\,E + 120\,Fx + \cdots,$$
$$\cos x = \qquad\qquad\qquad\qquad 120\,F + \cdots.$$

Placing $x = 0$ in each of these equations, we have

$$0 = A,\ 1 = B,\ 0 = 2\,C,\ -1 = 6\,D,\ 0 = 24\,E,\ 1 = 120\,F,$$

whence, $A = 0$, $B = 1$, $C = 0$, $D = -\frac{1}{6}$, $E = 0$, $F = \frac{1}{120}$.

Substituting these values in the first series, we have

$$\sin x = x - \frac{x^3}{6} + \frac{x^5}{120} + \cdots. \,*$$

We observe that there is no even power of x in the series as far as determined; this is because the left-hand sides of the equations from which A, C, and E are determined are either $\sin x$ or $-\sin x$ and hence become zero when $x = 0$. Moreover, the coefficients of the odd powers of x may be written so as to indicate how they are formed. Take, for example, the equation from which D is determined; the term $6\,D$ in this equation is the result of differentiating

---

*The last sign in the series indicates that more terms are to be added algebraically. It is not necessarily the sign of the following term.

Dx^3 three times in succession. But the first differentiation gives $3 Dx^2$, the second differentiation gives $3 D(2 x) = 3 \cdot 2 Dx$, and the third differentiation gives $3 \cdot 2 \cdot 1 D = 3! D$ since the product $3 \cdot 2 \cdot 1$ is denoted by $3!$ (§ 55). Using $3! D$ in place of $6 D$, we find $D = -\dfrac{1}{3!}$. In like manner we may prove $F = \dfrac{1}{5!}$.

If the expansion is carried out to five terms we should now expect the series to be

$$\sin x = x - \frac{x^3}{3!} + \frac{x^5}{5!} - \frac{x^7}{7!} + \frac{x^9}{9!} + \cdots,$$

and this is found to be the case when the work is completed.

Example 2. Expand $(a + x)^n$, where a and n are any constants, in a power series in x.

We place $(a + x)^n = A + Bx + Cx^2 + Dx^3 + Ex^4 + \cdots$.

Differentiating successively, we have

$$n(a + x)^{n-1} = B + 2 Cx + 3 Dx^2 + 4 Ex^3 + \cdots,$$
$$n(n - 1)(a + x)^{n-2} = 2! C + 3 \cdot 2 Dx + 4 \cdot 3 Ex^2 + \cdots,$$
$$n(n - 1)(n - 2)(a + x)^{n-3} = 3! D + 4 \cdot 3 \cdot 2 Ex + \cdots,$$
$$n(n-1)(n-2)(n-3)(a+x)^{n-4} = 4! E + \cdots.$$

Placing $x = 0$ in each of these equations and solving for the undetermined coefficients, we have

$$A = a^n, \quad B = na^{n-1}, \quad C = \frac{n (n - 1)}{2!} a^{n-2},$$
$$D = \frac{n(n - 1)(n - 2)}{3!} a^{n-3},$$
$$E = \frac{n(n - 1)(n - 2)(n - 3)}{4!} a^{n-4}.$$

Hence the required series is

$$(a + x)^n = a^n + na^{n-1}x + \frac{n(n - 1)}{2!} a^{n-2}x^2 + \frac{n(n - 1)(n - 2)}{3!} a^{n-3}x^3$$
$$+ \frac{n(n - 1)(n - 2)(n - 3)}{4!} a^{n-4}x^4 + \cdots.$$

This series is exactly what we should have found if we had expanded the expression $(a + x)^n$ by the rules of the *binomial theorem* learned in elementary algebra for a positive integral exponent. As a matter of fact, we have just proved that the binomial theorem holds for any exponent, positive or negative, fractional or integral. If n is a positive integer, the series will be a polynomial of $n + 1$ terms; in all other cases the series will be infinite.

Example 3. Expand $\ln (1 + x)$ in a power series in x.

The reason we take $\ln (1 + x)$ rather than $\ln x$, which might seem to be more natural, is that $\ln x$ is an example of a function which cannot be expanded into a power series in x, since we should find the coefficients infinite if we tried to use the method of the previous examples.

Accordingly we place

$$\ln (1 + x) = A + Bx + Cx^2 + Dx^3 + Ex^4 + Fx^5 + \cdots,$$

and by successive differentiation find

$$\frac{1}{1 + x} = (1 + x)^{-1} = B + 2\,Cx + 3\,Dx^2 + 4\,Ex^3 + 5\,Fx^4 + \cdots,$$
$$-1(1 + x)^{-2} = \qquad\quad 2\,C + 6\,Dx + 12\,Ex^2 + 20\,Fx^3 + \cdots,$$
$$2(1 + x)^{-3} = \qquad\qquad\qquad 6\,D + 24\,Ex + 60\,Fx^2 + \cdots,$$
$$-6(1 + x)^{-4} = \qquad\qquad\qquad\qquad\quad 24\,E + 120\,Fx + \cdots,$$
$$24(1 + x)^{-5} = \qquad\qquad\qquad\qquad\qquad\qquad 120\,F + \cdots.$$

Placing $x = 0$ in these equations and solving, we find

$$A = \ln 1 = 0, \quad B = 1, \quad C = -\tfrac{1}{2}, \quad D = \tfrac{1}{3}, \quad E = -\tfrac{1}{4}, \quad F = \tfrac{1}{5}.$$

Hence the required series is

$$\ln (1 + x) = x - \frac{x^2}{2} + \frac{x^3}{3} - \frac{x^4}{4} + \frac{x^5}{5} + \cdots.$$

The work of finding the coefficients may be abridged by stopping the differentiation with the second equation, for we know, by algebra, that

$$\frac{1}{1 + x} = 1 - x + x^2 - x^3 + x^4 + \cdots.$$

Substituting this value in the second equation, we have

$$1 - x + x^2 - x^3 + x^4 + \cdots = B + 2\,Cx + 3\,Dx^2 + 4\,Ex^3 + 5\,Fx^4 + \cdots.$$

Comparing coefficients of like powers of x, we have

$$B = 1, \quad 2\,C = -1, \quad 3\,D = 1, \quad 4\,E = -1, \quad 5\,F = 1;$$

whence we obtain the values of B, C, D, E, and F previously determined.

This method of abridgment can generally be used to advantage when the left-hand side of the first derived equation can be readily expanded into a power series by division or by the binomial theorem.

It is possible to embody the results of this discussion in a general formula. For that purpose let us write in place of any one of the specific functions used in the illustrative examples the general expression for a function $f(x)$. Let us denote the successive derivatives of this function by $f'(x), f''(x), f'''(x), \cdots$.

Placing

$$f(x) = A + Bx + Cx^2 + Dx^3 + Ex^4 + \cdots,$$

and differentiating, we have

$$f'(x) = B + 2\,Cx + \qquad 3\,Dx^2 + \qquad 4\,Ex^3 + \cdots,$$
$$f''(x) = \qquad 2!\,C + 3 \cdot 2\,Dx + \qquad 4 \cdot 3\,Ex^2 + \cdots,$$
$$f'''(x) = \qquad\qquad\qquad 3!\,D + 4 \cdot 3 \cdot 2\,Ex + \cdots,$$
$$f^{\mathrm{iv}}(x) = \qquad\qquad\qquad\qquad\qquad 4!\,E + \cdots.$$

Denoting by $f(0), f'(0), f''(0), f'''(0), f^{\mathrm{iv}}(0), \cdots$ the values of $f(x), f'(x), f''(x), f'''(x), f^{\mathrm{iv}}(x), \cdots$ when $x = 0$, and solving, we find

$$A = f(0), \quad B = f'(0), \quad C = \frac{f''(0)}{2!}, \quad D = \frac{f'''(0)}{3!}, \quad E = \frac{f^{\mathrm{iv}}(0)}{4!}, \cdots.$$

Hence the required general series is

$$f(x) = f(0) + f'(0)\,x + \frac{f''(0)}{2!}\,x^2 + \frac{f'''(0)}{3!}\,x^3 + \frac{f^{\mathrm{iv}}(0)}{4!}\,x^4 + \cdots.$$

This is called the *Maclaurin series*. The illustrative examples are special forms of this series.

EXERCISES

Expand each of the following functions into a Maclaurin series, obtaining the first four nonvanishing terms:

1. e^x.

2. $\cos x$.

3. $\tan x$.

4. $\sin^{-1} x$.

5. $\tan^{-1} x$.

6. $\sin\left(\dfrac{\pi}{4} + x\right)$.

7. $\ln(2 + x)$.

8. $\cos^2 x$.

9. $(e^x + e^{-x})^2$.

10. $\ln(1 + \sin x)$.

11. $\sqrt{1 + x^2}$.

66. Taylor series. Instead of expanding a function into a series of powers of x, as is done in the previous section, we may expand into powers of the binomial $x - a$, where a is a constant chosen at pleasure. The procedure is analogous to that of the previous section.

We equate the given function to

$$A + B(x - a) + C(x - a)^2 + D(x - a)^3 + \cdots$$

and differentiate successively. To determine the coefficients, we now place $x = a$ in order to make $x - a = 0$. The method is illustrated in the following examples:

Example 1. Expand $\sin x$ in powers of $x - \dfrac{\pi}{3}$.

We place

$$\sin x = A + B\left(x - \frac{\pi}{3}\right) + C\left(x - \frac{\pi}{3}\right)^2 + D\left(x - \frac{\pi}{3}\right)^3 + \cdots.$$

Differentiating successively, we have

$$\cos x = B + 2\,C\left(x - \frac{\pi}{3}\right) + 3\,D\left(x - \frac{\pi}{3}\right)^2 + \cdots,$$

$$-\sin x = \quad\quad 2\,C \quad\quad\quad\quad + 6\,D\left(x - \frac{\pi}{3}\right) + \cdots,$$

$$-\cos x = \quad\quad\quad\quad\quad\quad\quad\quad 6\,D \quad\quad\quad + \cdots.$$

Placing $x = \dfrac{\pi}{3}$, we have

$$\tfrac{1}{2}\sqrt{3} = A, \quad \tfrac{1}{2} = B, \quad -\tfrac{1}{2}\sqrt{3} = 2\,C, \quad -\tfrac{1}{2} = 6\,D,$$

whence $\quad A = \tfrac{1}{2}\sqrt{3}, \quad B = \tfrac{1}{2}, \quad C = -\tfrac{1}{4}\sqrt{3}, \quad D = -\tfrac{1}{12}.$

Therefore

$$\sin x = \tfrac{1}{2}\sqrt{3} + \tfrac{1}{2}\left(x - \frac{\pi}{3}\right) - \tfrac{1}{4}\sqrt{3}\left(x - \frac{\pi}{3}\right)^2 - \tfrac{1}{12}\left(x - \frac{\pi}{3}\right)^3 + \cdots.$$

Example 2. Expand $\ln x$ in powers of $x - 3$.

We place

$$\ln x = A + B(x - 3) + C(x - 3)^2 + D(x - 3)^3 + \cdots.$$

Differentiating, we have

$$\frac{1}{x} = B + 2\,C(x - 3) + 3\,D(x - 3)^2 + \cdots,$$

$$-\frac{1}{x^2} = \quad\quad 2\,C \quad\quad\quad + 6\,D(x - 3) \quad + \cdots,$$

$$\frac{2}{x^3} = \quad\quad\quad\quad\quad\quad\quad 6\,D \quad\quad\quad + \cdots.$$

Placing $x = 3$ and solving the resulting equations, we have

$$A = \ln 3, \quad B = \tfrac{1}{3}, \quad C = -\tfrac{1}{18}, \quad D = \tfrac{1}{81}.$$

Hence

$$\ln x = \ln 3 + \tfrac{1}{3}(x - 3) - \tfrac{1}{18}(x - 3)^2 + \tfrac{1}{81}(x - 3)^3 + \cdots.$$

It is possible to embody the results of this discussion in a general formula. Let $f(x)$ be any function which it is desired to expand in powers of $x - a$. Placing

$$f(x) = A + B(x - a) + C(x - a)^2 + D(x - a)^3 + \cdots$$

and differentiating, we have

$$f'(x) = B + 2\,C(x - a) + \quad 3\,D(x - a)^2 + \cdots,$$
$$f''(x) = \quad\quad 2!\,C \quad\quad + 3.2\,D(x - a) + \cdots,$$
$$f'''(x) = \quad\quad\quad\quad\quad 3!\,D \quad\quad + \cdots.$$

We now place $x = a$ in these equations, and denote by $f(a)$, $f'(a)$, $f''(a)$, etc. the values of $f(x)$, $f'(x)$, $f''(x)$, etc. when $x = a$. Solving for A, B, C, etc., we have

$$A = f(a), \quad B = f'(a), \quad C = \frac{f''(a)}{2!}, \quad D = \frac{f'''(a)}{3!}, \quad \cdots.$$

Hence the required general series is

$$f(x) = f(a) + f'(a)(x - a) + \frac{f''(a)}{2!}\,(x - a)^2 + \frac{f'''(a)}{3!}\,(x - a)^3 + \cdots.$$

This is called the *Taylor series*.

EXERCISES

Find the first four terms in the expansion of each of the following functions in a Taylor series, using the value of a given in each case:

1. e^x, $a = 5$.

2. $\dfrac{1}{1 + x}$, $a = 1$.

3. $\sin x$, $a = \dfrac{\pi}{6}$.

4. $\cos x$, $a = \dfrac{\pi}{4}$.

5. e^{2x}, $a = 3$.

6. $\tan^{-1} x$, $a = 1$.

7. $\sqrt{1 + x^2}$, $a = 1$.

8. $\tan x$, $a = \dfrac{\pi}{3}$.

9. $\ln(\sin x)$, $a = \dfrac{\pi}{4}$.

67. Computation by series. One important use of a series is in the computation of the value of a function for a given value of x. For this purpose it is necessary that the series should converge and it is also desirable that the series should converge rapidly. By this we mean that it should be possible to compute the value of the function by using only a few terms of the series. This consideration enables us to decide whether we should use a Maclaurin or a Taylor series.

If x is numerically less than unity, the powers x^2, x^3, etc. are successively smaller and smaller. Hence in this case the Maclaurin series is the one to use, and the smaller the value of x the fewer terms of the series will be necessary to compute the value of the function to a required degree of accuracy.

If x is numerically greater than unity, the powers of x are successively larger and larger, and in this case a Maclaurin series is not convenient. Hence we should use a Taylor series, first choosing a value of a such that $x - a$ is numerically less than unity. Then the powers $(x - a)^2$, $(x - a)^3$, . . . are successively smaller and smaller, and the nearer x is to a the fewer terms of the series will be necessary to compute the value of the function to a required degree of accuracy. We express this by saying that the Taylor series is useful in the *neighborhood* of $x = a$, while the Maclaurin series is useful in the neighborhood of $x = 0$. In choosing a it is necessary that we know the values of the function and its derivatives for $x = a$.

Example 1. Find the value of sin 10° to four decimal places.

It is necessary to express the angle in circular measure, since all formulas of the calculus which involve the trigonometric functions are based on that hypothesis. Now $10° = \dfrac{10\,\pi}{180}$ radians $= \dfrac{\pi}{18}$ radians $= .17453$ radians. Hence we place $x = \dfrac{10\,\pi}{180} = .17453$, where we take five significant figures in order to insure accuracy in the fourth significant figure of the result,* and substitute in the series of Example 1, § 65.

We have $\qquad \sin \dfrac{\pi}{18} = .17453 - \dfrac{(.17453)^3}{6} + \cdots$

$$= .17453 - .00089 = .17364.$$

Hence to four decimal places sin 10° = .1736.

We have used only two terms of the series, since a rough calculation, which may be made with $x = .2$, shows that the third term of the series will not affect the fourth decimal place.

Example 2. Find the value of sin 61° to four decimal places.

In radians the angle 61° is $\dfrac{61\,\pi}{180} = 1.0647$. Since this number is greater than unity, we will not use a Maclaurin series. We shall

---

* This is not a general rule. In other cases the student may need to carry two or even three more significant figures in the calculation than are needed in the result.

use a Taylor series, choosing for a the circular measure of an angle near $61°$ whose sine and cosine we know. This angle is evidently $60° = \dfrac{\pi}{3}$ radians. We take from Example 1, § 66, the expansion of $\sin x$ in the neighborhood of $\dfrac{\pi}{3}$, namely,

$$\sin x = \tfrac{1}{2}\sqrt{3} + \tfrac{1}{2}\left(x - \frac{\pi}{3}\right) - \tfrac{1}{4}\sqrt{3}\left(x - \frac{\pi}{3}\right)^2 + \cdots.$$

If we place $x = \dfrac{61\,\pi}{180}$, we have $x - \dfrac{\pi}{3} = \dfrac{\pi}{180} = .01745$. Therefore

$$\sin \frac{61\,\pi}{180} = \tfrac{1}{2}\sqrt{3} + \tfrac{1}{2}(.01745) - \tfrac{1}{4}\sqrt{3}(.01745)^2 + \cdots$$
$$= .8746 \cdots.$$

Another method of solving this problem is to expand $\sin\left(\dfrac{\pi}{3} + x\right)$ in a Maclaurin series. We find

$$\sin\left(\frac{\pi}{3} + x\right) = \tfrac{1}{2}\sqrt{3} + \tfrac{1}{2}\,x - \tfrac{1}{4}\sqrt{3}\,x^2 + \cdots.$$

Placing $x = \dfrac{\pi}{180} = .01745$ in this equation, we have

$$\sin \frac{61\,\pi}{180} = \tfrac{1}{2}\sqrt{3} + \tfrac{1}{2}(.01745) - \tfrac{1}{4}\sqrt{3}(.01745)^2 + \cdots$$
$$= .8746$$

as before.

EXERCISES

1. Compute $\sin 3°$ to four decimal places.

2. Compute $\cos 12°$ to four decimal places.

3. Compute $\cos 62°$ to four decimal places.

4. Compute $\sin 44°$ to four decimal places.

5. Compute $\cos 29°$ to four decimal places.

6. Compute $e^{\frac{1}{2}}$ to four decimal places.

7. Compute $e^{1.1}$ to four decimal places.

8. Compute $\ln (1.2)$ to four decimal places.

9. Compute the value of π to two decimal places, from the expansion of $\sin^{-1} x$ (Ex. 4, § 65) and the relationship $\sin^{-1}\dfrac{1}{2} = \dfrac{\pi}{6}$.

10. Compute $\sqrt[3]{9}$ to four decimal places by the binomial theorem, placing $a = 8$ and $x = 1$.

GENERAL EXERCISES

Expand each of the following functions into a Maclaurin series. If the given function contains only x^n, place $x^n = y$, expand in powers of y, and replace y by x^n.

1. $\ln \dfrac{1+x}{1-x}$.

2. $\sec x$.

3. $x \tan^{-1} x$.

4. e^{x^2}.

5. $e^{\sin x}$.

6. $e^{\tan x}$.

7. $\dfrac{1}{\sqrt{1+x^2}}$.

8. $\ln (x + \sqrt{1+x^2})$.

9. $\sin x^2$.

10. $\dfrac{1}{\sqrt{1-x^4}}$.

11. Obtain the expansion of $\tan x$ by dividing the series for $\sin x$ by that for $\cos x$.

12. Obtain the expansion of $\sec x$ by dividing 1 by the series for $\cos x$.

13. Expand $e^x \cos x$ into a Maclaurin series, and verify by multiplying the series for e^x by that for $\cos x$.

14. Find $\sqrt[5]{e}$ to four decimal places.

15. Compute $\sin 35°$ to four decimal places.

16. Compute $\tan 5°$ to four decimal places.

17. Compute $\ln \sec 46°$ to four decimal places.

18. Using the series in Ex. 1, compute $\ln \frac{3}{2}$ to five decimal places.

19. Using the series found in Ex. 1, compute $\ln 2$ to five decimal places, and thence, by aid of the result of Ex. 18, find $\ln 3$ to four decimal places.

20. Using the series found in Ex. 1, compute $\ln \frac{5}{4}$ to five decimal places, and thence, by aid of the first result of Ex. 19, find $\ln 5$ to four decimal places.

21. Using the series found in Ex. 1, compute $\ln \frac{7}{3}$ to four decimal places, and thence, by aid of the result of Ex. 19, find $\ln 7$ to three decimal places.

22. Compute the value of π to four decimal places, from the expansion of $\tan^{-1} x$ and the relation $\tan^{-1} \dfrac{1}{7} + 2 \tan^{-1} \dfrac{1}{3} = \dfrac{\pi}{4}$.

23. Compute $\sqrt[4]{15}$ to four decimal places by the binomial theorem.

24. Compute $\sqrt[3]{28}$ to four decimal places by the binomial theorem.

25. Obtain the integral $\displaystyle\int_0^x \frac{\sin x}{x}\, dx$ in the form of a series expansion.

26. Obtain the integral $\displaystyle\int_0^x e^{-x^2}\, dx$ in the form of a series expansion.

27. Obtain the integral $\displaystyle\int_0^x \frac{dx}{\sqrt{1-x^3}}$ in the form of a series expansion. $(x < 1.)$

CHAPTER IX

PARTIAL DIFFERENTIATION

68. Partial derivatives. A quantity is a function of two variables x and y when the values of x and y determine the quantity. Such a function is represented by the symbol $f(x, y)$. For example, the volume V of a right circular cylinder is a function of its radius r and its altitude h, and in this case

$$V = f(r, h) = \pi r^2 h.$$

Similarly, we may have a function of three or more variables represented by the symbols $f(x, y, z)$, $f(x, y, z, u)$, etc.

Consider now $f(x, y)$, where x and y are independent variables so that the value of x depends in no way upon the value of y nor does the value of y depend upon that of x. Then we may change x without changing y, and the change in x causes a change in f. The limit of the ratio of these changes is the derivative of f with respect to x when y is constant, and may be represented by the symbol $\left(\dfrac{df}{dx}\right)_y$.

Similarly, the derivative of f with respect to y when x is constant, is represented by the symbol $\left(\dfrac{df}{dy}\right)_x$. These derivatives are called *partial derivatives* of f with respect to x and y respectively. The symbol used indicates by the letter outside the parenthesis the variable held constant in the differentiation. When no ambiguity can arise as to this variable, the partial derivatives are represented by the symbols $\dfrac{\partial f}{\partial x}$ and $\dfrac{\partial f}{\partial y}$, thus:

$$\frac{\partial f}{\partial x} = \left(\frac{df}{dx}\right)_y = \operatorname*{Lim}_{\Delta x \to 0} \frac{f(x + \Delta x, y) - f(x, y)}{\Delta x},$$

$$\frac{\partial f}{\partial y} = \left(\frac{df}{dy}\right)_x = \operatorname*{Lim}_{\Delta y \to 0} \frac{f(x, y + \Delta y) - f(x, y)}{\Delta y}.$$

So, in general, if we have a function of any number of variables $f(x, y, \ldots, z)$, we may have a partial derivative with respect to each of the variables. These derivatives are expressed by the symbols $\dfrac{\partial f}{\partial x}, \dfrac{\partial f}{\partial y}, \ldots, \dfrac{\partial f}{\partial z}$, or sometimes by $f_x(x, y, \ldots, z)$, $f_y(x, y, \ldots, z), \ldots, f_z(x, y, \ldots, z)$.

To compute these derivatives we have to apply the formulas for the derivative of a function of one variable, regarding as constant all the variables except the one with respect to which we differentiate.

Example 1. Consider a perfect gas obeying the law $v = \dfrac{ct}{p}$. We may change the temperature while keeping the pressure unchanged. If Δt and Δv are corresponding increments of t and v, then

$$\Delta v = \frac{c(t + \Delta t)}{p} - \frac{ct}{p} = \frac{c\,\Delta t}{p}$$

and

$$\frac{\partial v}{\partial t} = \frac{c}{p}.$$

Or we may change the pressure while keeping the temperature unchanged. If Δp and Δv are corresponding increments of p and v, then

$$\Delta v = \frac{ct}{p + \Delta p} - \frac{ct}{p} = - \frac{ct\,\Delta p}{p^2 + p\,\Delta p}$$

and

$$\frac{\partial v}{\partial p} = - \frac{ct}{p^2}.$$

Example 2. $f = x^3 - 3\,x^2 y + y^3$,   **Example 3.** $f = \sin(x^2 + y^2)$,

$$\frac{\partial f}{\partial x} = 3\,x^2 - 6\,xy, \qquad\qquad\qquad \frac{\partial f}{\partial x} = 2\,x \cos(x^2 + y^2),$$

$$\frac{\partial f}{\partial y} = -3\,x^2 + 3\,y^2. \qquad\qquad\qquad \frac{\partial f}{\partial y} = 2\,y \cos(x^2 + y^2).$$

Example 4. $x = r \cos \theta$, $y = r \sin \theta$.

We may here regard x and y as explicit functions of r and θ and differentiate accordingly with the following results:

$$\left.\begin{aligned} \frac{\partial x}{\partial r} &= \cos \theta, & \frac{\partial x}{\partial \theta} &= -r \sin \theta, \\[2mm] \frac{\partial y}{\partial r} &= \sin \theta, & \frac{\partial y}{\partial \theta} &= r \cos \theta. \end{aligned}\right\} \tag{1}$$

We may also regard r and θ as functions of x and y, and find the partial derivatives $\dfrac{\partial r}{\partial x}, \dfrac{\partial \theta}{\partial x}, \dfrac{\partial r}{\partial y}$, and $\dfrac{\partial \theta}{\partial y}$. These derivatives may be found in two ways.

1. Solving for r and θ in terms of x and y, we have

$$r = \sqrt{x^2 + y^2}, \quad \theta = \tan^{-1}\frac{y}{x},$$

whence we find

$$\left.\begin{array}{ll}
\dfrac{\partial r}{\partial x} = \dfrac{x}{\sqrt{x^2 + y^2}} = \cos\theta, & \dfrac{\partial r}{\partial y} = \dfrac{y}{\sqrt{x^2 + y^2}} = \sin\theta, \\[3mm]
\dfrac{\partial \theta}{\partial x} = -\dfrac{y}{x^2 + y^2} = -\dfrac{\sin\theta}{r}, & \dfrac{\partial \theta}{\partial y} = \dfrac{x}{x^2 + y^2} = \dfrac{\cos\theta}{r}.
\end{array}\right\} \quad (2)$$

2. We may differentiate the equations $x = r\cos\theta$, $y = r\sin\theta$ as they stand, regarding r and θ as implicit functions of x and y. Differentiating with respect to x, we have

$$1 = \cos\theta\,\frac{\partial r}{\partial x} - r\sin\theta\,\frac{\partial \theta}{\partial x},$$

$$0 = \sin\theta\,\frac{\partial r}{\partial x} + r\cos\theta\,\frac{\partial \theta}{\partial x},$$

since $\dfrac{dx}{dx} = 1$ and the derivative of y with respect to x is zero since y is held constant in the differentiation. Solving these equations for $\dfrac{\partial r}{\partial x}$ and $\dfrac{\partial \theta}{\partial x}$, we find

$$\frac{\partial r}{\partial x} = \cos\theta, \quad \frac{\partial \theta}{\partial x} = -\frac{\sin\theta}{r}.$$

Differentiating with respect to y, we have

$$0 = \cos\theta\,\frac{\partial r}{\partial y} - r\sin\theta\,\frac{\partial \theta}{\partial y},$$

$$1 = \sin\theta\,\frac{\partial r}{\partial y} + r\cos\theta\,\frac{\partial \theta}{\partial y}.$$

Solving these equations for $\dfrac{\partial r}{\partial y}$ and $\dfrac{\partial \theta}{\partial y}$, we find

$$\frac{\partial r}{\partial y} = \sin\theta, \quad \frac{\partial \theta}{\partial y} = \frac{\cos\theta}{r}.$$

These results agree with (2).

It may be inferred that if we have two equations containing four variables, any two may be taken as the independent variables and the remaining two as the dependent variables, and that we can find the corresponding partial derivatives even if we cannot express the dependent variables as explicit functions of the independent variables.

It is to be emphasized that $\dfrac{\partial x}{\partial r}$ in (1) is not the reciprocal of $\dfrac{\partial r}{\partial x}$

in (2). In fact, in (1) $\dfrac{\partial x}{\partial r} = \left(\dfrac{dx}{dr}\right)_\theta$, and in (2) $\dfrac{\partial r}{\partial x} = \left(\dfrac{dr}{dx}\right)_y$; and because the variable held constant is different in the two cases, there is no reason that one should be the reciprocal of the other. It happens in this case that the two are equal, but this is not a general rule. In fact $\dfrac{\partial x}{\partial \theta}$ in (1) and $\dfrac{\partial \theta}{\partial x}$ in (2) are neither equal nor reciprocal.

EXERCISES

Find $\dfrac{\partial z}{\partial x}$ and $\dfrac{\partial z}{\partial y}$ in each of the following cases:

1. $z = x^5 + x^3y^2 + xy^4 - y^5.$

2. $z = \dfrac{xy}{y^2 - x^2}.$

3. $z = \tan^{-1}\dfrac{x+y}{1-xy}.$

4. $z = \sin^{-1}xy.$

5. $z = \ln\left(\dfrac{x}{y} + \dfrac{y}{x}\right).$

6. $z = \cos\dfrac{xy}{x-y}.$

7. $z = e^{\frac{x}{y}}\sin\dfrac{y}{x}.$

8. $z = \ln\left(x + \sqrt{x^2 + y^2}\right).$

9. If $z = \sin\dfrac{x-y}{x+y}$, prove $x\dfrac{\partial z}{\partial x} + y\dfrac{\partial z}{\partial y} = 0.$

10. If $z = \sqrt{x^2 + y^2}\, e^{\frac{y}{x}}$, prove $x\dfrac{\partial z}{\partial x} + y\dfrac{\partial z}{\partial y} = z.$

69. Higher partial derivatives. The partial derivatives of $f(x, y)$ are themselves functions of x and y which may have partial derivatives, called the *second partial derivatives* of $f(x, y)$. They are $\dfrac{\partial}{\partial x}\left(\dfrac{\partial f}{\partial x}\right)$, $\dfrac{\partial}{\partial y}\left(\dfrac{\partial f}{\partial x}\right)$, $\dfrac{\partial}{\partial x}\left(\dfrac{\partial f}{\partial y}\right)$, $\dfrac{\partial}{\partial y}\left(\dfrac{\partial f}{\partial y}\right)$. But it may be shown* that the order of differentiation with respect to x and y is immaterial when the functions and their derivatives fulfill the ordinary conditions as to continuity,† so that the second

---

* See Woods's "Advanced Calculus," p. 68. Ginn and Company.

† A function of x is said to be *continuous* if the increment of the function approaches zero when the increment of x approaches zero. Then

$$\underset{\Delta x \to 0}{\text{Lim}}\ [f(x + \Delta x) - f(x)] = 0$$

or

$$\underset{\Delta x \to 0}{\text{Lim}}\ f(x + \Delta x) = f(x),$$

whence

$$f(x + \Delta x) = f(x) + \epsilon$$

where

$$\epsilon \to 0 \quad \text{as} \quad \Delta x \to 0.$$

A function of two or more variables is continuous if the increment of the function approaches zero as the increments of the variables approach zero in any manner whatever.

partial derivatives are three in number, expressed by the symbols

$$\frac{\partial}{\partial x}\left(\frac{\partial f}{\partial x}\right) = \frac{\partial^2 f}{\partial x^2} = f_{xx},$$

$$\frac{\partial}{\partial x}\left(\frac{\partial f}{\partial y}\right) = \frac{\partial}{\partial y}\left(\frac{\partial f}{\partial x}\right) = \frac{\partial^2 f}{\partial x \partial y} = f_{xy},$$

$$\frac{\partial}{\partial y}\left(\frac{\partial f}{\partial y}\right) = \frac{\partial^2 f}{\partial y^2} = f_{yy}.$$

Similarly, the *third partial derivatives* of $f(x, y)$ are four in number; namely,

$$\frac{\partial}{\partial x}\left(\frac{\partial^2 f}{\partial x^2}\right) = \frac{\partial^3 f}{\partial x^3},$$

$$\frac{\partial}{\partial y}\left(\frac{\partial^2 f}{\partial x^2}\right) = \frac{\partial}{\partial x}\left(\frac{\partial^2 f}{\partial x \partial y}\right) = \frac{\partial^2}{\partial x^2}\left(\frac{\partial f}{\partial y}\right) = \frac{\partial^3 f}{\partial x^2 \partial y},$$

$$\frac{\partial}{\partial x}\left(\frac{\partial^2 f}{\partial y^2}\right) = \frac{\partial}{\partial y}\left(\frac{\partial^2 f}{\partial x \partial y}\right) = \frac{\partial^2}{\partial y^2}\left(\frac{\partial f}{\partial x}\right) = \frac{\partial^3 f}{\partial x \partial y^2},$$

$$\frac{\partial}{\partial y}\left(\frac{\partial^2 f}{\partial y^2}\right) = \frac{\partial^3 f}{\partial y^3}.$$

So, in general, $\dfrac{\partial^{p+q} f}{\partial x^p \partial y^q}$ signifies the result of differentiating $f(x, y)$ p times with respect to x, and q times with respect to y, the order of differentiating being immaterial.

In like manner, $\dfrac{\partial^{p+q+r} f}{\partial x^p \partial y^q \partial z^r}$ signifies the result of differentiating $f(x, y, z)$ p times with respect to x, q times with respect to y, and r times with respect to z, in any order.

EXERCISES

1. If $z = (x^2 + y^2)\,\mathrm{ctn}^{-1}\dfrac{x}{y}$, find $\dfrac{\partial^2 z}{\partial x \partial y}$.

2. If $z = e^x \cos(y - x)$, find $\dfrac{\partial^2 z}{\partial x^2}$.

3. If $z = \ln(y^2 + 2\,xy)$, find $\dfrac{\partial^2 z}{\partial y \partial x}$.

Verify $\dfrac{\partial}{\partial x}\left(\dfrac{\partial z}{\partial y}\right) = \dfrac{\partial}{\partial y}\left(\dfrac{\partial z}{\partial x}\right)$ in each of the following cases:

4. $z = x^2y^2 + 2\,e^{xy}$.　　　　　　　　**6.** $z = x\sin^{-1}\dfrac{y}{x}$.

5. $z = \dfrac{x^2 + y^2}{x - y}$.　　　　　　　　**7.** $z = \dfrac{y}{\sqrt{x^2 - y^2}}$.

8. If $z = \tan^{-1}\dfrac{y}{x}$, prove $\dfrac{\partial^2 z}{\partial x^2} + \dfrac{\partial^2 z}{\partial y^2} = 0$.

9. If $z = \ln\,(a^2x^2 + b^2y^2)$, prove $b^2\dfrac{\partial^2 z}{\partial x^2} + a^2\dfrac{\partial^2 z}{\partial y^2} = 0$.

10. If $V = r^m \sin n\phi$, prove $n^2 r\,\dfrac{\partial^2 (rV)}{\partial r^2} + m(m+1)\,\dfrac{\partial^2 V}{\partial \phi^2} = 0$.

70. Total differential. In § 68 we considered the change in $f(x, y)$ due to changing x alone, y being kept constant, and found the partial derivative $\dfrac{\partial f}{\partial x}$. In like manner we held x constant and changed y alone and found the partial derivative $\dfrac{\partial f}{\partial y}$. We now wish to consider the change in f due to changing both x and y at the same time. Accordingly we give x an increment Δx and y an increment Δy and denote the corresponding increment of f by Δf, where

$$\Delta f = f(x + \Delta x,\, y + \Delta y) - f(x, y). \tag{1}$$

The computation of Δf for given values of x, y, Δx, and Δy is a question of arithmetic or algebra.

For example, let 　$f = x^2 + xy + y^2,$　　　　　　(2)

and let 　　　　$x_1 = 1 \quad \text{and} \quad y_1 = 2.$

Then 　　　　$f_1 = (1)^2 + (1)(2) + (2)^2 = 7. \tag{3}$

Now let 　　　　$\Delta x = .1 \text{ and } \Delta y = .2.$

Then 　　　　$x_2 = 1.1, \quad y_2 = 2.2$

and 　　$f_2 = (1.1)^2 + (1.1)(2.2) + (2.2)^2 = 8.47; \tag{4}$

whence 　　　　$\Delta f = f_2 - f_1 = 1.47. \tag{5}$

More generally, we may let the first value of f be

$$f_1 = x^2 + xy + y^2. \tag{6}$$

Adding increments Δx and Δy to x and y respectively, we have

whence 　$f_2 = (x + \Delta x)^2 + (x + \Delta x)(y + \Delta y) + (y + \Delta y)^2; \tag{7}$

$\Delta f = f_2 - f_1 = (2x+y)\Delta x + (x+2y)\Delta y + (\Delta x)^2 + \Delta x\Delta y + (\Delta y)^2. \tag{8}$

An examination of (8) shows that Δf may be divided into two parts, namely, $\quad (2\,x + y)\Delta x + (x + 2\,y)\Delta y,\qquad\qquad (9)$

which is of the first degree in Δx and Δy, and

$$(\Delta x)^2 + \Delta x \Delta y + (\Delta y)^2, \qquad\qquad (10)$$

which is of the second degree in Δx and Δy.

Now if Δx and Δy are small, as, for example,

$$\Delta x = .001, \quad \Delta y = .0002,$$

then $\quad (\Delta x)^2 = .000001, \quad \Delta x \Delta y = .0000002, \quad (\Delta y)^2 = .00000004,$ all of which are much smaller than Δx and Δy. Hence the expression in (10) is very small in comparison with the expression in (9), (at least, unless x and y are themselves very small). Hence we may call (9) the *principal part* of the increment (8).

Now the coefficient of Δx in (8) is $\dfrac{\partial f}{\partial x}$ and the coefficient of Δy is $\dfrac{\partial f}{\partial y}$, so that (8) may be written

$$\Delta f = \frac{\partial f}{\partial x}\,\Delta x + \frac{\partial f}{\partial y}\,\Delta y + (\Delta x)^2 + \Delta x\,\Delta y + (\Delta y)^2. \qquad (11)$$

We shall now show that (11) is a special case of a general formula $\quad \Delta f = \dfrac{\partial f}{\partial x}\,\Delta x + \dfrac{\partial f}{\partial y}\,\Delta y + \epsilon_1\Delta x + \epsilon_2\Delta y, \qquad (12)$

where f is any continuous function of x and y which can be differentiated and $\epsilon_1 \to 0$, $\epsilon_2 \to 0$, as $\Delta x \to 0$, $\Delta y \to 0$.

To prove this, we note that (1) is unaltered by writing it in the form $\quad \Delta f = \{f(x + \Delta x, y + \Delta y) - f(x, y + \Delta y)\}$
$$+ \{f(x, y + \Delta y) - f(x, y)\}. \quad (13)$$

Consider the expression in the first brace of (13). By § 68 and the definition of a limit,

$$f(x + \Delta x, y + \Delta y) - f(x, y + \Delta y) = [\,f_x(x, y + \Delta y) + \epsilon'\,]\,\Delta x, \quad (14)$$

where $f_x(x, y + \Delta y)$ is $\dfrac{\partial f}{\partial x}$ with y replaced by $y + \Delta y$, and $\epsilon' \to 0$ as $\Delta x \to 0$. Now we assume that $\dfrac{\partial f}{\partial x}$ is continuous.* Hence $\quad f_x(x, y + \Delta y) = f_x(x, y) + \epsilon''$,

where $\epsilon'' \to 0$ as $\Delta y \to 0$. Hence (14) gives

$$f(x + \Delta x, y + \Delta y) - f(x, y + \Delta y) = [\,f_x(x, y) + \epsilon_1\,]\,\Delta x, \quad (15)$$

where $\qquad\qquad\qquad \epsilon_1 = \epsilon' + \epsilon''.$

* See footnote, p. 214.

Similarly, considering the quantity in the second brace in (13), we have

$$f(x, y + \Delta y) - f(x, y) = [f_y(x, y) + \epsilon_2] \Delta y. \tag{16}$$

Substituting these two values in (13), we have

$$\Delta f = f_x(x, y)\Delta x + f_y(x, y)\Delta y + \epsilon_1 \Delta x + \epsilon_2 \Delta y, \tag{17}$$

which is the same as (12), which we set out to prove.

Now the value of Δf in (12) consists of two parts, one of which we call the *principal part*, namely,

$$\frac{\partial f}{\partial x} \Delta x + \frac{\partial f}{\partial y} \Delta y, \tag{18}$$

which contains Δx and Δy multiplied by coefficients which do not become small with Δx and Δy, and the other part,

$$\epsilon_1 \Delta x + \epsilon_2 \Delta y, \tag{19}$$

where the coefficients of Δx and Δy are quantities which approach zero as Δx and Δy approach zero. The quantity (19) is accordingly very small as compared with (18), at least in general. We now take the principal part of the increment Δf and call it the *total differential* of f and denote it by df.

We cannot define dx and dy in this way when x and y are the independent variables. We shall therefore, as in § 18, define the differential of an independent variable as equal to its increment. Hence we have

$$dx = \Delta x, \quad dy = \Delta y, \tag{20}$$

and

$$df = \frac{\partial f}{\partial x} dx + \frac{\partial f}{\partial y} dy.^* \tag{21}$$

It is evident that the total differential expresses approximately the change in the function caused by changes in both the independent variables.

Example. The period of a simple pendulum with small oscillations is

$$T = 2\pi\sqrt{\frac{l}{g}},$$

whence

$$g = \frac{4\pi^2 l}{T^2}.$$

---

* This formula has been obtained on the hypothesis that x and y are independent values. It is also true when x and y are functions of other variables. See Woods's "Advanced Calculus," p. 78.

Let $l = 100$ cm. with a possible error of $\frac{1}{2}$ mm. in measuring, and $T = 2$ sec. with a possible error of $\frac{1}{100}$ sec. in measuring.

Let it be required to find approximately the largest error made in computing g due to the errors in l and T. We have, by (20) and (21),

$$dl = \pm \tfrac{1}{20}, \quad dT = \pm \tfrac{1}{100}$$

and
$$dg = \frac{4\,\pi^2}{T^2}\,dl + \left(-\frac{8\,\pi^2 l}{T^3}\right)dT.$$

We obtain the largest possible error in g by taking dl and dT of opposite signs, say $dl = \frac{1}{20}$, $dT = -\frac{1}{100}$.

Then
$$dg = \frac{\pi^2}{20} + \pi^2 = 1.05\,\pi^2 = 10.36.$$

The ratio of error is
$$\frac{dg}{g} = \frac{dl}{l} - 2\,\frac{dT}{T} = .0005 + .01 = .0105 = 1.05\%.$$

EXERCISES

1. Calculate the numerical difference between Δz and dz when $z = x^3 + y^3 - 3\,x^2 y$, $x = 2$, $y = 3$, $\Delta x = dx = .01$, and $\Delta y = dy = .001$.

2. The base AB of a triangle is 10 in. long, the side AC is 15 in. long, and the angle A is 45°. Calculate the change in the area caused by increasing AC by .1 in. and the angle A by 1°. Calculate also the differential of area corresponding to the same increments.

3. A right circular cone has an altitude of 10 ft., and the radius of its base is 4 ft. Find approximately the change in the volume of the cone caused by increasing the altitude by .1 in. and decreasing the radius of the base by $\frac{1}{2}$ in.

4. The equal sides of an isosceles triangle are each 5 ft. long, and the base is 8 ft. long. Find approximately the greatest possible error in the computed area of the triangle caused by possible errors of .02 ft. in the length of each of the equal sides and .04 ft. in the length of the base.

5. If C is the strength of an electric current due to an electro-motive force E along a circuit of resistance R, by Ohm's law

$$C = \frac{E}{R}.$$

If an error of 1 per cent is made in measuring E, and an error of 2 per cent in measuring R, find approximately the greatest possible percentage of error in computing C.

6. The density D of a body is determined by the formula

$$D = \frac{W}{W - W'},$$

where W is the weight of the body in air and W' the weight in water. If $W = 240,000$ gr. and $W' = 220,000$ gr., find approximately the greatest possible error in D caused by an error of 4 gr. in W and an error of 8 gr. in W'.

7. The velocity v, with which vibrations travel along a flexible string, is given by the formula

$$v = \sqrt{\frac{t}{m}},$$

where t is the tension of the string and m the mass of a unit length of it. Find approximately the greatest possible error in the computation of v if t is found to be 6,000,000 dynes and m to be .005 gr. per centimeter, the measurement of t being subject to a possible error of 1000 dynes and that of m to a possible error of .0005 gr.

8. An acute angle ϕ is determined from the formula $\phi = \sin^{-1} \frac{x}{y}$, where x is a side and y the hypotenuse of a right triangle. The lengths of x and y are, respectively, 5 ft. and 13 ft., with a possible error of 1 in. in the measurement of each. Find approximately the greatest possible error in the computed value of ϕ.

71. Exact differential. We have just seen (21) § 70, that if $f(x, y)$ is a function of x and y, we have

$$df = \frac{\partial f}{\partial x}\, dx + \frac{\partial f}{\partial y}\, dy. \tag{1}$$

When the function $f(x, y)$ is known, the partial derivatives $\frac{\partial f}{\partial x}$ and $\frac{\partial f}{\partial y}$ may be found. Let us denote them by M and N respectively, so that

$$\frac{\partial f}{\partial x} = M, \quad \frac{\partial f}{\partial y} = N, \tag{2}$$

where M and N are certain functions of x and y. The second member of (1) is then of the form

$$M\, dx + N\, dy. \tag{3}$$

Now expressions of the form (3) may arise in practice by other methods than by differentiation, or may be written down at pleasure, M and N being any two functions whatever. Hence it is important to know when (3) is the same as (1). We shall accordingly prove the following theorem:

The necessary and sufficient condition that an expression

$$M\,dx + N\,dy$$

shall be a total differential of some function $f(x, y)$ is that M and N should satisfy the equation

$$\frac{\partial M}{\partial y} = \frac{\partial N}{\partial x}. \tag{4}$$

To prove that the condition is necessary, we assume that (3) is equal to the differential of some function $f(x, y)$, that is, that

$$df = M\,dx + N\,dy, \tag{5}$$

and shall prove that (4) necessarily follows.

We have, by (2),

$$M = \frac{\partial f}{\partial x}, \quad N = \frac{\partial f}{\partial y};$$

whence

$$\frac{\partial M}{\partial y} = \frac{\partial}{\partial y}\!\left(\frac{\partial f}{\partial x}\right), \quad \frac{\partial N}{\partial x} = \frac{\partial}{\partial x}\!\left(\frac{\partial f}{\partial y}\right).$$

But from § 69 these results are equal, and hence (4) must be true, as was to be proved.

To prove that the condition is sufficient, we assume that we have $M\,dx + N\,dy$ with M and N such that (4) is true. We must then be able to find a function $f(x, y)$ such that

$$\frac{\partial f}{\partial x} = M, \quad \frac{\partial f}{\partial y} = N. \tag{6}$$

If the first equation of (6) is to be true, we may integrate that equation, holding y constant. In place of the usual constant of integration we may have a function of y alone, which we will denote by $\phi(y)$, since the derivative of such a function with respect to x would be zero. Hence we have

$$f(x, y) = \int M\,dx + \phi(y). \tag{7}$$

But this value of $f(x, y)$ must satisfy the second equation of (6), and, substituting in that equation, we have

$$\frac{\partial}{\partial y} \int M \, dx + \frac{d\phi}{dy} = N,$$

or
$$\frac{d\phi}{dy} = N - \frac{\partial}{\partial y} \int M \, dx. \tag{8}$$

By hypothesis, the first member of (8) does not contain x. Hence if the second member should contain x, the equation would be absurd, and the work would stop.

The condition that the second member of (8) should not contain x is that its derivative with respect to x should be zero. That is, we must have

$$\frac{\partial N}{\partial x} - \frac{\partial}{\partial x}\left[\frac{\partial}{\partial y} \int M \, dx\right] = 0,$$

which is the same as

$$\frac{\partial N}{\partial x} - \frac{\partial}{\partial y}\left[\frac{\partial}{\partial x} \int M \, dx\right] = 0,$$

which is the same as
$$\frac{\partial N}{\partial x} - \frac{\partial M}{\partial y} = 0,$$

which is a true equation according to the hypothesis, (4). Hence $\phi(y)$ can be found from (8) and substituted in (7). The function $f(x, y)$ has therefore been found.

Hence (4) is a sufficient condition to make any expression (3) a total differential. Since in this case (3) may be exactly found by differentiation, it is also called an *exact* differential.

Example. The expression $(3 x^2 + 6 xy)dx + (3 x^2 + 3 y^2)dy$ is an exact differential, since
$$\frac{\partial}{\partial y} (3 x^2 + 6 xy) = 6 x$$

and
$$\frac{\partial}{\partial x} (3 x^2 + 3 y^2) = 6 x,$$

and the results are equal.

The expression $(x^2 + 2 xy)dx + (y^2 - x^2)dy$ is not an exact differential, since
$$\frac{\partial}{\partial y} (x^2 + 2 xy) = 2 x$$

and
$$\frac{\partial}{\partial x} (y^2 - x^2) = - 2 x,$$

and the results are not equal.

EXERCISES

Find which of these expressions are exact differentials:

1. $(5 x^4 - 3 x^2 y + 2 xy^2)dx + (2 x^2 y - x^3 + 5 y^4)dy.$

2. $x(1 - y)dx + y(1 - x)dy.$

3. $(2 x - y + 1)dx + (2 y - x - 1)dy.$

4. $\left(y + \dfrac{1}{x}\right)dx + \left(x + \dfrac{1}{y}\right)dy.$

5. $y^2 dx - (x^2 + 2 xy)dy.$

6. $\dfrac{1 + y^2}{x^3} dx - \dfrac{1 + x^2}{x} y dy.$

7. $(y - x^2 - 1)dx - x dy.$

8. $dx + (x - y)dy.$

9. $(x + y)^2 dx + (x^2 + 2 xy + 3 y^2)dy.$

10. $\dfrac{x \, dx}{\sqrt{x^2 + y^2}} + \left(-1 + \dfrac{y}{\sqrt{x^2 + y^2}}\right)dy.$

11. $(y + xy^2)dx - dy.$

12. $\dfrac{1}{y} e^{-\frac{x}{y}}dx - \left(\dfrac{x}{y^2} e^{-\frac{x}{y}} + \dfrac{1}{y}\right) dy.$

72. Rate of change. If we differentiate any function $f(x, y)$ with respect to x, the resulting partial derivative $\dfrac{\partial f}{\partial x}$ gives the rate of change of f with respect to x when x alone varies. In like manner, the partial derivative $\dfrac{\partial f}{\partial y}$ gives the rate of change of f with respect to y when y alone varies.

Now suppose that x and y are functions of a single variable t. Then f is a function of that single variable t, and we may wish to find $\dfrac{df}{dt}$. To do this, we divide $\Delta f((12), \S 70)$ by Δt and take the limit as $\Delta t \to 0$. The result is

$$\frac{df}{dt} = \frac{\partial f}{\partial x}\frac{dx}{dt} + \frac{\partial f}{\partial y}\frac{dy}{dt}, \tag{1}$$

for, as $\Delta t \to 0$, $\Delta x \to 0$ and $\Delta y \to 0$, and hence $\epsilon_1 \to 0$ and $\epsilon_2 \to 0$.

Or we might have divided df ((21), § 70) by dt, thus finding (1) directly.

If x and y are functions of more than one variable t, then f is a function of more variables than t, and hence the corresponding derivative of f with respect to t is a partial derivative and is denoted by $\dfrac{\partial f}{\partial t}$. To find this derivative, we divide $\Delta f((12),\ \S\ 70)$ by Δt and take the limit as $\Delta t \to 0$. The result is

$$\frac{\partial f}{\partial t} = \frac{\partial f}{\partial x}\frac{\partial x}{\partial t} + \frac{\partial f}{\partial y}\frac{\partial y}{\partial t}, \tag{2}$$

the derivatives of x and y with respect to t being partial derivatives.

The partial derivative $\dfrac{\partial f}{\partial x}$ gives, as already noted, the rate of change of f with respect to x when x alone varies; that is, as we move from one point in the xy-plane to any second point in that plane in a direction parallel to OX. Hence we may regard $\dfrac{\partial f}{\partial x}$ as giving the rate of change of f in a direction parallel to OX. In like manner, $\dfrac{\partial f}{\partial y}$ gives the rate of change of f in the xy-plane in a direction parallel to OY. Formula (1) now enables us to find the rate of change of f in any direction in the xy-plane.

Let $P(x, y)$ (Fig. 94) be any point in the plane, and $Q(x + \Delta x, y + \Delta y)$ be any second point in the plane. Let the value of $f(x, y)$ at P be denoted by f and the value at Q be denoted by $f + \Delta f$. Divide Δf by Δs, the length of the arc PQ of a curve drawn through P and Q, and take the limit of $\dfrac{\Delta f}{\Delta s}$ as

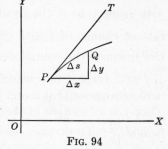

FIG. 94

$\Delta s \to 0$. This limit will be denoted by $\dfrac{df}{ds}$ and will measure the rate of change of f in the direction of the tangent line to the curve PQ at the point P in exactly the same way that $\dfrac{\partial f}{\partial x}$ and $\dfrac{\partial f}{\partial y}$ measure the rates of change of f in directions parallel to OX and OY respectively.

But, by (1), $$\frac{df}{ds} = \frac{\partial f}{\partial x}\frac{dx}{ds} + \frac{\partial f}{\partial y}\frac{dy}{ds};$$ (3)

and if the tangent line makes an angle ϕ with OX, we have, by § 39,

$$\frac{dx}{ds} = \cos \phi \text{ and } \frac{dy}{ds} = \sin \phi,$$

and hence (3) becomes

$$\frac{df}{ds} = \frac{\partial f}{\partial x}\cos \phi + \frac{\partial f}{\partial y}\sin \phi,$$ (4)

and gives the rate of change of f in a direction making an angle ϕ with OX.

We may visualize (4) by thinking of the profile map of a country built up on the xy-plane, with f as the height of the country above sea level. Then $\frac{\partial f}{\partial x}$ gives the rate of change of the height of the country as one moves from any point in a direction whose projection on the xy-plane is parallel to OX, that is, gives the slope or the grade of a road through that point in that direction. In like manner, $\frac{\partial f}{\partial y}$ gives the grade of a road whose projection is parallel to OY, and (4) gives the grade of a road whose projection makes an angle ϕ with OX.

In particular, if a road is such that at all points of it $\frac{df}{ds} = 0$, the road is level, that is, all points of it are at the same height above sea level; and if at any point, ϕ is so taken as to make $\frac{df}{ds}$ have its greatest value, the corresponding road is the steepest road through the point. By following on the xy-plane from point to point the direction in which $\frac{df}{ds} = 0$ we may construct "contour lines" often seen on maps.

But f need not necessarily be height. It may have other physical meanings, such as the electrical potential at $P(x, y)$, or the temperature at that point, and the profile map may be considered a graphical representation of the function.

Example 1. If the radius of a right circular cylinder is increasing at the rate of 2 in. per second, and the altitude is increasing at the rate of 3 in. per second, how fast is the volume increasing when the altitude is 15 in. and the radius 5 in.?

Let V be the volume, r the radius, and h the altitude. Then

$$V = \pi r^2 h.$$

By (1),
$$\frac{dV}{dt} = \frac{\partial V}{\partial r}\frac{dr}{dt} + \frac{\partial V}{\partial h}\frac{dh}{dt}$$

$$= 2\,\pi r h \frac{dr}{dt} + \pi r^2 \frac{dh}{dt}.$$

By hypothesis, $\frac{dr}{dt} = 2$, $\frac{dh}{dt} = 3$, $r = 5$, $h = 15$. Therefore $\frac{dV}{dt}$ $= 375\,\pi$ cu. in. per second.

The same result may be obtained without partial differentiation by expressing V directly in terms of t. For, by hypothesis, $r = 5 + 2\,t$, $h = 15 + 3\,t$, if we choose $t = 0$ when $r = 5$ and $h = 15$. Therefore
$$V = (375 + 375\,t + 120\,t^2 + 12\,t^3)\pi\,;$$

whence
$$\frac{dV}{dt} = (375 + 240\,t + 36\,t^2)\pi.$$

When $t = 0$, $\frac{dV}{dt} = 375\,\pi$ cu. in. per second, as before.

Example 2. The temperature u at a point in the xy-plane is given by the formula
$$u = \ln \sqrt{x^2 + y^2}. \tag{1}$$

The rate of change of temperature in a direction parallel to OX is
$$\frac{\partial u}{\partial x} = \frac{x}{x^2 + y^2}\,; \tag{2}$$

the rate of change of temperature in a direction parallel to OY is
$$\frac{\partial u}{\partial y} = \frac{y}{x^2 + y^2}\,; \tag{3}$$

and the rate of change of temperature in a direction making an angle ϕ with OX is, by (4) above,
$$\frac{du}{ds} = \frac{x \cos\phi + y \sin\phi}{x^2 + y^2}. \tag{4}$$

If $\frac{du}{ds} = 0$ at all points of any curve, then u is constant on that curve, and the temperature is the same at all points of that curve. Such a curve is called an *isothermal* line.

Placing
$$\frac{du}{ds} = 0, \text{ we find}$$
$$\tan\phi = -\frac{x}{y}, \tag{5}$$

or
$$\frac{dy}{dx} = -\frac{x}{y} \tag{6}$$

for any isothermal line.

Writing (6) in the form

$$x \, dx + y \, dy = 0, \tag{7}$$

we can integrate and obtain the result

$$x^2 + y^2 = a^2, \tag{8}$$

where a^2 is a constant.

Hence the isothermal lines in this problem are concentric circles with their common center at O.

Since equation (1) gives the temperature at any point, we could have found the equation of an isothermal line by placing $u = c$ in (1). The result is

$$c = \ln \sqrt{x^2 + y^2}, \tag{9}$$

which can be put in the form

$$x^2 + y^2 = e^{2c}, \tag{10}$$

a result in agreement with (8).

We will now determine the direction in which the rate of change of temperature is greatest, that is, we will determine ϕ when $\dfrac{du}{ds}$ is a maximum.

Differentiating (4) with respect to ϕ, we have

$$\frac{d}{d\phi}\left(\frac{du}{ds}\right) = \frac{-x \sin \phi + y \cos \phi}{x^2 + y^2}. \tag{11}$$

When $\qquad \dfrac{d}{d\phi}\left(\dfrac{du}{ds}\right) = 0$, we have

$$- x \sin \phi + y \cos \phi = 0, \tag{12}$$

whence $\qquad\qquad \tan \phi = \dfrac{y}{x} \, ; \tag{13}$

and it can readily be shown that when ϕ satisfies (13), $\dfrac{du}{ds}$ is a maximum.

Comparing (13) with (5), we see that the direction of most rapid change of temperature is normal to the isothermal lines. This result agrees with the general theorem that any function $f(x, y)$ increases most rapidly in the direction normal to the contour lines.

EXERCISES

1. If $z = e^{\tan^{-1} \frac{y}{x}}$, $x = \sin t$, $y = \cos t$, find the rate of change of z with respect to t.

2. If $z = \ln \dfrac{y}{x}$, $x = \cos t$, $y = \sin t$, find the rate of change of z with respect to t when $t = \dfrac{\pi}{4}$.

3. If $z = e^x \sin xy$, $x = \dfrac{\pi}{2} t$, $y = t$, find the rate of change of z with respect to t when $t = 1$.

4. The equal sides of an isosceles triangle are increasing at the uniform rate of .02 in. per second, and the vertical angle is decreasing at the uniform rate of 1′ per second. How fast is the area of the triangle increasing when the equal sides are each 3 ft. long and the angle at the vertex is 60°?

5. If $V = (e^{ax} - e^{-ax})\cos ay$, prove that V and its derivatives in any direction are all equal to zero at the point $\left(0, \dfrac{\pi}{2\,a}\right)$.

6. If $V = \dfrac{1}{\sqrt{x^2 + y^2}}$, find the rate of change of V at the point $(3, 4)$ in a direction making an angle of 135° with OX.

7. At any point in the plane XOY the electrical potential is defined by the equation
$$V = \ln \frac{\sqrt{(x - 1)^2 + y^2}}{\sqrt{x^2 + y^2}}.$$

Find the rate of change of V at the point $(1, 1)$ in a direction making an angle of 45° with OX.

8. In what direction from the point $(1, 1)$ is the rate of change of V (Ex. 7) the greatest?

9. Prove that the rate of change of $z = \ln (x + \sqrt{x^2 + y^2})$ in the direction of the line drawn from the origin of coördinates to any point $P(x, y)$ is equal to the reciprocal of the length of OP.

10. In what direction from any point (x, y) is the rate of change of the function $z = e^{-ax} \cos ay$ the greatest?

73. Differentiation of a definite integral. From the definition of a definite integral given in Chapter III

$$\int_a^x f(x)dx = F(x) - F(a), \tag{1}$$

where the upper limit x is left as a variable. Then

$$\frac{d}{dx}\int_a^x f(x)dx = F'(x) = f(x). \tag{2}$$

Similarly, $\displaystyle\int_x^b f(x)dx = F(b) - F(x),$

and $\dfrac{d}{dx}\displaystyle\int_x^b f(x)dx = -F'(x) = -f(x). \tag{3}$

Consider now the integral $\displaystyle\int_a^b f(x, \alpha)dx$, where α is a parameter independent of x. This parameter does not affect the in-

9. From the integral $\int_1^x x^\alpha\, dx$ obtain by differentiating with respect to α the value of $\int_1^x x^\alpha \ln x\, dx$.

10. From the integral $\int_0^x e^{\alpha x}\, dx$ obtain by differentiating with respect to α the value of $\int_0^x x e^{\alpha x}\, dx$.

GENERAL EXERCISES

1. If $z = \ln (xy^2 - x^2 y)$, find the value of $\dfrac{\partial z}{\partial x} + \dfrac{\partial z}{\partial y}$.

2. If $z = \ln \dfrac{x^2 + y^2}{x^2 - y^2}$, find the value of $x \dfrac{\partial z}{\partial x} + y \dfrac{\partial z}{\partial y}$.

3. If $z = y^3 + y e^{\frac{1}{x}}$, prove $x^2 \dfrac{\partial z}{\partial x} + y \dfrac{\partial z}{\partial y} = 3\, y^3$.

4. If $z = \ln [(x + y)(x^2 + y^2)]$, prove $x \dfrac{\partial z}{\partial x} + y \dfrac{\partial z}{\partial y} = 3$.

5. If $z = \sqrt{y^2 - x^2}\, \sin^{-1}\dfrac{y}{x}$, prove $x \dfrac{\partial z}{\partial x} + y \dfrac{\partial z}{\partial y} = z$.

6. If $z = (x^2 + y^2) \tan^{-1}\dfrac{x}{y}$, prove $x \dfrac{\partial z}{\partial x} + y \dfrac{\partial z}{\partial y} = 2\, z$.

7. If $z = x^2 y\, e^{\frac{y}{x}}$, prove $x \dfrac{\partial z}{\partial x} + y \dfrac{\partial z}{\partial y} = 3\, z$.

8. If $z = e^{-ay} \sin a(k + x)$, prove $\dfrac{\partial^2 z}{\partial x^2} + \dfrac{\partial^2 z}{\partial y^2} = 0$.

9. If $z = e^{-(b^2 + a^2 k^2)t} \cos kx$, prove $\dfrac{\partial z}{\partial t} = a^2 \dfrac{\partial^2 z}{\partial x^2} - b^2 z$.

10. If $z = e^{-kx} \sin \left(my + x\sqrt{a^2 m^2 - k^2}\right)$, prove $\dfrac{\partial^2 z}{\partial x^2} + 2\, k \dfrac{\partial z}{\partial x} = a^2 \dfrac{\partial^2 z}{\partial y^2}$.

11. If $V = e^{a\phi} \cos (a \ln r)$, prove $\dfrac{\partial^2 V}{\partial r^2} + \dfrac{1}{r} \dfrac{\partial V}{\partial r} + \dfrac{1}{r^2} \dfrac{\partial^2 V}{\partial \phi^2} = 0$.

12. If $u = (e^{ax} + e^{ay})^2$, prove $\dfrac{\partial^2 u}{\partial x^2} + 2 \dfrac{\partial^2 u}{\partial x \partial y} + \dfrac{\partial^2 u}{\partial y^2} = 4\, a^2 u$.

13. The hypotenuse and one side of a right triangle are 10 in. and 6 in. If the hypotenuse is increased by .02 in. and the given side is decreased by .01 in., find approximately the change in the other side, the triangle being kept a right triangle.

14. The eccentricity e of a hyperbola is given by the formula

$$e = \frac{\sqrt{a^2 + b^2}}{a},$$

where a and b are the semi-axes of the hyperbola. Find approximately the greatest possible error in the computed value of e if a and b are, respectively, 4 ft. and 3 ft., with a possible error of 1 in. in the measurement of each.

15. If F denotes the focal length of a combination of two lenses in contact, their thickness being neglected, and f_1 and f_2 denote the respective focal lengths of the two lenses, then

$$\frac{1}{F} = \frac{1}{f_1} + \frac{1}{f_2}.$$

If f_1 and f_2 are said to be 8 in. and 4 in. respectively, find approximately the greatest possible error in the computation of F from the above formula if errors of .02 in. in f_1 and .01 in. in f_2 are made.

16. The distance between two points A and B on opposite sides of a pond is determined by taking a third point C and measuring $AC = 40$ ft., $BC = 100$ ft., and $BCA = 60°$. Find approximately the greatest possible error in the computed length of AB caused by possible errors of 3 in. in the measurement of both AC and BC.

17. The distance of an inaccessible object A from a point B is found by measuring a base line $BC = 200$ ft., the angle $CBA = \alpha$ $= 45°$, and the angle $BCA = \beta = 30°$. Find the greatest possible error in the computed length of AB caused by errors of $2'$ in measuring both α and β.

18. The horizontal range R of a bullet having an initial velocity of v_0, fired at an elevation α, is given by the formula

$$R = \frac{v_0{}^2 \sin 2\,\alpha}{g}.$$

Find approximately the greatest possible error in the computation of R if $v_0 = 8000$ ft. per second with a possible error of 12 ft. per second, and $\alpha = 60°$ with a possible error of $2'$ (take $g = 32$).

19. The area of a circular segment bounded by a chord and an arc subtending an angle $2\,\theta$ at the center of the circle is given by the formula
$$A = r^2\theta - \tfrac{1}{2}\,r^2 \sin 2\,\theta.$$

Assuming r to be 6 ft. with a possible error of .1 ft., and θ to be $\dfrac{\pi}{6}$ with a possible error of .01 radian, find approximately the greatest possible error in the computation of A.

20. The stiffness of a rectangular beam varies as the product of its breadth and the cube of its depth. From a circular log 10 in. in diameter a rectangular beam of breadth 6 in. is sawed, having the greatest possible depth. If the measurements of the diameter of the log and the breadth of the beam may each be inaccurate by

.01 in., find approximately the greatest possible error in the computed stiffness of the beam.

21. If $z = \sin^{-1} \dfrac{x}{1+y}$, $x = \sin t$, $y = \cos t$, find the rate of change of z with respect to t when $t = \dfrac{\pi}{3}$.

22. The altitude of a right circular cone decreases at the uniform rate of .01 in. per second, and its radius increases at the uniform rate of .02 in. per second. How fast is the lateral surface of the cone increasing when its altitude is 3 ft. and its radius 2 ft.?

23. If $u = \ln \dfrac{1}{\sqrt{x^2 + y^2}}$ find the rate of change of u at the point $(3, 4)$ in the direction toward the point $(7, 7)$.

24. If the electric potential V at any point of a plane is given by the formula $V = \ln[(x-1)^2 + (y-1)^2]^{\frac{1}{2}}$ find the rate of change of potential at any point: (1) in a direction from $(1, 1)$ to (x, y); (2) in a direction perpendicular to the above direction.

25. If the electric potential V at any point of a plane is given by the formula $V = \ln \dfrac{\sqrt{x^2 + (y+a)^2}}{\sqrt{x^2 + (y-a)^2}}$, find the rate of change of potential at the point (a, a) in the direction toward the origin and at the point $(a, 2\,a)$ in the direction toward the point $(0, 4\,a)$.

26. In what direction from the point $(3, 4)$ is the rate of change of the function $z = kxy$ a maximum, and what is the value of that maximum rate?

27. Find a general expression for the rate of change of the function $u = e^{-y} \sin x + \dfrac{1}{3} e^{-3y} \sin 3\,x$ at the point $\left(\dfrac{\pi}{3}, 0\right)$. Find also the maximum value of the rate of change.

28. From the integral $\displaystyle\int_0^x \sin \alpha x \, dx$ find by successive differentiation the value of $\displaystyle\int_0^x x^2 \sin \alpha x \, dx$.

29. From the integral $\displaystyle\int_0^x \cos \alpha x \, dx$ find by successive differentiation the value of $\displaystyle\int_0^x x^2 \cos \alpha x \, dx$.

30. From the integral $\displaystyle\int_0^x e^{\alpha x} \, dx$ find by successive differentiation the value of $\displaystyle\int_0^x x^3 e^{\alpha x} \, dx$.

31. From the integral $\displaystyle\int_1^x x^\alpha \, dx$ find by successive differentiation the value of $\displaystyle\int_1^x x^\alpha (\ln x)^2 \, dx$.

CHAPTER X

INTEGRATION

74. Introduction. The process of *integration* has been defined, (§ 20), as the determination of a function when its derivative or its differential is known. Some formulas of integration have already been written down and applied in the solution of problems. We will now make a more systematic study of integration and derive a more complete list of formulas which will include those already found. These formulas will be proved anew, however, in order that this chapter may be a self-contained discussion of methods of integration.

By definition, if
$$f(x)dx = dF(x),$$

then
$$\int f(x)dx = F(x) + C,$$

where C is the *constant of integration.*

The expression $f(x)dx$ is said to be under the sign of integration, and $f(x)$ is called the *integrand.* The expression $F(x) + C$ is called the *indefinite integral* to distinguish it from the *definite integral* defined in Chapter III.

In all the formulas which will be derived the constant C will be omitted, since it is independent of the form of the integrand; but it is to be added in all the indefinite integrals found by means of the formulas.

The two formulas
$$\int c\,du = c\int du \tag{1}$$

and
$$\int (du + dv + dw + \cdots) = \int du + \int dv + \int dw + \cdots \tag{2}$$

are of fundamental importance. Stated in words they are as follows:

(1) *A constant factor may be changed from one side of the sign of integration to the other.*

(2) *The integral of the sum of a finite number of functions is the sum of the integrals of the separate functions.*

To prove (1), we note that since $c\,du = d(cu)$, it follows that

$$\int c\,du = \int d(cu) = cu = c\int du.$$

In like manner, to prove (2), since

$$du + dv + dw + \cdots = d(u + v + w + \cdots),$$

we have

$$\int (du + dv + dw + \cdots) = \int d(u + v + w + \cdots)$$

$$= u + v + w + \cdots$$

$$= \int du + \int dv + \int dw + \cdots.$$

The application of these formulas is illustrated in the following articles.

75. Integral of u^n. Since for all values of m except $m = 0$

$$d(u^m) = mu^{m-1}\,du,$$

or

$$d\left(\frac{u^m}{m}\right) = u^{m-1}\,du,$$

it follows that

$$\int u^{m-1}\,du = \frac{u^m}{m}.$$

Placing $m = n + 1$, we have

$$\int u^n\,du = \frac{u^{n+1}}{n+1} \tag{1}$$

for all values of n except $n = -1$.

In the case $n = -1$, the expression under the sign of integration in (1) becomes $\dfrac{du}{u}$, which is recognized as $d(\ln u)$.

Therefore

$$\int \frac{du}{u} = \ln u. \tag{2}$$

It is evident that formulas (3), § 42, and (2), § 57, are but special cases of (1) and (2) respectively, where $u = x$. To apply these formulas to more general cases, it is evident that we must choose for u some function of the variable which will bring the integral, if possible, under one of the formulas. The form of the integrand suggests the function of the variable which should be chosen for u, as will be seen in the solutions of the following illustrative examples :

Example 1. Find the value of $\int \left(ax^2 + bx + \dfrac{c}{x} + \dfrac{k}{x^2} \right) dx$. Applying (2), § 74, and then (1), § 74, we have

$$\int \left(ax^2 + bx + \frac{c}{x} + \frac{k}{x^2} \right) dx = a \int x^2 \, dx + b \int x \, dx + c \int \frac{dx}{x} + k \int x^{-2} dx$$

$$= \frac{1}{3} \, ax^3 + \frac{1}{2} \, bx^2 + c \ln x - \frac{k}{x} + C.$$

Example 2. Find the value of $\int \sqrt{x^2 + 2} \; x \, dx$. Let us try placing $x^2 + 2 = u$. Then, by differentiation, $2 \, x \, dx = du$, so that $x \, dx = \frac{1}{2} \, du$. Hence

$$\int \sqrt{x^2 + 2} \; x \, dx = \int u^{\frac{1}{2}} \frac{1}{2} \, du = \frac{1}{2} \int u^{\frac{1}{2}} \, du = \frac{1}{2} \cdot \frac{u^{\frac{3}{2}}}{\frac{3}{2}} + C$$

$$= \frac{1}{3} \, u^{\frac{3}{2}} + C = \frac{1}{3} \, (x^2 + 2)^{\frac{3}{2}} + C.$$

Example 3. Find the value of $\int \dfrac{4(ax + b)}{ax^2 + 2 \, bx} \; dx$.

Here we will place $ax^2 + 2 \, bx = u$.

Then $(2 \, ax + 2 \, b)dx = du$, so that $(ax + b)dx = \frac{1}{2} \, du$.

Hence $\quad \int \dfrac{4(ax + b)dx}{ax^2 + 2 \, bx} = \int \dfrac{2 \, du}{u} = 2 \int \dfrac{du}{u}$

$$= 2 \ln u + C$$

$$= 2 \ln(ax^2 + 2 \, bx) + C$$

$$= \ln(ax^2 + 2 \, bx)^2 + C.$$

Example 4. Find the value of $\int (e^{ax} + b)^2 e^{ax} \, dx$.

Let $e^{ax} + b = u$. Then $e^{ax} a \, dx = du$.

Hence $\quad \int (e^{ax} + b)^2 e^{ax} \, dx = \int u^2 \dfrac{du}{a}$

$$= \frac{1}{a} \int u^2 \, du$$

$$= \frac{1}{3 \, a} \, u^3 + C$$

$$= \frac{1}{3 \, a} \, (e^{ax} + b)^3 + C.$$

If the integrand is a trigonometric expression it is often possible to carry out the integration by either formula (1) or formula (2). This may happen when the integrand can be expressed in terms of one of the elementary trigonometric functions, the whole expression being multiplied by the differential of that function. For instance, the expression to be integrated may consist of a function of sin x multiplied by cos $x\,dx$, or a function of cos x multiplied by $(-\sin x\,dx)$, etc.

Example 5. Find the value of $\int \cos^3 4\,x\,dx$. Since $d(\sin 4\,x)$ $= 4\cos 4\,x\,dx$, we will separate out the factor cos $4\,x\,dx$ and try to express the rest of the integrand in terms of sin $4\,x$. We have

$$\cos^3 4\,x\,dx = \cos^2 4\,x(\cos 4\,x\,dx) = (1 - \sin^2 4\,x)(\cos 4\,x\,dx).$$

Since we have succeeded in expressing the rest of the integrand in terms of sin $4\,x$, we let sin $4\,x = u$, whence cos $4\,x\,dx = \frac{1}{4}\,du$. Hence

$$\int \cos^3 4\,x\,dx = \int (1 - \sin^2 4\,x)(\cos 4\,x\,dx)$$
$$= \int (1 - u^2)(\tfrac{1}{4}\,du)$$
$$= \tfrac{1}{4}\int (1 - u^2)\,du$$
$$= \frac{1}{4}\left(u - \frac{u^3}{3}\right) + C$$
$$= \tfrac{1}{4}(\sin 4\,x - \tfrac{1}{3}\sin^3 4\,x) + C$$
$$= \tfrac{1}{12}(3\sin 4\,x - \sin^3 4\,x) + C.$$

Example 6. Find the value of $\int \sec^6 2\,x\,dx$.

Since $d(\tan 2\,x) = 2\sec^2 2\,x\,dx$, we separate out the factor $\sec^2 2\,x\,dx$ and express the rest of the integrand in terms of tan $2\,x$.

Thus $\sec^6 2\,x\,dx = \sec^4 2\,x(\sec^2 2\,x\,dx)$
$$= (1 + \tan^2 2\,x)^2(\sec^2 2\,x\,dx)$$
$$= (1 + 2\tan^2 2\,x + \tan^4 2\,x)(\sec^2 2\,x\,dx).$$

Now place tan $2\,x = u$, and we have

$$\int \sec^6 2\,x\,dx = \tfrac{1}{2}\int (1 + 2\,u^2 + u^4)\,du$$
$$= \tfrac{1}{2}(u + \tfrac{2}{3}\,u^3 + \tfrac{1}{5}\,u^5) + C$$
$$= \tfrac{1}{2}\tan 2\,x + \tfrac{1}{3}\tan^3 2\,x + \tfrac{1}{10}\tan^5 2\,x + C.$$

EXERCISES

Find the values of the following integrals:

1. $\int \left(8\,x^3 + 6\,x - \dfrac{3}{x^4}\right) dx.$ 11. $\int \dfrac{e^{ax} + \sin ax}{(e^{ax} - \cos ax)^2}\, dx.$

2. $\int \left(5\sqrt[3]{x^2} - \dfrac{4}{\sqrt[3]{x}}\right) dx.$ 12. $\int \dfrac{1 + \sin 2\,x}{(2\,x - \cos 2\,x)^{\frac{3}{2}}}\, dx.$

3. $\int \left(3\,x^2\sqrt{x} - \dfrac{2}{x\sqrt{x}}\right) dx.$ 13. $\int \dfrac{(x^2 - x)\,dx}{2\,x^3 - 3\,x^2 + 1}.$

4. $\int \dfrac{(x^2 + 1)^2}{x^3}\, dx.$ 14. $\int \dfrac{\sec^2 ax}{1 + \tan ax}\, dx.$

5. $\int \dfrac{x^3}{x - 1}\, dx.$ 15. $\int \sin^2 3\,x \cos 3\,x\,dx.$

6. $\int (x^3 + 3)^3\, x^2\,dx.$ 16. $\int \cos (2\,x + 3) \sin (2\,x + 3)dx.$

7. $\int \sqrt{(x^4 - 8)^3}\, x^3\,dx.$ 17. $\int \sin^3 5\,x \cos^3 5\,x\,dx.$

8. $\int \dfrac{x^2}{\sqrt[3]{x^3 + 3}}\, dx.$ 18. $\int \sec^4 2\,x\,dx.$

9. $\int \dfrac{e^{2x} + e^{-2x}}{e^{2x} - e^{-2x}}\, dx.$ 19. $\int \operatorname{ctn}(3\,x + 2)\csc^3(3\,x + 2)dx.$

10. $\int \dfrac{1 - \sin 3\,x}{3\,x + \cos 3\,x}\, dx.$ 20. $\int \sin^5(3\,x - 1)dx.$

76. Other algebraic integrands. The following formulas of integration, in which the integrands are algebraic functions of u, can easily be verified by differentiation, and this verification should be made by the student.

$$\int \frac{du}{u^2 + a^2} = \frac{1}{a}\tan^{-1}\frac{u}{a}. \tag{1}$$

$$\int \frac{du}{u^2 - a^2} = \frac{1}{2\,a}\ln\frac{u - a}{u + a}. \tag{2}$$

$$\int \frac{du}{\sqrt{a^2 - u^2}} = \sin^{-1}\frac{u}{a}. \tag{3}$$

$$\int \frac{du}{\sqrt{u^2 + a^2}} = \ln(u + \sqrt{u^2 + a^2}). \tag{4}$$

$$\int \frac{du}{\sqrt{u^2 - a^2}} = \ln(u + \sqrt{u^2 - a^2}). \tag{5}$$

In the verification of (3) the student will observe that the formula holds only if $\sin^{-1}\dfrac{u}{a}$ is in the first or the fourth quadrant, since the plus sign before the radical in 1, § 48, holds only for those quadrants. If, however, it is necessary to have $\sin^{-1}\dfrac{u}{a}$ in the second or the third quadrant, it will be necessary to prefix the minus sign on the right-hand side of the equation.

On the other hand (1) holds for all quadrants.

Example 1. Find the value of $\displaystyle\int \frac{dx}{4\,x^2 + 7}$.

Letting $2\,x = u$, we have $2\,dx = du$, whence $dx = \frac{1}{2}\,du$. Hence

$$\int \frac{dx}{4\,x^2 + 7} = \int \frac{\frac{1}{2}\,du}{u^2 + 7}$$

$$= \frac{1}{2} \int \frac{du}{u^2 + 7}$$

$$= \frac{1}{2} \cdot \frac{1}{\sqrt{7}} \tan^{-1} \frac{u}{\sqrt{7}} + C$$

$$= \frac{1}{2\sqrt{7}} \tan^{-1} \frac{2\,x}{\sqrt{7}} + C.$$

Example 2. Find the value of $\displaystyle\int \frac{dx}{\sqrt{3 - 2\,x^2}}$.

Letting $\sqrt{2}\,x = u$, we have $\sqrt{2}\,dx = du$, whence $dx = \dfrac{1}{\sqrt{2}}\,du$. Hence

$$\int \frac{dx}{\sqrt{3 - 2\,x^2}} = \int \frac{\dfrac{1}{\sqrt{2}}\,du}{\sqrt{3 - u^2}}$$

$$= \frac{1}{\sqrt{2}} \int \frac{du}{\sqrt{3 - u^2}}$$

$$= \frac{1}{\sqrt{2}} \sin^{-1} \frac{u}{\sqrt{3}} + C$$

$$= \frac{1}{\sqrt{2}} \sin^{-1} \frac{\sqrt{2}\,x}{\sqrt{3}} + C$$

$$= \frac{1}{\sqrt{2}} \sin^{-1} \frac{x\,\sqrt{6}}{3} + C.$$

Example 3. Find the value of $\int \dfrac{dx}{x^2 + 2\,x + 5}$.

Since there are terms of both the first and the second degree in x, we place those terms in a parenthesis, and write

$$x^2 + 2\,x + 5 = (x^2 + 2\,x) + 5.$$

We may make the terms in parenthesis a perfect square by adding 1 (the square of half the coefficient of x), and in order not to change the value of the expression we subtract 1 from 5. Thus

$$\begin{aligned}
x^2 + 2\,x + 5 &= (x^2 + 2\,x) + 5 \\
&= (x^2 + 2\,x + 1) + (5 - 1) \\
&= (x + 1)^2 + 4.
\end{aligned}$$

We can now place $x + 1 = u$, whence $dx = du$. Hence

$$\begin{aligned}
\int \frac{dx}{x^2 + 2\,x + 5} &= \int \frac{dx}{(x + 1)^2 + 4} \\
&= \int \frac{du}{u^2 + 4} \\
&= \frac{1}{2} \tan^{-1} \frac{u}{2} + C \\
&= \frac{1}{2} \tan^{-1} \frac{x + 1}{2} + C.
\end{aligned}$$

Example 4. Find the value of $\int \dfrac{dx}{2\,x^2 + x - 15}$.

We first divide out the coefficient of x^2, writing the integrand in the form

$$\frac{1}{2} \cdot \frac{1}{x^2 + \frac{1}{2}\,x - \frac{15}{2}} = \frac{1}{2} \cdot \frac{1}{(x + \frac{1}{4})^2 - \frac{121}{16}},$$

the second fraction having been transformed by the method used in Example 3. We now let $x + \frac{1}{4} = u$, whence $dx = du$. Hence

$$\begin{aligned}
\int \frac{dx}{2\,x^2 + x - 15} &= \frac{1}{2} \int \frac{dx}{(x + \frac{1}{4})^2 - \frac{121}{16}} \\
&= \frac{1}{2} \int \frac{du}{u^2 - \frac{121}{16}} \\
&= \frac{1}{2} \cdot \frac{1}{2(\frac{11}{4})} \ln \frac{u - \frac{11}{4}}{u + \frac{11}{4}} + C \\
&= \frac{1}{11} \ln \frac{x - \frac{5}{2}}{x + 3} + C \\
&= \frac{1}{11} \ln \frac{2\,x - 5}{x + 3} + K,
\end{aligned}$$

where $C = \frac{1}{11} \ln 2 + K$.

By expressing the first constant of integration as the sum of the constant $\frac{1}{11}\ln 2$ and a new constant K, we have been able to simplify the form of the integral; but the two forms of answer really differ only in the constants of integration.

In this connection it may be noted that if the same integral is evaluated by using different formulas, the resulting integrals may seem to be different, but it can always be shown that they differ only in the constants of integration.

Example 5. Find the value of $\int \dfrac{dx}{\sqrt{1+2\,x-3\,x^2}}\cdot$ We first factor out the coefficient of x^2 and write the terms containing x in a parenthesis with the minus sign before it, since the term in x^2 is negative. Thus

$$\frac{1}{\sqrt{1+2\,x-3\,x^2}} = \frac{1}{\sqrt{3}} \cdot \frac{1}{\sqrt{\frac{1}{3} - (x^2 - \frac{2}{3}\,x)}}\cdot$$

We now complete the square of the terms in x, as in Examples 3 and 4, with the result that

$$\frac{1}{\sqrt{1+2\,x-3\,x^2}} = \frac{1}{\sqrt{3}} \cdot \frac{1}{\sqrt{\frac{4}{9} - (x - \frac{1}{3})^2}}\cdot$$

Placing $x - \frac{1}{3} = u$, we have $dx = du$.

Hence
$$\int \frac{dx}{\sqrt{1+2\,x-3\,x^2}} = \frac{1}{\sqrt{3}} \int \frac{dx}{\sqrt{\frac{4}{9} - (x - \frac{1}{3})^2}}$$

$$= \frac{1}{\sqrt{3}} \int \frac{du}{\sqrt{\frac{4}{9} - u^2}}$$

$$= \frac{1}{\sqrt{3}} \cdot \sin^{-1} \frac{u}{\frac{2}{3}} + C$$

$$= \frac{1}{\sqrt{3}} \sin^{-1} \frac{3\,x-1}{2} + C.$$

Example 6. Find the value of $\int \dfrac{5\,x-2}{2\,x^2+3}\,dx.$

Separating the integrand into two fractions

$$\frac{5\,x}{2\,x^2+3} - \frac{2}{2\,x^2+3},$$

and using (2), § 74, we have

$$\int \frac{5\,x-2}{2\,x^2+3}\,dx = \int \frac{5\,x\,dx}{2\,x^2+3} - \int \frac{2\,dx}{2\,x^2+3}\cdot$$

If we let $2\,x^2 + 3 = u$ in the first integral, then $du = 4\,x\,dx$, and

$$\int \frac{5\,x\,dx}{2\,x^2 + 3} = \frac{5}{4} \int \frac{du}{u} = \frac{5}{4} \ln u = \frac{5}{4} \ln(2\,x^2 + 3) \,;$$

and if we let $\sqrt{2}\,x = u$ in the second integral, then $du = \sqrt{2}\,dx$,

and $\int \dfrac{2\,dx}{2\,x^2 + 3} = \sqrt{2} \int \dfrac{du}{u^2 + 3} = \sqrt{2} \cdot \dfrac{1}{\sqrt{3}} \tan^{-1} \dfrac{u}{\sqrt{3}} = \dfrac{\sqrt{6}}{3} \tan^{-1} \dfrac{x\sqrt{6}}{3} .$

Therefore $\int \dfrac{5\,x - 2}{2\,x^2 + 3}\,dx = \dfrac{5}{4} \ln(2\,x^2 + 3) - \dfrac{\sqrt{6}}{3} \tan^{-1} \dfrac{x\sqrt{6}}{3} + C.$

EXERCISES

Find the values of the following integrals:

1. $\int \dfrac{dx}{\sqrt{9 - 16\,x^2}} .$

2. $\int \dfrac{dx}{\sqrt{8 - 5\,x^2}} .$

3. $\int \dfrac{dx}{x^2 + 5} .$

4. $\int \dfrac{dx}{7\,x^2 + 3} .$

5. $\int \dfrac{dx}{\sqrt{x^2 + 3}} .$

6. $\int \dfrac{dx}{\sqrt{4\,x^2 - 9}} .$

7. $\int \dfrac{dx}{4\,x^2 - 16} .$

8. $\int \dfrac{dx}{3\,x^2 - 5} .$

9. $\int \dfrac{dx}{\sqrt{4\,x - 3\,x^2}} .$

10. $\int \dfrac{dx}{\sqrt{2 + 6\,x - x^2}} .$

11. $\int \dfrac{dx}{x^2 + 6\,x} .$

12. $\int \dfrac{dx}{5\,x^2 + 3\,x - 1} .$

13. $\int \dfrac{dx}{x^2 + 8\,x + 17} .$

14. $\int \dfrac{dx}{2\,x^2 - 3\,x + 5} .$

15. $\int \dfrac{dx}{\sqrt{2 - 4\,x - 3\,x^2}} .$

16. $\int \dfrac{dx}{\sqrt{x^2 + 4\,x}} .$

17. $\int \dfrac{dx}{\sqrt{2\,x^2 + x + 1}} .$

18. $\int \dfrac{x + 3}{x^2 - 4}\,dx.$

19. $\int \dfrac{3\,x + 7}{4\,x^2 + 9}\,dx.$

20. $\int \dfrac{x - 2}{\sqrt{9 - x^2}}\,dx.$

21. $\int \dfrac{2\,x + 3}{\sqrt{3\,x^2 + 4}}\,dx.$

77. Integrals of trigonometric functions. Of the following formulas for the integration of the trigonometric functions, each of the first six is the direct converse of the corresponding formula of differentiation (§ 46), and the last four can readily be verified by differentiation, which is left to the student.

$$\int \sin u\,du = -\cos u. \tag{1}$$

$$\int \cos u\,du = \sin u. \tag{2}$$

$$\int \sec^2 u\, du = \tan u. \tag{3}$$

$$\int \csc^2 u\, du = -\operatorname{ctn} u. \tag{4}$$

$$\int \sec u \tan u\, du = \sec u. \tag{5}$$

$$\int \csc u \operatorname{ctn} u\, du = -\csc u. \tag{6}$$

$$\int \tan u\, du = -\ln \cos u. \tag{7}$$

$$\int \operatorname{ctn} u\, du = \ln \sin u. \tag{8}$$

$$\int \sec u\, du = \ln (\sec u + \tan u). \tag{9}$$

$$\int \csc u\, du = \ln (\csc u - \operatorname{ctn} u). \tag{10}$$

Often a trigonometric transformation of the integrand facilitates the carrying out of the integration, as shown in the following examples:

Example 1. Find the value of $\int \sin 7\, x dx$.

If we let $\qquad\qquad u = 7\, x,$

then $\qquad\qquad\qquad du = 7\, dx;$

whence $\qquad\qquad\quad dx = \tfrac{1}{7}\, du,$

and $\qquad\qquad \int \sin 7\, x\, dx = \int \sin u(\tfrac{1}{7}\, du)$

$$= \tfrac{1}{7} \int \sin u\, du$$

$$= -\tfrac{1}{7} \cos u + C$$

$$= -\tfrac{1}{7} \cos 7\, x + C.$$

Example 2. Find the value of $\int \sec(2\, x + 1)\tan(2\, x + 1)dx$.

If we let $u = 2\, x + 1$, then $du = 2\, dx$,

and $\int \sec(2\, x + 1)\tan(2\, x + 1)dx = \tfrac{1}{2} \int \sec u \tan u\, du$

$$= \tfrac{1}{2} \sec u + C$$

$$= \tfrac{1}{2} \sec(2\, x + 1) + C.$$

Example 3. Find the value of $\int \cos^2 3\,x\,dx.$

Since by (8), § 43, $\qquad \cos^2 3\,x = \frac{1}{2}(1 + \cos 6\,x),$

$$\int \cos^2 3\,x\,dx = \int (\tfrac{1}{2} + \tfrac{1}{2} \cos 6\,x)dx$$

$$= \tfrac{1}{2} \int dx + \tfrac{1}{2} \int \cos 6\,x\,dx$$

$$= \frac{1}{2}\,x + \frac{1}{12} \sin 6\,x + C,$$

the second integral being evaluated by formula (2) with $u = 6\,x.$

Example 4. Find the value of $\int \sqrt{1 + \cos 5\,x}\,dx.$

Since by (9), § 43,
$$\sqrt{1 + \cos 5\,x} = \sqrt{2}\,\cos \frac{5\,x}{2},$$

$$\int \sqrt{1 + \cos 5\,x}\,dx = \int \sqrt{2}\,\cos \frac{5\,x}{2}\,dx$$

$$= \sqrt{2} \int \cos \frac{5\,x}{2}\,dx$$

$$= \frac{2}{5}\sqrt{2} \sin \frac{5\,x}{2} + C.$$

Example 5. Find the value of $\int \tan^2 3\,x\,dx.$

Since $\qquad\qquad \tan^2 3\,x = \sec^2 3\,x - 1,$

$$\int \tan^2 3\,x\,dx = \int (\sec^2 3\,x - 1)dx$$

$$= \int \sec^2 3\,x\,dx - \int dx$$

$$= \tfrac{1}{3} \tan 3\,x - x,$$

the first integral being evaluated by formula (3) with $u = 3\,x.$

EXERCISES

Find the values of the following integrals:

1. $\int \sin (4\,x + 3)dx.$

2. $\int \cos (3\,x - 2)dx.$

3. $\int \tan \frac{2\,x}{3}\,dx.$

4. $\int \operatorname{ctn} (4\,x - 2)dx.$

5. $\int \sec (2\,x + 4)dx.$

6. $\int \csc (3\,x - 2)dx.$

7. $\int \sec (2 - 3\,x) \tan (2 - 3\,x)dx.$

8. $\int \csc^2 (1 - 3\,x)dx.$

9. $\int \sec^2 \frac{x}{3}\, dx.$

15. $\int \frac{\cos 4\, x}{\cos 2\, x}\, dx.$

10. $\int \csc (2 - 5\, x) \operatorname{ctn} (2 - 5\, x) dx.$

16. $\int \cos^2 \frac{x}{4}\, dx.$

11. $\int \sin^2 \frac{2\, x}{5}\, dx.$

17. $\int \sin^2 \frac{x}{3} \cos^2 \frac{x}{3}\, dx.$

12. $\int \tan^2 (2\, x + 3) dx.$

18. $\int \sqrt{1 + \cos \frac{2\, x}{3}}\, dx.$

13. $\int \sqrt{1 - \cos 3\, x}\, dx.$

19. $\int \sin 3\, x \cos 2\, x\, dx.$

14. $\int \left(\sin \frac{3\, x}{2} - \cos \frac{3\, x}{2}\right)^2 dx.$

20. $\int \frac{dx}{\sqrt{1 - \cos 4\, x}}.$

78. Integrals of exponential functions. The formulas

$$\int e^u\, du = e^u \tag{1}$$

and

$$\int a^u\, du = \frac{1}{\ln a}\, a^u \tag{2}$$

are derived immediately from the corresponding formulas of differentiation.

Example 1. Find the value of $\int e^{3\, x} dx.$
If we let $3\, x = u$, we have

$$\int e^{3\, x} dx = \tfrac{1}{3} \int e^u\, du$$

$$= \tfrac{1}{3}\, e^u + C$$

$$= \tfrac{1}{3}\, e^{3x} + C.$$

Example 2. Find the value of $\int \frac{\sqrt[x]{5}}{x^2}\, dx.$

If we place $\sqrt[x]{5} = 5^{\frac{1}{x}}$ and let $\frac{1}{x} = u$, we have

$$\int \frac{\sqrt[x]{5}}{x^2}\, dx = - \int 5^u\, du$$

$$= - \frac{1}{\ln 5}\, 5^u + C$$

$$= - \frac{1}{\ln 5} \cdot \sqrt[x]{5} + C$$

EXERCISES

Find the values of the following integrals:

1. $\int e^{5x+3} dx.$

5. $\int \dfrac{e^{2x} - 1}{e^{2x} + 1} dx.$

9. $\int (e^x + x^e) dx.$

2. $\int x e^{x^2} dx.$

6. $\int \dfrac{1 - e^x}{1 + e^x} dx.$

10. $\int (10^x + x^{10}) dx.$

3. $\int (e^{3x} + e^{-3x})^2 dx.$

7. $\int e^{\cos x} \sin x \, dx.$

11. $\int e^{a+bx} c^{a+bx} dx.$

4. $\int \dfrac{e^x - e^{-x}}{e^x + e^{-x}} dx.$

8. $\int \dfrac{e^{\tan^{-1} x}}{1 + x^2} dx.$

12. $\int \dfrac{e^{\frac{1}{x}}}{x^2} dx.$

79. Substitutions. In all the integrations that have been made in the previous sections we have substituted a new variable u for some function of x, thereby making the given integral identical with one of the formulas. There are other cases in which the choice of the new variable u is not so evident, but in which, nevertheless, it is possible to reduce the given integral to one of the known integrals by an appropriate choice and *substitution* of a new variable. We shall suggest in this section a few of the more common substitutions which it is desirable to try.

1. *Integrand involving powers of $a + bx$.* The substitution of some power of z for $a + bx$ is usually desirable.

Example 1. Find the value of $\int \dfrac{x^2 dx}{(1 + 2x)^{\frac{1}{3}}}$.

Here we let $1 + 2x = z^3$; then $x = \frac{1}{2}(z^3 - 1)$ and $dx = \frac{3}{2} z^2 dz$.

Therefore
$$\int \frac{x^2 dx}{(1 + 2x)^{\frac{1}{3}}} = \frac{3}{8} \int (z^7 - 2z^4 + z) dz$$
$$= \frac{3}{8}\left(\frac{1}{8} z^8 - \frac{2}{5} z^5 + \frac{1}{2} z^2\right) + C$$
$$= \frac{3}{320} z^2 (5 z^6 - 16 z^3 + 20) + C.$$

Replacing z by its value $(1 + 2x)^{\frac{1}{3}}$ and simplifying, we have

$$\int \frac{x^2 dx}{(1 + 2x)^{\frac{1}{3}}} = \frac{3}{320} (1 + 2x)^{\frac{2}{3}}(9 - 12x + 20x^2) + C.$$

2. *Integrand involving powers of* $a + bx^n$. If the integrand contains $x^{n-1}dx$ as a factor, but otherwise contains only powers of x^n and of $a + bx^n$, the substitution of some power of z for $a + bx^n$ is desirable, since $d(a + bx^n) = bnx^{n-1}dx$.

Example 2. Find the value of $\int \dfrac{\sqrt{x^2 + a^2}}{x}\, dx$.

We may write the integral in the form

$$\int \frac{\sqrt{x^2 + a^2}}{x^2}\,(x\,dx)$$

and place $x^2 + a^2 = z^2$. Then $x\,dx = z\,dz$, and the integral becomes

$$\int \frac{z^2 dz}{z^2 - a^2} = \int \left(1 + \frac{a^2}{z^2 - a^2}\right)\,dz = z + \frac{a}{2}\ln\frac{z - a}{z + a} + C.$$

Replacing z by its value in terms of x, we have

$$\int \frac{\sqrt{x^2 + a^2}}{x}\,dx = \sqrt{x^2 + a^2} + \frac{a}{2}\ln\frac{\sqrt{x^2 + a^2} - a}{\sqrt{x^2 + a^2} + a} + C.$$

Example 3. Find the value of $\int x^5(1 + 2\,x^3)^{\frac{1}{2}}dx$.

We may write the integral in the form

$$\int x^3(1 + 2\,x^3)^{\frac{1}{2}}(x^2\,dx),$$

and place $1 + 2\,x^3 = z^2$. Then $x^2\,dx = \frac{1}{3}\,z\,dz$, and the new integral in z is

$$\frac{1}{6}\int (z^4 - z^2)dz = \frac{1}{90}\,z^3(3\,z^2 - 5) + C.$$

Replacing z by its value, we have

$$\int x^5(1 + 2\,x^3)^{\frac{1}{2}}dx = \frac{1}{45}(1 + 2\,x^3)^{\frac{3}{2}}(3\,x^3 - 1) + C.$$

3. *Integrand involving square roots.* This occurs very frequently in practice.

If the square root is of the type $\sqrt{a + bx}$, the substitution $a + bx = z^2$ is to be made in accordance with 1.

If the square root is one of the types $\sqrt{a^2 - x^2}$, $\sqrt{x^2 - a^2}$, or $\sqrt{x^2 + a^2}$ and the integrand is of the type described in 2, the substitution of z for the radical is to be made as illustrated in Example 2. In other cases a trigonometric substitution may be made as shown in 4, 5, and 6.

If the square root is of the type $\sqrt{a + bx + cx^2}$, it may be put into one of the forms $\sqrt{a^2 - u^2}$, $\sqrt{u^2 - a^2}$, or $\sqrt{u^2 + a^2}$ as shown in Example 5, § 76, and the above directions followed.

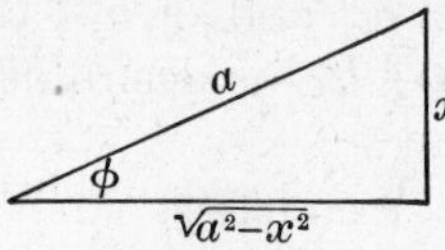

4. *Integrand involving* $\sqrt{a^2 - x^2}$. If a right triangle is constructed with one leg equal to x and with the hypotenuse equal to a (Fig. 95), the substitution $x = a \sin \phi$ is suggested.

FIG. 95

Example 4. Find the value of $\int \sqrt{a^2 - x^2}\, dx$.

Let $x = a \sin \phi$. Then $dx = a \cos \phi\, d\phi$ and, from the triangle, $\sqrt{a^2 - x^2} = a \cos \phi$.

Therefore
$$\int \sqrt{a^2 - x^2}\, dx = a^2 \int \cos^2 \phi\, d\phi$$
$$= \tfrac{1}{2} a^2 \int (1 + \cos 2\phi) d\phi$$
$$= \tfrac{1}{2} a^2 (\phi + \tfrac{1}{2} \sin 2\phi) + C.$$

But
$$\phi = \sin^{-1} \frac{x}{a},$$

and
$$\sin 2\phi = 2 \sin \phi \cos \phi$$
$$= \frac{2 x \sqrt{a^2 - x^2}}{a^2};$$

for, from the triangle, $\sin \phi = \dfrac{x}{a}$ and $\cos \phi = \dfrac{\sqrt{a^2 - x^2}}{a}$.

Finally, by substitution, we have
$$\int \sqrt{a^2 - x^2}\, dx = \frac{1}{2} \left(x \sqrt{a^2 - x^2} + a^2 \sin^{-1} \frac{x}{a} \right) + C.$$

5. *Integrand involving* $\sqrt{x^2 + a^2}$. If a right triangle is constructed with the two legs equal to x and a respectively (Fig. 96), the substitution $x = a \tan \phi$ is suggested.

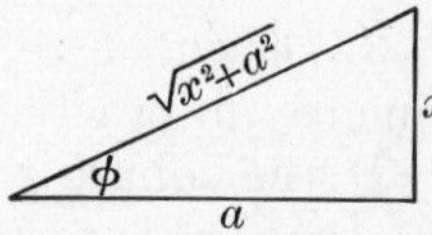

Example 5. Find the value of $\int \dfrac{dx}{(x^2 + a^2)^{\frac{3}{2}}}$.

FIG. 96

Let $x = a \tan \phi$. Then $dx = a \sec^2 \phi\, d\phi$ and, from the triangle, $\sqrt{x^2 + a^2} = a \sec \phi$.

Therefore $\int \dfrac{dx}{(x^2 + a^2)^{\frac{3}{2}}} = \dfrac{1}{a^2} \int \dfrac{d\phi}{\sec \phi} = \dfrac{1}{a^2} \int \cos \phi\, d\phi = \dfrac{1}{a^2} \sin \phi + C.$

But, from the triangle, $\sin\phi = \dfrac{x}{\sqrt{x^2 + a^2}}$; so that, by substitution,

$$\int \frac{dx}{(x^2 + a^2)^{\frac{3}{2}}} = \frac{x}{a^2\sqrt{x^2 + a^2}} + C.$$

6. *Integrand involving* $\sqrt{x^2 - a^2}$. If a right triangle is constructed with the hypotenuse equal to x and with one leg equal to a (Fig. 97), the substitution $x = a \sec\phi$ is suggested.

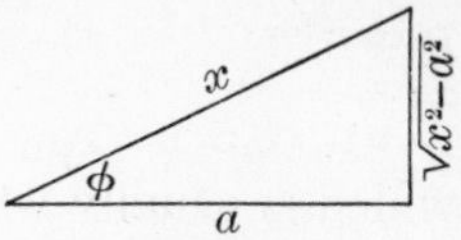

Example 6. Find the value of

$$\int x^3\sqrt{x^2 - a^2}\,dx.$$

FIG. 97

Let $x = a\sec\phi$. Then $dx = a\sec\phi\tan\phi\,d\phi$ and, from the triangle, $\sqrt{x^2 - a^2} = a\tan\phi$.

Therefore
$$\int x^3\sqrt{x^2 - a^2}\,dx = a^5\int \tan^2\phi\sec^4\phi\,d\phi$$
$$= a^5\int (\tan^2\phi + \tan^4\phi)\sec^2\phi\,d\phi$$
$$= a^5(\tfrac{1}{3}\tan^3\phi + \tfrac{1}{5}\tan^5\phi) + C.$$

But, from the triangle, $\tan\phi = \dfrac{\sqrt{x^2 - a^2}}{a}$; so that, by substitution, we have

$$\int x^3\sqrt{x^2 - a^2}\,dx = \tfrac{1}{15}(2a^2 + 3x^2)\sqrt{(x^2 - a^2)^3} + C.$$

We might have written this integral in the form $\int x^2\sqrt{x^2 - a^2}\,(x\,dx)$ and solved by letting $z^2 = x^2 - a^2$.

EXERCISES

Find the values of the following integrals:

1. $\int \dfrac{dx}{x\sqrt{x+3}}.$

2. $\int \dfrac{x^2\,dx}{(5x+1)^{\frac{2}{5}}}.$

3. $\int \dfrac{(2x+5)^{\frac{3}{2}}}{x}\,dx.$

4. $\int \dfrac{dx}{(3-x^2)^{\frac{3}{2}}}.$

5. $\int \dfrac{dx}{x^4\sqrt{x^2-25}}.$

6. $\int \dfrac{x^3\,dx}{(x^2+4)^{\frac{3}{2}}}.$

7. $\int \dfrac{x^2\,dx}{(x^2+4)^2}.$

8. $\int \dfrac{dx}{(x^2-4)^{\frac{3}{2}}}.$

9. $\int \dfrac{x^2\,dx}{(9-x^2)^{\frac{3}{2}}}.$

10. $\int \dfrac{x^2\,dx}{(4x^2+9)^{\frac{5}{2}}}.$

11. $\int x^5(x^3+8)^{\frac{2}{3}}\,dx.$

12. $\int \dfrac{(4x^2-9)^{\frac{3}{2}}}{x^6}\,dx.$

13. $\int \dfrac{dx}{x^2\sqrt{9+4x^2}}.$

14. $\int \dfrac{x^2\,dx}{(3-x^2)^{\frac{7}{2}}}.$

15. $\int \dfrac{\sqrt{x^3+4}}{x}\,dx.$

80. Integration by parts. Another method of importance in the reduction of a given integral to a known type is that of *integration by parts*, the formula for which is derived from the formula for the differential of a product,

$$d(uv) = u\,dv + v\,du.$$

From this formula we derive

$$uv = \int u\,dv + \int v\,du,$$

which is usually written in the form

$$\int u\,dv = uv - \int v\,du.$$

In the use of this formula the aim is evidently to make the original integration depend upon the evaluation of a simpler integral.

Example 1. Find the value of $\int xe^x\,dx$.

If we let $x = u$ and $e^x\,dx = dv$, we have $du = dx$ and $v = e^x$. Substituting in our formula, we have

$$\int xe^x\,dx = xe^x - \int e^x\,dx$$
$$= xe^x - e^x + C$$
$$= (x-1)e^x + C.$$

It is evident that in selecting the expression for dv it is desirable, if possible, to choose an expression that is easily integrated.

Example 2. Find the value of $\int \sin^{-1} x\,dx$.

Here we may let $\sin^{-1} x = u$ and $dx = dv$, whence $du = \dfrac{dx}{\sqrt{1 - x^2}}$ and $v = x$.

Substituting in our formula, we have

$$\int \sin^{-1} x\,dx = x \sin^{-1} x - \int \frac{x\,dx}{\sqrt{1 - x^2}}$$
$$= x \sin^{-1} x + \sqrt{1 - x^2} + C,$$

the last integral being evaluated by § 79.

Sometimes an integral may be evaluated by successive integration by parts.

Example 3. Find the value of $\int x^2 e^x \, dx$.

Here we let $x^2 = u$ and $e^x \, dx = dv$. Then $du = 2 \, x \, dx$ and $v = e^x$.

Therefore $\qquad \int x^2 e^x \, dx = x^2 e^x - 2 \int x e^x \, dx$.

The integral $\int x e^x \, dx$ may be evaluated by integration by parts (see Example 1) so that finally

$$\int x^2 e^x \, dx = x^2 e^x - 2(x - 1)e^x + C = e^x(x^2 - 2\,x + 2) + C.$$

Example 4. Find the value of $\int e^{ax} \sin bx \, dx$.

Letting $\sin bx = u$ and $e^{ax} \, dx = dv$, we have

$$\int e^{ax} \sin bx \, dx = \frac{1}{a} \, e^{ax} \sin bx - \frac{b}{a} \int e^{ax} \cos bx \, dx.$$

In the integral $\int e^{ax} \cos bx \, dx$ we let $\cos bx = u$ and $e^{ax} \, dx = dv$, and have

$$\int e^{ax} \cos bx \, dx = \frac{1}{a} \, e^{ax} \cos bx + \frac{b}{a} \int e^{ax} \sin bx \, dx.$$

Substituting this value above, we have

$$\int e^{ax} \sin bx \, dx = \frac{1}{a} \, e^{ax} \sin bx - \frac{b}{a} \left(\frac{1}{a} \, e^{ax} \cos bx + \frac{b}{a} \int e^{ax} \sin bx \, dx \right).$$

Now bringing to the left-hand member of the equation all the terms containing the integral, we have

$$\left(1 + \frac{b^2}{a^2} \right) \int e^{ax} \sin bx \, dx = \frac{1}{a} \, e^{ax} \sin bx - \frac{b}{a^2} \, e^{ax} \cos bx,$$

whence $\qquad \int e^{ax} \sin bx \, dx = \dfrac{e^{ax}(a \sin bx - b \cos bx)}{a^2 + b^2}.$

Example 5. Find the value of $\int \sqrt{x^2 + a^2} \, dx$.

Placing $\sqrt{x^2 + a^2} = u$ and $dx = dv$, whence $du = \dfrac{x \, dx}{\sqrt{x^2 + a^2}}$ and $v = x$, we have

$$\int \sqrt{x^2 + a^2} \, dx = x \sqrt{x^2 + a^2} - \int \frac{x^2 \, dx}{\sqrt{x^2 + a^2}}. \tag{1}$$

Since $x^2 = (x^2 + a^2) - a^2$, the second integral of (1) may be written as

$$\int \frac{(x^2 + a^2) \, dx}{\sqrt{x^2 + a^2}} - a^2 \int \frac{dx}{\sqrt{x^2 + a^2}},$$

which equals $\qquad \int \sqrt{x^2 + a^2} \, dx - a^2 \int \dfrac{dx}{\sqrt{x^2 + a^2}}.$

Evaluating this last integral and substituting in (1), we have

$$\int \sqrt{x^2 + a^2}\,dx = x\sqrt{x^2 + a^2} - \int \sqrt{x^2 + a^2}\,dx + a^2 \ln\left(x + \sqrt{x^2 + a^2}\right),$$

whence $\int \sqrt{x^2 + a^2}\,dx = \tfrac{1}{2}\left[x\sqrt{x^2 + a^2} + a^2 \ln\left(x + \sqrt{x^2 + a^2}\right)\right].$

EXERCISES

Find the values of the following integrals:

1. $\int xe^{2x}\,dx.$

2. $\int x^2 e^{3x}\,dx.$

3. $\int \cos^{-1} x\,dx.$

4. $\int \tan^{-1} x\,dx.$

5. $\int x \sin x\,dx.$

6. $\int x^2 \sin 2x\,dx.$

7. $\int x^2 \ln x\,dx.$

8. $\int x \cos^2 3x\,dx.$

9. $\int x^3 \tan^{-1} x\,dx.$

10. $\int x \sec^{-1} 2x\,dx.$

11. $\int x^2 \cos x\,dx.$

12. $\int (\ln \cos x) \sin x\,dx.$

81. Integration of rational fractions. A *rational fraction* is a fraction whose numerator and denominator are polynomials. It can often be integrated by expressing it as the sum of *partial fractions* whose denominators are factors of the denominator of the original fraction. We shall illustrate only the case in which the degree of the numerator is less than the degree of the denominator and in which the factors of the denominator are all different. If the degree of the numerator is equal to, or greater than, the degree of the denominator, the fraction should be reduced by division to a polynomial plus a fraction whose numerator is of lower degree than its denominator.

Example 1. Find the value of $\int \dfrac{x^2 + 11x + 14}{(x + 3)(x^2 - 4)}\,dx.$

The factors of the denominator are $x + 3$, $x - 2$, and $x + 2$. We assume

$$\frac{x^2 + 11x + 14}{(x + 3)(x^2 - 4)} = \frac{A}{x + 3} + \frac{B}{x - 2} + \frac{C}{x + 2}, \tag{1}$$

where A, B, and C are constants to be determined.

Clearing (1) of fractions by multiplying by $(x+3)(x^2-4)$, we have

$$x^2+11x+14=A(x-2)(x+2)+B(x+3)(x+2)+C(x+3)(x-2), \quad (2)$$

or

$$x^2+11x+14=(A+B+C)x^2+(5B+C)x+(-4A+6B-6C). \quad (3)$$

Since A, B, and C are to be determined so that the right-hand member of (3) shall be identical with the left-hand member, the coefficients of like powers of x on the two sides of the equation must be equal.

Therefore, equating the coefficients of like powers of x in (3), we obtain the equations

$$A+B+C=1,$$
$$5B+C=11,$$
$$-4A+6B-6C=14,$$

whence we find $A=-2$, $B=2$, $C=1$.

Substituting these values in (1), we have

$$\frac{x^2+11x+14}{(x+3)(x^2-4)}=-\frac{2}{x+3}+\frac{2}{x-2}+\frac{1}{x+2},$$

and

$$\int\frac{x^2+11x+14}{(x+3)(x^2-4)}\,dx=-\int\frac{2\,dx}{x+3}+\int\frac{2\,dx}{x-2}+\int\frac{dx}{x+2}$$

$$=-2\ln(x+3)+2\ln(x-2)+\ln(x+2)+C$$

$$=\ln\frac{(x+2)(x-2)^2}{(x+3)^2}+C.$$

Example 2. Find the value of $\int\frac{3x^2-4x-1}{x^3+1}\,dx$.

The factors of the denominator are $x+1$ and x^2-x+1. We assume

$$\frac{3x^2-4x-1}{x^3+1}=\frac{A}{x+1}+\frac{Bx+C}{x^2-x+1}. \quad (1)$$

Clearing of fractions and rearranging terms, we have

$$3x^2-4x-1=(A+B)x^2+(-A+B+C)x+(A+C). \quad (2)$$

Since A, B, and C are to be determined so that the right-hand member of (2) shall be identical with the left-hand member, the coefficients of like powers of x on the two sides of the equation must be equal.

Therefore we have

$$A+B=3,$$
$$-A+B+C=-4,$$
$$A+C=-1,$$

whence we find $A=2$, $B=1$, $C=-3$.

Hence $\int\frac{3x^2-4x-1}{x^3+1}\,dx=\int\frac{2\,dx}{x+1}+\int\frac{x-3}{x^2-x+1}\,dx.$

The value of the first integral is $2\ln(x+1)$. To evaluate the second integral we write

$$x^2 - x + 1 = (x^2 - x + \tfrac{1}{4}) + 1 - \tfrac{1}{4} = (x - \tfrac{1}{2})^2 + \tfrac{3}{4},$$

which suggests the substitution $u = x - \tfrac{1}{2}$. Then

$$\int \frac{x-3}{x^2-x+1}\,dx = \int \frac{u-\tfrac{5}{2}}{u^2+\tfrac{3}{4}}\,du = \int \frac{u\,du}{u^2+\tfrac{3}{4}} - \tfrac{5}{2}\int \frac{du}{u^2+\tfrac{3}{4}}$$

$$= \frac{1}{2}\ln\left(u^2+\frac{3}{4}\right) - \frac{5}{\sqrt{3}}\tan^{-1}\frac{2u}{\sqrt{3}}$$

$$= \frac{1}{2}\ln(x^2-x+1) - \frac{5}{\sqrt{3}}\tan^{-1}\frac{2x-1}{\sqrt{3}}.$$

We have finally

$$\int \frac{3x^2-4x-1}{x^3+1}\,dx = 2\ln(x+1) + \frac{1}{2}\ln(x^2-x+1) - \frac{5}{\sqrt{3}}\tan^{-1}\frac{2x-1}{\sqrt{3}}.$$

EXERCISES

Find the values of the following integrals:

1. $\int \dfrac{x+1}{2x^2+3x}\,dx.$

2. $\int \dfrac{8x+13}{6x^2+7x+2}\,dx.$

3. $\int \dfrac{6x^2+6}{6x^2-x-1}\,dx.$

4. $\int \dfrac{6x^3+3x^2-x+1}{2x^2+x-1}\,dx.$

5. $\int \dfrac{x^2+4x-4}{x^3-4x}\,dx.$

6. $\int \dfrac{4x+2}{x^3+2x^2-x-2}\,dx.$

7. $\int \dfrac{4x^3-6x-1}{2x^3-x^2-x}\,dx.$

8. $\int \dfrac{18x^3+20x^2-8x-8}{9x^3-4x}\,dx.$

9. $\int \dfrac{5x^2-x+4}{x^3-x^2+2x}\,dx.$

10. $\int \dfrac{5x^2+x-1}{8x^3-1}\,dx.$

82. Definite integrals. As shown in Chapter III,

$$\int_a^b f(x)\,dx = [F(x)+C]_a^b = [F(b)+C] - [F(a)+C]$$
$$= F(b) - F(a).$$

It appears that the constant of integration cancels out and may be omitted in evaluating a definite integral.

When a definite integral is evaluated by substitution it is usually desirable to change the limits to the values of the new variable which correspond to the values of the old variable.

Example 1. Find $\int_0^a \sqrt{a^2 - x^2}\,dx$.

Let $x = a \sin \phi$. The limits of the given integral are $x = 0$ and $x = a$. Substituting these values in the equation $x = a \sin \phi$, we find that when $x = 0$, $\phi = 0$; and when $x = a$, $\phi = \dfrac{\pi}{2}$, so that ϕ varies from 0 to $\dfrac{\pi}{2}$ as x varies from 0 to a. Accordingly,

$$\int_0^a \sqrt{a^2 - x^2}\,dx = a^2 \int_0^{\frac{\pi}{2}} \cos^2\phi\,d\phi$$
$$= \left[\frac{a^2}{2}\left(\phi + \frac{1}{2}\sin 2\,\phi\right)\right]_0^{\frac{\pi}{2}}$$
$$= \frac{\pi a^2}{4}.$$

When a definite integral is evaluated by integration by parts, the limits may be handled as follows:

If $f(x)\,dx$ is denoted by $u\,dv$, the definite integral $\int_a^b f(x)\,dx$ may be denoted by $\int_a^b u\,dv$, where it is understood that a and b are the values of the independent variable. Then

$$\int_a^b u\,dv = [uv]_a^b - \int_a^b v\,du.$$

To prove this, note that it follows at once from the equation

$$[uv]_a^b = \int_a^b d\,(uv) = \int_a^b (u\,dv + v\,du) = \int_a^b u\,dv + \int_a^b v\,du.$$

Example 2. $\displaystyle\int_0^{\frac{\pi}{2}} x^2 \sin x\,dx = \left[-x^2 \cos x\right]_0^{\frac{\pi}{2}} + 2\int_0^{\frac{\pi}{2}} x \cos x\,dx$

$$= 2\int_0^{\frac{\pi}{2}} x \cos x\,dx$$
$$= \left[2\,x \sin x\right]_0^{\frac{\pi}{2}} - 2\int_0^{\frac{\pi}{2}} \sin x\,dx$$
$$= \pi + \left[2 \cos x\right]_0^{\frac{\pi}{2}}$$
$$= \pi - 2.$$

A special difficulty occurs in evaluating a definite integral by (1) and (3), § 76, which involve inverse trigonometric functions. Consider in the first place

$$\int_a^b \frac{dx}{x^2 + 1} = [\tan^{-1} x]_a^b = \tan^{-1} b - \tan^{-1} a.$$

There is an ambiguity, since $\tan^{-1}a$ and $\tan^{-1}b$ have each an infinite number of values. Let us draw the curve $y = \tan^{-1}x$ (Fig. 98), which consists of an infinite number of separate parts, or *branches*. If we take $OM = a$, $\tan^{-1}a$ is the distance of any one of the points $P_1, P_2, P_3, \cdots$ from OX, distances which are represented by the lines MP_1, MP_2, MP_3, $\cdots$. In like manner, if we take $ON = b$, then $\tan^{-1}b$ is represented by any one of the lines $NQ_1, NQ_2, NQ_3, \cdots$. It follows that $\tan^{-1}b - \tan^{-1}a$ may be represented by the difference found by subtracting from any line representing $\tan^{-1}b$ any line representing $\tan^{-1}a$; and it is obvious that unless we choose

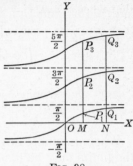

FIG. 98

$\tan^{-1}a$ and $\tan^{-1}b$ according to some system, we may get a great variety of values for our integral. It would seem reasonable to choose the values of $\tan^{-1}a$ and $\tan^{-1}b$ so that they may be represented by the ordinates of two points on the same branch of the curve. That this is correct may be shown as follows:

From the definition of a definite integral as given in § 23, if we hold a fixed and let b approach a as a limit, the value of the integral approaches zero as a limit. Accordingly whatever point Q is taken to determine $\tan^{-1}b$, it should approach the point P, which determines $\tan^{-1}a$, as ON approaches OM. Hence P and Q should be on the same branch of the curve. It is immaterial which branch of the curve is taken, and, for convenience, we shall always take the branch so that $\tan^{-1}a$ *and* $\tan^{-1}b$ *shall lie between* $-\dfrac{\pi}{2}$ *and* $\dfrac{\pi}{2}$.

Example 3. $\displaystyle\int_{-1}^{\sqrt{3}} \frac{dx}{x^2 + 1} = \tan^{-1}\sqrt{3} - \tan^{-1}(-1) = \frac{\pi}{3} - \left(-\frac{\pi}{4}\right) = \frac{7\,\pi}{12}.$

Let us now consider the integral

$$\int_a^b \frac{dx}{\sqrt{1 - x^2}} = \left[\sin^{-1}x\right]_a^b = \sin^{-1}b - \sin^{-1}a,$$

where we have the same kind of ambiguity as that just discussed. A similar discussion leads to a similar result; namely, $\sin^{-1}a$

and $\sin^{-1}b$ *must be taken between* $-\dfrac{\pi}{2}$ *and* $\dfrac{\pi}{2}$. This is also indicated by the fact, pointed out in § 76, that the formula of integration used is valid only when $\sin^{-1}\dfrac{x}{a}$ is in the first or the fourth quadrant.

Example 4. $\displaystyle\int_{-\frac{1}{2}}^{1}\frac{dx}{\sqrt{1-x^2}} = \sin^{-1}1 - \sin^{-1}\left(-\frac{1}{2}\right) = \frac{\pi}{2} - \left(-\frac{\pi}{6}\right) = \frac{2\pi}{3}$.

EXERCISES

Find the values of the following integrals:

1. $\displaystyle\int_{\frac{5}{4}}^{\frac{5}{3}}\frac{x\,dx}{(x^2-1)^{\frac{3}{2}}}$.

2. $\displaystyle\int_{1}^{3}\frac{(1+x^2)\,dx}{(3x+x^3)^{\frac{3}{2}}}$.

3. $\displaystyle\int_{0}^{\frac{\pi}{8}}\tan 2x\sec^3 2x\,dx$.

4. $\displaystyle\int_{0}^{2}\frac{dx}{\sqrt{4x-x^2}}$.

5. $\displaystyle\int_{-\frac{a}{2}}^{\frac{a}{2}}\frac{dx}{\sqrt{a^2-x^2}}$.

6. $\displaystyle\int_{-3}^{3}\frac{dx}{x^2+9}$.

7. $\displaystyle\int_{3}^{5}\frac{dx}{\sqrt{x^2-9}}$.

8. $\displaystyle\int_{0}^{1}x^2 e^{x^3}\,dx$.

9. $\displaystyle\int_{\frac{1}{3}}^{1}e^{3x-1}\,dx$.

10. $\displaystyle\int_{3}^{6}\frac{dx}{x\sqrt{x^3+9}}$.

11. $\displaystyle\int_{2}^{\sqrt[3]{15}}\frac{x^5}{(x^3+1)^{\frac{3}{2}}}\,dx$.

12. $\displaystyle\int_{3\sqrt{2}}^{6}\frac{dx}{x^2\sqrt{x^2-9}}$.

13. $\displaystyle\int_{\frac{2}{3}}^{\frac{4}{3\sqrt{3}}}\frac{\sqrt{9x^2-4}}{x^4}\,dx$.

14. $\displaystyle\int_{1}^{\sqrt{3}}\frac{dx}{(x^2+1)^{\frac{5}{2}}}$.

15. $\displaystyle\int_{\sqrt{3}}^{3\sqrt{3}}\frac{dx}{x^2\sqrt{x^2+9}}$.

16. $\displaystyle\int_{0}^{1}\frac{x^4\,dx}{(2-x^2)^{\frac{7}{2}}}$.

17. $\displaystyle\int_{0}^{2}(4-x^2)^{\frac{3}{2}}\,dx$.

18. $\displaystyle\int_{2}^{5}\frac{x^2\,dx}{\sqrt{x-1}}$.

19. $\displaystyle\int_{2}^{7}\frac{x\,dx}{\sqrt[4]{3x-5}}$.

20. $\displaystyle\int_{\frac{1}{2}}^{1}\frac{\ln 2x}{x^2}\,dx$.

21. $\displaystyle\int_{0}^{\frac{\pi}{4}}x\sin 2x\,dx$.

22. $\displaystyle\int_{1}^{2}x(\ln x)^2\,dx$.

83. Table of integrals. Much time and labor in integration may be saved by using a table in which are collected those formulas of integration which are frequently required in the applications of the calculus. In order that the student may become familiar with the use of such a table, a brief one has been placed at the end of this text. In it we have collected the formulas of integration already used in this chapter and have added a few others which may be derived from them by substitutions or by integration by parts. In all cases they can be verified by differentiating both sides of the equation.

It will be noticed that some of the formulas express the given integral only in terms of a simpler integral.

It will often happen that the integral to be evaluated is exactly like one of the formulas of the table; in such cases the integral can be written down immediately. In other cases, it will be necessary, as in the previous work, to choose some function of the variable for x or u and make the corresponding transformation.

GENERAL EXERCISES

Find the values of the following integrals:

1. $\int \dfrac{x^5}{x^2+1}\,dx.$

2. $\int \dfrac{4\,x+3}{x^2+3}\,dx.$

3. $\int \dfrac{dx}{2\,x^2-x+1}.$

4. $\int \dfrac{dx}{3\,x^2+2\,x-1}.$

5. $\int \dfrac{2\,x+2}{x^2+x+3}\,dx.$

6. $\int \dfrac{4\,x+5}{2\,x^2+3\,x+5}\,dx.$

7. $\int \dfrac{3\,x+4}{6\,x^2+6\,x-5}\,dx.$

8. $\int \dfrac{3\,x+2}{2\,x^2-x+1}\,dx.$

9. $\int \dfrac{dx}{\sqrt{6\,x-x^2}}.$

10. $\int \dfrac{dx}{\sqrt{2\,x^2+4\,x-5}}.$

11. $\int \dfrac{dx}{\sqrt{1-2\,x-2\,x^2}}.$

12. $\int \dfrac{dx}{\sqrt{3\,x^2-2\,x-1}}.$

13. $\int \dfrac{3\,x-5}{\sqrt{3\,x^2+2\,x+1}}\,dx.$

14. $\int \dfrac{3\,x+7}{\sqrt{1-4\,x-5\,x^2}}\,dx.$

15. $\int \dfrac{x+5}{\sqrt{2+2\,x-3\,x^2}}\,dx.$

16. $\int \dfrac{3\,x+2}{8\,x^2+24\,x+15}\,dx.$

17. $\int \cos^3 \dfrac{x}{3}\,dx.$

18. $\int \csc^4 \dfrac{x}{6}\,dx.$

19. $\int \sin^3(2\,x+3)\cos^2(2\,x+3)\,dx.$

20. $\int \sec^3(x+3)\tan^3(x+3)\,dx$

21. $\int \dfrac{\sin x}{\cos 2\,x}\,dx.$

22. $\int \left(\tan \dfrac{x}{2}-\operatorname{ctn}\dfrac{x}{2}\right)^2 dx.$

23. $\int \dfrac{1+\cos 6\,x}{1-\cos 6\,x}\,dx.$

24. $\int \dfrac{\sin 4\,x}{\sin 2\,x}\,dx.$

25. $\int \dfrac{\cos 8\,x}{\cos 4\,x+\sin 4\,x}\,dx.$

26. $\int \left(\dfrac{\sin 2\,x}{\cos x}+\dfrac{\cos 2\,x}{\sin x}\right) dx.$

27. $\int \dfrac{dx}{1 + \cos 4\,x}.$

28. $\int \dfrac{\sin 4\,x}{\cos x}\,dx.$

29. $\int \sqrt{1 - \sin 4\,x}\,dx.$

30. $\int \dfrac{2\,x - 5}{(x - 2)^2}\,dx.$

31. $\int x^2 (2\,x + 3)^{\frac{1}{2}}\,dx.$

32. $\int \dfrac{dx}{x^2 \sqrt{9 - x^2}}.$

33. $\int \dfrac{dx}{x^2 (x^2 + 4)^2}.$

34. $\int \dfrac{x\,dx}{(3\,x - 2)^{\frac{3}{4}}}.$

35. $\int \dfrac{x^5\,dx}{(x^3 + 1)^{\frac{1}{3}}}.$

36. $\int \dfrac{\sqrt{2 - x^2}}{x^2}\,dx.$

37. $\int \dfrac{(4\,x^2 + 1)^{\frac{3}{2}}}{x^6}\,dx.$

38. $\int \dfrac{x^5\,dx}{(1 + x^3)^{\frac{1}{2}}}.$

39. $\int \dfrac{x^4\,dx}{(5 - x^2)^{\frac{5}{2}}}.$

40. $\int \dfrac{x^4\,dx}{(4\,x^2 - 1)^{\frac{7}{2}}}.$

41. $\int \dfrac{x^7\,dx}{\sqrt{x^4 + 4}}.$

42. $\int \dfrac{x^2\,dx}{(9\,x^2 + 4)^{\frac{3}{2}}}.$

43. $\int xe^{\frac{x}{3}}\,dx.$

44. $\int x^2 \ln 3\,x\,dx.$

45. $\int x^2 \tan^{-1} x\,dx.$

46. $\int \dfrac{2\,x - 11}{2\,x^2 - x - 6}\,dx.$

47. $\int \dfrac{3\,x^3 + 2\,x^2 - 5\,x - 2}{3\,x^2 - 4\,x}\,dx.$

48. $\int \dfrac{2 - 3\,x + 16\,x^2}{4\,x^3 - 8\,x^2 - x + 2}\,dx.$

49. $\int \dfrac{3\,x^2 + 4\,x - 23}{x^3 + x^2 - 9\,x - 9}\,dx.$

50. $\int \dfrac{2\,x^3 + x^2 - 12\,x - 18}{x^3 - 9\,x}\,dx.$

51. $\int \dfrac{1 - x - x^2}{x^3 + x^2 + x}\,dx.$

52. $\int_{-1}^{1} \dfrac{x^2\,dx}{x + 2}.$

53. $\int_{0}^{\frac{\pi}{2}} \dfrac{\cos x\,dx}{1 + \sin x}.$

54. $\int_{0}^{\frac{\pi}{2}} \sqrt{1 + 3\tan \dfrac{x}{2}}\,\sec^2 \dfrac{x}{2}\,dx.$

55. $\int_{-2}^{0} \dfrac{dx}{x^2 + 4}.$

56. $\int_{2}^{3} \dfrac{dx}{4\,x^2 - 9}.$

57. $\int_{0}^{1} \dfrac{dx}{\sqrt{4\,x^2 + 1}}.$

58. $\int_{\frac{\pi}{2}}^{\pi} \sin^3 \dfrac{x}{3}\,dx.$

59. $\int_{0}^{\frac{\pi}{2}} \sqrt{1 - \cos 2\,x}\,\cos x\,dx.$

60. $\int_{-\frac{\pi}{4}}^{\frac{\pi}{4}} \sin^2 \left(\dfrac{x}{2} + \dfrac{\pi}{4}\right) dx.$

61. $\int_{0}^{\frac{\pi}{2}} \sin x \sin 2\,x\,dx.$

62. $\int_{\frac{\pi}{12}}^{\frac{\pi}{6}} (1 + \cos 6\,x)^{\frac{3}{2}}\,dx.$

63. $\int_{0}^{\frac{\pi}{4}} \cos^6 x\,dx.$

64. $\int_{0}^{\frac{\pi}{9}} \dfrac{dx}{\sqrt{1 + \cos 3\,x}}.$

65. $\int_{2}^{\frac{11}{2}} x \sqrt[3]{2\,x - 3}\,dx.$

66. $\int_{\frac{3}{5}}^{\frac{4}{5}} \dfrac{x^3\,dx}{(1 - x^2)^{\frac{5}{2}}}.$

67. $\int_{1}^{\sqrt{3}} \dfrac{dx}{x^2 (4 - x^2)^{\frac{3}{2}}}.$

68. $\int_{-1}^{1} x^2 \sqrt{2 - x^2}\,dx.$

69. $\int_{1}^{2} \dfrac{x^4\,dx}{(x^5 + 3)^{\frac{3}{2}}}.$

70. $\int_{1}^{\sqrt{3}} \dfrac{dx}{x^2 (x^2 + 1)^{\frac{3}{2}}}.$

71. $\int_{1}^{2} \dfrac{\sqrt{x^2 - 1}}{x}\,dx.$

72. $\int_{\frac{3}{4}}^{\frac{4}{3}} \dfrac{dx}{x \sqrt{x^2 + 1}}.$

73. $\int_{0}^{\frac{1}{3}} \cos^{-1} 3\,x\,dx.$

74. $\int_{0}^{\frac{\pi}{2}} x^2 \sin x\,dx.$

75. $\int_{\frac{1}{4}}^{\frac{1}{2}} \sin^{-1} 2\,x\,dx.$

CHAPTER XI

APPLICATIONS

84. Fundamental theorem. In Chapter III we have solved certain problems involving areas, pressures, and volumes by use of the definite integral. The general method used in each case was to analyze the problem into the limit of the sum of an infinite number of terms of the form $f(x_i)\Delta x$, where Δx is an increment of x which is taken as positive and may be replaced by dx when x is the independent variable. We made use of the following formula, derived in § 22,

$$\underset{n \to \infty}{\text{Lim}} \sum_{i=0}^{i=n-1} f(x_i)\Delta x = \int_a^b f(x)dx, \tag{1}$$

which is the *fundamental theorem of integral calculus*.

The term $f(x)dx$, as well as the concrete object it represents, is called the element of the sum or the element of integration. In each problem we first found this element of integration and then proceeded to the integration.

We now wish to extend this method to a larger type of problems. Before doing this, however, certain theoretical questions need to be considered.

In finding the element of integration, it is often not possible to express the terms of the sum (1) exactly as $f(x_i)\Delta x$, the more exact expression being $[f(x_i) + \epsilon_i]\Delta x$, where the quantities ϵ_i are not fully determined but are known to approach zero as a limit as Δx approaches zero. It is consequently of the highest importance to show that

$$\underset{n \to \infty}{\text{Lim}} \sum_{i=0}^{i=n-1} \epsilon_i \, \Delta x = 0,$$

so that

$$\underset{n \to \infty}{\text{Lim}} \sum_{i=0}^{i=n-1} [f(x_i) + \epsilon_i]\Delta x = \underset{n \to \infty}{\text{Lim}} \sum_{i=0}^{i=n-1} f(x_i)\Delta x = \int_a^b f(x)dx.$$

For that purpose, let γ be a positive quantity which is equal to the largest numerical value of any ϵ_i in the sum. Then

$$- \gamma \gtreqless \epsilon_i \gtreqless \gamma$$

and
$$- \Sigma\gamma\,\Delta x \gtreqless \Sigma\epsilon_i\,\Delta x \gtreqless \Sigma\gamma\,\Delta x.$$

But
$$\Sigma\gamma\,\Delta x = \gamma\Sigma\,\Delta x = \gamma(b - a)$$

and $\underset{n \to \infty}{\text{Lim}}\ \Sigma\gamma\,\Delta x = 0$ since γ approaches zero as Δx approaches zero. Hence $\underset{n \to \infty}{\text{Lim}}\ \overset{i = n-1}{\underset{i=0}{\Sigma}}\epsilon_i\,\Delta x = 0$.

Hence the quantities ϵ_i which may appear in expressing the sum do not affect the value of the integral and may be omitted.

Quantities such as Δx and ϵ_i, which approach zero as a limit, are called *infinitesimals*. Terms such as $f(x)\Delta x$, which are formed by multiplying Δx by a finite quantity, not zero, are called infinitesimals of the same order as Δx. Quantities such as $\epsilon_i\,\Delta x$, which are the products of two infinitesimals approaching zero together, are called *infinitesimals of higher order* than either infinitesimal.

The theorem above proved may be restated in the following way:

In forming the element of integration infinitesimals of higher order than $f(x)\Delta x$ may be disregarded.

For example, consider the area under a curve considered in § 22, Fig. 24. We have obtained the area by considering it as the limit of the sum of the areas of rectangles each of which has the area $y\,\Delta x$. Suppose that in place of rectangles we should use trapezoids formed by drawing chords DP_1, P_1P_2, etc. (Fig. 24). The parallel sides of one of these trapezoids are, respectively, y and $y + \Delta y$, and hence its area is $y\,\Delta x + \frac{1}{2}\,\Delta y\,\Delta x$. The term $\frac{1}{2}\,\Delta y\,\Delta x$ is an infinitesimal of higher order than $y\,\Delta x$ and our theorem asserts that no error is made in neglecting it in finding the limit of the sum. In fact it is geometrically evident that the limit of the sum of the areas of the trapezoids is the same as the limit of the sum of the areas of the rectangles.

85. Infinite limits or integrand. There are cases in which it may seem to be necessary to use infinity for one or both of the limits of a definite integral, or in which the integrand becomes infinite. We shall restrict the discussion of these cases to the solution of the following illustrative examples:

Example 1. Find the area bounded by the curve $y = \dfrac{1}{x^2}$ (Fig. 99), the axis of x, and the ordinate $x = 1$.

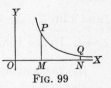

It is seen that the curve has the axis of x as an asymptote; and hence, strictly speaking, the required area is not completely bounded, since the curve and its asymptote do not intersect. Accordingly, in Fig. 99 let $OM = 1$ and $ON = b(b > 1)$ and draw the ordinates MP and NQ. Then

Fig. 99

$$\text{Area } MNQP = \int_1^b \frac{dx}{x^2} = \left[-\frac{1}{x}\right]_1^b = 1 - \frac{1}{b}.$$

If the value of b is increased, the boundary line NQ moves to the right; and the greater b becomes, the nearer the area approaches unity.

We may, accordingly, define the area bounded by the curve, the axis of x, and the ordinate $x = 1$ as the limit of the area $MNQP$ as b increases indefinitely, and denote it by the symbol

$$\int_1^\infty \frac{dx}{x^2} = \operatorname*{Lim}_{b \to \infty} \int_1^b \frac{dx}{x^2} = 1.$$

Example 2. Find the area bounded by the curve $y = \dfrac{1}{\sqrt{a^2 - x^2}}$ (Fig. 100), the axis of x, and the ordinates $x = 0$ and $x = a$.

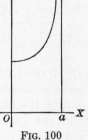

Since the line $x = a$ is an asymptote of the curve, $y \to \infty$ when $x \to a$; furthermore, the area is not, strictly speaking, bounded. We may, however, find the area bounded on the right by the ordinate $x = a - h$, where h is a small quantity, with the result

$$\int_0^{a-h} \frac{dx}{\sqrt{a^2 - x^2}} = \left[\sin^{-1} \frac{x}{a}\right]_0^{a-h} = \sin^{-1} \frac{a - h}{a}.$$

If $h \to 0$, $\quad \sin^{-1} \dfrac{a - h}{a} \to \sin^{-1} 1 = \dfrac{\pi}{2}.$

Hence we may regard $\dfrac{\pi}{2}$ as the value of the area required, and express it by the integral

Fig. 100

$$\int_0^a \frac{dx}{\sqrt{a^2 - x^2}} = \operatorname*{Lim}_{h \to 0} \int_0^{a-h} \frac{dx}{\sqrt{a^2 - x^2}} = \frac{\pi}{2}.$$

Example 3. Find the value of $\int_1^\infty \dfrac{dx}{\sqrt{x}}$.

Proceeding as in Example 1, we place

$$\int_1^\infty \frac{dx}{\sqrt{x}} = \operatorname*{Lim}_{b \to \infty} \int_1^b \frac{dx}{\sqrt{x}}.$$

But $\qquad \int_1^b \dfrac{dx}{\sqrt{x}} = \left[2\,\sqrt{x}\,\right]_1^b = 2\,\sqrt{b} - 2,$

an expression which increases indefinitely as $b \to \infty$; hence the given integral has no finite value.

We accordingly conclude that in each case we must determine a limit, and that the problem has no solution if we cannot find a limit.

86. Element of integration. We shall collect in this section under the headings Area, Pressure, and Volume some of the elements of integration which are useful in determining those quantities. Some of these elements have already been used in previous sections, and some of them are derived here for the first time in this text.

Area. Let the required area (Fig. 101) be bounded below by the curve $y = f_1(x)$ and above by the curve $y = f_2(x)$, where $f_2(x) > f_1(x)$. To form elements of area we draw a series of straight lines parallel to OY and dx apart, and form a series of rectangles such as P_1P_2RS. If we denote MP_2 by y_2 and MP_1 by y_1,

FIG. 101

the length P_1P_2 of this rectangle is $y_2 - y_1$, and its width is dx. Hence, if the area of such a rectangle is taken as the element of area dA, $\quad dA = (y_2 - y_1)dx = [f_2(x) - f_1(x)]\,dx.$ \hfill (1)

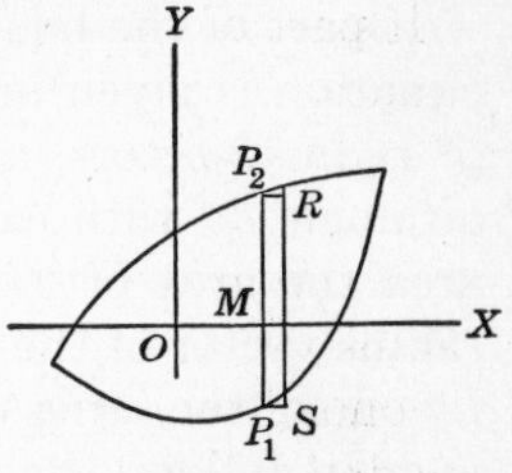

If one of the boundary curves is replaced by the axis of x, and the equation of the other curve is $y = f(x)$, we can form, as in § 22, a similar series of elementary rectangles having one end on OX and have as a special case of (1) the formula

$$dA = y\,dx = f(x)dx. \tag{2}$$

In (1) and (2) we assume that dx is positive. Then in (1), dA is always positive; in (2), however, dA is positive where the axis of x is the lower boundary, and is negative where the axis of x is the upper boundary, of the required area.

Similarly, if the required area is bounded on the left by the curve $x = f_1(y)$, and on the right by the curve $x = f_2(y)$, we may form the elementary rectangles of area by drawing a series of straight lines parallel to OX and dy apart. With this construction the area of any rectangle is $(x_2 - x_1)dy$, where x_1 and x_2 are the respective values of x for the points of the two curves in which they are intersected by one of the series of parallel lines. Hence

$$dA = (x_2 - x_1)dy = [f_2(y) - f_1(y)]dy. \tag{3}$$

As a special case of (3) we have the formula

$$dA = x\, dy = f(y)dy, \tag{4}$$

when one of the curves coincides with the axis of y.

In (3) and (4) we assume that dy is positive. Then in (3) dA is always positive; in (4), however, dA is positive where the axis of y is the left-hand boundary, and is negative where the axis of y is the right-hand boundary.

If part of the boundary of the required area is a curve whose equation is given in polar coördinates, we draw (§ 63) a series of radius vectors, any two consecutive radius vectors making an angle $d\theta$ with each other. We then take as the element of area the area of a sector of circle of radius r, where r is the radius vector of the point of the curve at which it is intersected by one of the series of radius vectors. As the angle of the sector is $d\theta$, it follows that

$$dA = \tfrac{1}{2}\, r^2\, d\theta. \tag{5}$$

Or we may proceed as follows if the equation of the boundary curve is in polar coördinates. We may divide the required area up into circular rings by drawing a series of concentric circles having their common center at the origin O, the radii of two consecutive circles differing by Δr (Fig. 102).

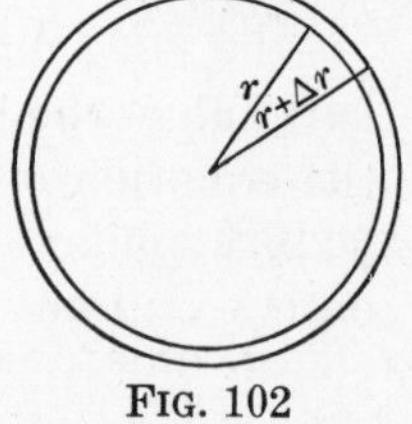

Then the area of such a ring is

$$\pi(r + \Delta r)^2 - \pi r^2 = 2\,\pi r\,\Delta r + \pi\,\Delta r^2$$
$$= 2\,\pi r\,\Delta r + \epsilon\,\Delta r,$$

FIG. 102

where $\epsilon = \pi \Delta r$ and is hence an infinitesimal since it vanishes when Δr vanishes.

By the theorem of § 84,

$$\text{Lim}_{n \to \infty} \sum_{i=0}^{i=n-1} (2\pi r_i + \epsilon_i)\Delta r = \text{Lim}_{n \to \infty} \sum_{i=0}^{i=n-1} 2\pi r_i \, \Delta r.$$

Hence we may take as the element of area a circular ring of this type and let

$$dA = 2 \, \pi r \, dr. \tag{6}$$

Pressure. To find the hydrostatic pressure on any vertical plane area, we may draw a series of straight lines across the area parallel to the surface of the liquid (§ 24), each pair of consecutive lines being at an infinitesimal distance apart. We can then form a series of infinitesimal rectangles of area dA with their long sides parallel to the surface of the liquid. Then if h is the depth of either of the long sides below the surface of the liquid and w is the weight of a unit volume of the liquid, we have the element of pressure dP given by the formula

$$dP = hw \, dA. \tag{7}$$

Another method is to draw a series of straight lines (Fig. 103) perpendicular to the surface of the liquid MN, each pair of consecutive lines being an infinitesimal distance apart, and let

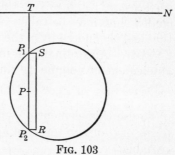

FIG. 103

dA be the area of an infinitesimal rectangle such as P_1P_2RS. It is easy to show that the pressure on any rectangle is equal to its area multiplied by w and the depth of its middle point (see Ex. 24, p. 77). If $TP_1 = h_1$ and $TP_2 = h_2$, and P is the middle point of P_1P_2, then $TP = \frac{1}{2}(h_1 + h_2)$.

Hence the element of pressure dP is given, in this method, by the formula

$$dP = \frac{1}{2}(h_1 + h_2)w \, dA. \tag{8}$$

To evaluate either (7) or (8) it is necessary to express both h and dA in terms of the same variable.

Volume. To form an element of volume, dV, we pass through the solid a series of planes (§ 25) all perpendicular to some chosen straight line, each pair of consecutive planes being at an infinitesimal distance apart. As these planes are parallel, they cut the given solid up into slices of infinitesimal thickness. Let A represent the area of either face of a slice. Let h represent the distance of the face of the slice from some chosen fixed point on the straight line to which all the cutting planes are perpendicular. Then the thickness of a slice may be denoted by dh, and the volume of the slice is approximately $A\, dh$. Accurately speaking, $A\, dh$ is the volume of a solid of base A and sides of length dh perpendicular to the base, but the volumes of this solid and the slice differ by an infinitesimal of higher order. Hence we take the slice as the element of volume dV and let

$$dV = A\, dh. \tag{9}$$

If we are to carry out the work by evaluating a definite integral, we must be able to express A in terms of h, or both of them in terms of a third variable.

Another element of volume may be found as follows: Through the solid pass a series of right circular cylinders having a common axis. These cylindrical surfaces divide the solid up into cylindrical shells. If the radii of two consecutive cylindrical surfaces are r and $r + dr$, the area of the cross section of the included shell may be taken by (6) as $2\,\pi r\, dr$. If the altitude of the shell is denoted by h, the volume of the shell is approximately $2\,\pi rh\, dr$. Accordingly we may take such a cylindrical shell as an element of volume dV and write

$$dV = 2\,\pi rh\, dr. \tag{10}$$

To use this element of volume it is necessary to express h in terms of r, or r in terms of h, or both r and h in terms of a third variable.

The use of some of these elements is illustrated in the following examples:

Example 1. Find the area of the ellipse $\dfrac{x^2}{a^2} + \dfrac{y^2}{b^2} = 1$.

It is evident from the symmetry of the curve (Fig. 104) that one fourth of the required area is bounded by the axis of y, the axis of x, and the curve.

Constructing the rectangle $MNQP$ as the element of area dA, we have

$$dA = y\,dx = \frac{b}{a}\sqrt{a^2 - x^2}\,dx.$$

Hence

$$A = 4\int_0^a \frac{b}{a}\sqrt{a^2 - x^2}\,dx$$

$$= \frac{2}{a}\frac{b}{a}\left[x\sqrt{a^2 - x^2} + a^2\sin^{-1}\frac{x}{a}\right]_0^a$$

$$= \pi ab.$$

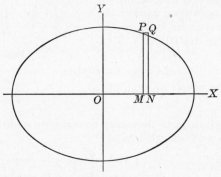

Fig. 104

Example 2. Let the ellipse of Example 1 be represented by the equations

$$x = a\cos\phi, \qquad y = b\sin\phi.$$

Using the same element of area, and expressing y and dx in terms of ϕ, we have

$$dA = (b\sin\phi)(-a\sin\phi\,d\phi)$$

$$= -ab\sin^2\phi\,d\phi.$$

As x varies from 0 to a, ϕ varies from $\frac{\pi}{2}$ to 0;

hence

$$A = 4\int_0^a y\,dx = -4\int_{\frac{\pi}{2}}^0 ab\sin^2\phi\,d\phi.$$

It is evident from formula (1), § 23, that the sign of a definite integral is changed by interchanging the limits. Hence

$$A = 4\,ab\int_0^{\frac{\pi}{2}}\sin^2\phi\,d\phi$$

$$= 4\,ab\left[\frac{\phi}{2} - \frac{\sin 2\phi}{4}\right]_0^{\frac{\pi}{2}} = \pi ab.$$

Example 3. Find the area bounded by the axis of x, the parabola $y^2 = kx$, and the straight line $y + 2x - k = 0$ (Fig. 105).

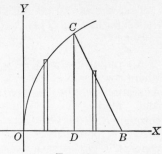

The straight line and the parabola intersect at the point $C\left(\dfrac{k}{4}, \dfrac{k}{2}\right)$, and the straight line intersects OX at $B\left(\dfrac{k}{2}, 0\right)$. Draw CD perpendicular to OX. If we construct the elements of area as in Example 1, they will be of different form according as they are to the left or to the right of the line CD; for on the left of CD we shall have

Fig. 105

$$dA = y\,dx = k^{\frac{1}{2}}x^{\frac{1}{2}}\,dx,$$

and on the right of CD we shall have

$$dA = y\,dx = (k - 2\,x)dx.$$

It will, accordingly, be necessary to compute separately the areas ODC and DBC and take their sum.

$$\text{Area } ODC = \int_0^{\frac{k}{4}} k^{\frac{1}{2}}x^{\frac{1}{2}}\,dx = \left[\tfrac{2}{3}\,k^{\frac{1}{2}}x^{\frac{3}{2}}\right]_0^{\frac{k}{4}} = \tfrac{1}{12}\,k^2.$$

$$\text{Area } DBC = \int_{\frac{k}{4}}^{\frac{k}{2}} (k - 2\,x)dx = \left[kx - x^2\right]_{\frac{k}{4}}^{\frac{k}{2}} = \tfrac{1}{16}\,k^2.$$

Hence the required area is $\tfrac{7}{48}\,k^2$. It is to be noted that the area DBC, since it is that of a right triangle, could have been found by the formulas of plane geometry; for the altitude $DC = \dfrac{k}{2}$ and the base $DB = \dfrac{k}{2} - \dfrac{k}{4} = \dfrac{k}{4}$, and hence the area $= \dfrac{k^2}{16}$.

Or we may construct the element of area as shown in Fig. 106.

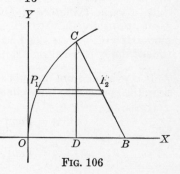

Then, if x_1 and x_2 are the abscissas, respectively, of P_1 and P_2,

$$dA = (x_2 - x_1)dy = \left(\dfrac{k - y}{2} - \dfrac{y^2}{k}\right)dy.$$

Hence

$$A = \int_0^{\frac{k}{2}} \left(\dfrac{k - y}{2} - \dfrac{y^2}{k}\right)dy$$

$$= \left[\dfrac{ky}{2} - \dfrac{y^2}{4} - \dfrac{y^3}{3\,k}\right]_0^{\frac{k}{2}} = \dfrac{7}{48}\,k^2.$$

Fig. 106

Example 4. Find the volume of the ring solid generated by revolving a circle of radius a about an axis in its plane b units from its center ($b > a$).

Take the axis of revolution as OY (Fig. 107) and the line through the center as OX. Then the equation of the circle is

$$(x - b)^2 + y^2 = a^2.$$

A straight line parallel to OX meets the circle in two points: P_1, where $x = x_1 = b - \sqrt{a^2 - y^2}$, and P_2, where $x = x_2 = b + \sqrt{a^2 - y^2}$.

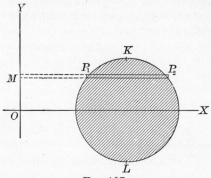

A section of the required solid made by a plane through P_1P_2 perpendicular to OY is bounded by two concentric circles with radii $MP_1 = x_1$ and $MP_2 = x_2$ respectively. Hence

$$dV = (\pi x_2{}^2 - \pi x_1{}^2)dy$$
$$= 4\ \pi b \sqrt{a^2 - y^2}\, dy.$$

The summation extends from the point L, where $y = -a$, to the point K, where $y = a$. On account of

FIG. 107

symmetry, however, we may take twice the integral from $y = 0$ to $y = a$. Hence

$$V = 2 \int_0^a 4\ \pi b \sqrt{a^2 - y^2}\, dy = 2\ \pi^2 a^2 b.$$

Example 5. Find the volume of a hemisphere of radius a by use of formula (10).

Let a quarter of the hemisphere be represented in Fig. 108. Let OX be perpendicular to the base of the hemisphere at its middle point O. Let $P_1R_1S_1T_1$ and $P_2R_2S_2T_2$ be quarters of right circular cylinders of radii r and $r + dr$, respectively, with OX as a common axis. If P_1T_1 is taken as the altitude of the cylindrical shell thus formed,

$$P_1T_1 = \sqrt{a^2 - r^2},$$

since $OT_1 = a$, $OP_1 = r$, and $OP_1T_1 = 90°$.

Hence $dV = 2\ \pi r \sqrt{a^2 - r^2}\, dr,$

and $\qquad V = \int_0^a 2\ \pi r \sqrt{a^2 - r^2}\, dr$

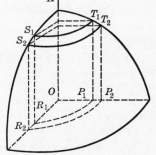

FIG. 108

$$= \left[-\frac{2\ \pi}{3} (a^2 - r^2)^{\frac{3}{2}} \right]_0^a = \frac{2}{3}\ \pi a^3.$$

1. Find the area of one of the closed figures bounded by the curves $y^2 = 9\,x$ and $y^2 = x^3$.

2. Find the area bounded by the curve $y^2 = 4(x - 2)$ and the line $2\,x - 3\,y = 0$.

3. Find the area between the axis of x and one arch of the cycloid $x = a(\phi - \sin \phi)$, $y = a(1 - \cos \phi)$. *p. 267*

4. Find the area bounded by the hyperbola $xy = 16$ and the line $x + y - 10 = 0$.

5. Find the total area bounded by the curve $4\,y^2 = 9\,x^2 - x^4$.

6. Find the area bounded by the parabola $x^2 = 4\,ay$ and the curve $y = \dfrac{8\,a^3}{x^2 + 4\,a^2}$.

7. Find the total area bounded by the curve $r = a(1 - \cos 2\,\theta)$.

8. Find the area of that part of the circle $r = 8 \cos \theta$ which is outside the circle $r = 4$.

9. Find the total area bounded by the curve $r = 4 + 2 \cos 3\,\theta$.

10. Find the area inside the curve $r = 5 + 3 \cos 2\,\theta$ which is outside the circle $r = 5$.

11. Find the area inside the circle $r = a \cos \theta$ and outside the curve $r = a(1 - \cos \theta)$.

12. Find the area inside the curve $r = 1 + 2 \cos \theta$ which is outside the small loop of that curve.

13. Find the volume of the solid formed by revolving about OX the area bounded by OX, OY, and the curve $x^{\frac{1}{2}} + y^{\frac{1}{2}} = a^{\frac{1}{2}}$.

14. The area bounded by the ellipse $x^2 + 4\,y^2 = 16$ is revolved about the line $x + 4 = 0$ as an axis. Find the volume of the solid generated.

15. Find the volume of the solid formed by revolving about the axis of x the area in the first quadrant bounded by OY and the curves $y = 8 - 2\,x^2$ and $y = 4\,x^2$.

16. Find the volume of the solid generated by revolving about the line $x = 4$ as an axis the area bounded by the line $x = 4$ and the hyperbola $9\,x^2 - 4\,y^2 = 36$.

17. The section of a certain solid made by any plane perpendicular to OX is a square with the ends of one diagonal on the hyperbola $4\,x^2 - 9\,y^2 = 36$. Find the volume of this solid between the planes perpendicular to OX at the points for which $x = 3$ and $x = 6$.

18. The section of a given solid made by any plane perpendicular to OX is an equilateral triangle with the ends of one of its sides on the curve $y^2 = 9 x^2 - x^4$. Find the total volume of the solid.

19. The surface of the water in a given reservoir is 8 ft. above the bottom of the dam. In the side of the dam is a semicircular gate of 2 ft. radius, the diameter of the semicircle being on a level with the bottom of the dam. What is the pressure on the gate?

20. A gasoline tank is in the form of a right circular cylinder of radius 2 ft., with its axis horizontal. Find the pressure on one end in terms of w, the weight of a cubic foot of gasoline, when the gasoline is 3 ft. deep in the tank.

21. The vertical end of a given water tank is in the form of a parabolic segment, the base of which is horizontal and 4 ft. long, and the vertex of which is 2 ft. below the base. Determine the pressure on the end of the tank: (1) when the tank is full; (2) when the surface of the water is 1 ft. below the top of the tank.

87. Mean value of a function. Let $f(x)$ be any function of x, and let $y = f(x)$ be represented by the curve AB (Fig. 109), where $OM = a$ and $ON = b$. Take the points $M_1, M_2, \cdots, M_{n-1}$ so as to divide the distance MN into n *equal* parts, each equal to dx; then $b - a = n\,dx$. At the points $M, M_1, M_2, \cdots, M_{n-1}$ erect the ordinates $y_0, y_1, y_2, \cdots, y_{n-1}$. Then the average, or mean, value of these n ordinates is

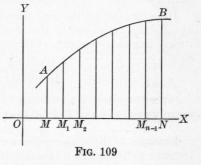

FIG. 109

$$\frac{y_0 + y_1 + y_2 + \cdots + y_{n-1}}{n}.$$

This fraction is equal to

$$\frac{(y_0 + y_1 + y_2 + \cdots + y_{n-1})dx}{n\,dx} = \frac{y_0\,dx + y_1\,dx + y_2\,dx + \cdots + y_{n-1}\,dx}{b - a}.$$

If n is indefinitely increased, this expression approaches as a limit the value

$$\frac{1}{b - a}\int_a^b f(x)dx.$$

This is evidently the mean value of an "infinite number" of values of the function $f(x)$ taken at equal distances between the values $x = a$ and $x = b$. It is called the *mean value* of the function for that interval.

If we now draw the ordinate NB, the integral

$$\int_a^b f(x)dx$$

is graphically represented by the area $MNBA$. Hence the mean value of the function is graphically represented by the altitude of a rectangle with the base MN which has the same area as $MNBA$.

We see from the above discussion that the average of the function y depends upon the variable x of which the equal intervals dx are taken, and we say that the function is averaged with respect to x. If the function can also be averaged with respect to some other variable which is divided into equal parts, the result may be different. This is illustrated in the examples which follow.

Example 1. Find the mean velocity of a body falling from rest during the time t_1 if the velocity is averaged with respect to the time.

Here we imagine the time from 0 to t_1 divided into equal intervals dt and the velocities at the beginning of each interval averaged. Proceeding as in the text, we find, since $v = gt$, that the mean velocity equals

$$\frac{1}{t_1 - 0}\int_0^{t_1} gt\, dt = \tfrac{1}{2}\, gt_1.$$

Since the velocity is gt_1 when $t = t_1$, it appears that in this case the mean velocity is half the final velocity.

Example 2. Find the mean velocity of a body falling from rest through a distance s_1 if the velocity is averaged with respect to the distance.

Here we imagine the distance from 0 to s_1 divided into equal intervals ds and the velocities at the beginning of each interval averaged. Proceeding as in the text, we find, since $v = \sqrt{2\, gs}$, that the mean velocity is

$$\frac{1}{s_1 - 0}\int_0^{s_1} \sqrt{2\, gs}\, ds = \tfrac{2}{3}\sqrt{2\, gs_1}.$$

Since the velocity is $\sqrt{2\, gs_1}$ when $s = s_1$, we see that in this case the mean velocity is two thirds the final velocity.

EXERCISES

1. Find the mean value of the lengths of the perpendiculars from a diameter of a semicircle to the circumference, assuming the perpendiculars to be drawn at equal distances on the diameter.

2. Find the mean length of the perpendiculars drawn from the circumference of a semicircle to its diameter, assuming the perpendiculars to be drawn at equal distances on the circumference.

3. Find the mean length of the radii of a loop of the curve $r = a \cos 4\theta$, the angle between successive radii being constant.

4. From a point 1 in. from the center of a circle of radius 4 in. straight lines are drawn to points equally spaced along the circumference. Find the mean of the squares of the lengths of these lines.

5. Find the mean area of the plane sections of a right circular cone of altitude h and radius a made by planes perpendicular to the axis at equal distances apart.

6. In a right circular cone of altitude 2 and radius of base 1, all possible right circular cylinders with their upper bases equally spaced along the altitude of the cone are inscribed. What is the mean volume of the inscribed cylinders?

7. The angular velocity of a certain wheel is proportional to the square of the time. It starts from rest and in 3 minutes acquires an angular velocity of 300 revolutions per minute. Find the average angular velocity in that time.

8. Find the mean width of one arch of the curve $y = \sin x$.

9. A particle vibrates according to the law $s = a \sin kt$. Find the average velocity of the particle during the time of vibration from an extreme to the mean position of its path.

10. The formula connecting the pressure p in pounds per square inch and the volume v in cubic inches of a certain gas is $pv = 40$. Find the average pressure as the gas expands from 4 cu. in. to 8 cu. in.

88. Length of a plane curve. To find the length of any plane curve AB (Fig. 110), we assume $n-1$ points $P_1(x_1, y_1)$, $P_2(x_2, y_2)$, $P_3(x_3, y_3)$, $\cdots$, $P_{n-1}(x_{n-1}, y_{n-1})$ on the curve between A and B, and connect each pair of consecutive points by a straight line. The length of AB is then defined as the limit of the sum of the lengths of the n chords as n is increased with-

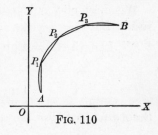

FIG. 110

out limit and the length of each chord at the same time approaches zero as a limit.

The length of any chord $P_i P_{i+1}$ is, by § 27,

$$\sqrt{(x_{i+1} - x_i)^2 + (y_{i+1} - y_i)^2} = \sqrt{\overline{\Delta x_i}^2 + \overline{\Delta y_i}^2} \qquad (1)$$

if we denote $x_{i+1} - x_i$ by Δx_i and $y_{i+1} - y_i$ by Δy_i.

Hence the length of the n chords is

$$\sum_{i=0}^{i=n-1} \sqrt{\overline{\Delta x_i}^2 + \overline{\Delta y_i}^2}, \qquad (2)$$

and, by definition,

$$\text{Length } AB = \operatorname*{Lim}_{n \to \infty} \sum_{i=0}^{i=n-1} \sqrt{\overline{\Delta x_i}^2 + \overline{\Delta y_i}^2}. \qquad (3)$$

To bring this into the form of a definite integral we need to have the equation of the curve so given that x and y are both functions of an independent variable t. Here t is a third independent variable, or it may be either x or y.

Then we may write (3) in the form

$$\text{Length } AB = \operatorname*{Lim}_{n \to \infty} \sum_{i=0}^{i=n-1} \sqrt{\left(\frac{\Delta x_i}{\Delta t}\right)^2 + \left(\frac{\Delta y_i}{\Delta t}\right)^2} \Delta t. \qquad (4)$$

Now as $\Delta t \to 0$, $\dfrac{\Delta x}{\Delta t} \to \dfrac{dx}{dt}$ and $\dfrac{\Delta y}{\Delta t} \to \dfrac{dy}{dt}$,

and hence $\quad \sqrt{\left(\dfrac{\Delta x}{\Delta t}\right)^2 + \left(\dfrac{\Delta y}{\Delta t}\right)^2} \to \sqrt{\left(\dfrac{dx}{dt}\right)^2 + \left(\dfrac{dy}{dt}\right)^2},$

and therefore, by (2), § 1,

$$\sqrt{\left(\frac{\Delta x}{\Delta t}\right)^2 + \left(\frac{\Delta y}{\Delta t}\right)^2} = \sqrt{\left(\frac{dx}{dt}\right)^2 + \left(\frac{dy}{dt}\right)^2} + \epsilon. \qquad (5)$$

We may now substitute in (4) by means of (5), with the result that

$$\text{Length } AB = \operatorname*{Lim}_{n \to \infty} \sum_{i=0}^{i=n-1} \left[\sqrt{\left(\frac{dx_i}{dt}\right)^2 + \left(\frac{dy_i}{dt}\right)^2} + \epsilon_1 \right] dt$$

$$= \operatorname*{Lim}_{n \to \infty} \sum_{i=0}^{i=n-1} \sqrt{\left(\frac{dx_i}{dt}\right)^2 + \left(\frac{dy_i}{dt}\right)^2} \, dt \qquad (6)$$

according to § 84.

Hence, we have

$$\text{Length } AB = \int_{t_0}^{t_1} \sqrt{\left(\frac{dx}{dt}\right)^2 + \left(\frac{dy}{dt}\right)^2} \, dt \tag{7}$$

where t_0 and t_1 are the values of t which determine the points A and B respectively.

We may write (7) in the more convenient form

$$\text{Length } AB = \int \sqrt{dx^2 + dy^2}, \tag{8}$$

the appropriate limits of integration to be substituted.

It is to be noted that the expression $\sqrt{dx^2 + dy^2}$ under the sign of integration is the ds of § 39. Accordingly we may express this ds in terms of polar coördinates, and obtain the formula

$$\text{Length } AB = \int \sqrt{dr^2 + r^2 d\theta^2} \tag{9}$$

to be used in case the equation of AB is in polar coördinates.

To evaluate either (8) or (9) we must express one of the variables involved in terms of the other, or both in terms of a third. The limits of integration may then be determined.

Example 1. Find the length of the parabola $y^2 = kx$ from the vertex to the point (a, b).

From the equation of the parabola we find $2\,y\,dy = k\,dx$. Hence formula (8) becomes either

$$s = \int_0^a \sqrt{1 + \frac{k^2}{4\,y^2}}\, dx = \int_0^a \sqrt{\frac{4\,x + k}{4\,x}}\, dx,$$

or

$$s = \int_0^b \sqrt{\frac{4\,y^2}{k^2} + 1}\, dy = \frac{1}{k}\int_0^b \sqrt{4\,y^2 + k^2}\, dy.$$

Either integral leads to the result

$$s = \frac{b}{2\,k}\sqrt{4\,b^2 + k^2} + \frac{k}{4}\ln\frac{2\,b + \sqrt{4\,b^2 + k^2}}{k}.$$

Example 2. Find the length of one arch of the cycloid

$$x = a(\phi - \sin\phi), \qquad y = a(1 - \cos\phi).$$

We have $\quad dx = a(1 - \cos\phi)d\phi, \quad dy = a\sin\phi\, d\phi$;

whence $\quad ds = a\sqrt{2 - 2\cos\phi}\, d\phi = 2\,a\sin\frac{\phi}{2}\, d\phi.$

Therefore $\quad s = 2\,a\int_0^{2\pi}\sin\frac{\phi}{2}\, d\phi = 8\,a.$

EXERCISES

1. Find the length of the curve $2 y^2 = (x - 2)^3$ from its point of intersection with OX to the point $(4, 2)$.

2. Find the total length of the curve $8 y^2 = x^2 - x^4$.

3. The position of a body moving in the plane XOY is given at any time t by the equations $x = t^2 - 3$, $y = t^3 + 2$. How far will the body move during the first five seconds if the unit of time is the second and the unit of distance is the foot?

4. Find the length of the curve $x = e^{-2t}\sin 2 t$, $y = e^{-2t} \cos 2 t$ between the points for which $t = 0$ and $t = \dfrac{\pi}{2}$.

5. A point is moving along the curve $r = a \sin^5 \dfrac{\theta}{5}$. If it starts from the pole, how far will it go before it gets back to the pole again?

6. Find the total length of the curve $r = a(1 - \cos \theta)$.

7. Find the length of the catenary $y = \dfrac{a}{2}\left(e^{\frac{x}{a}} + e^{-\frac{x}{a}}\right)$ from $x = 0$ to $x = h$.

8. Find the length of the curve $y = \ln \dfrac{e^x - 1}{e^x + 1}$ between the points for which $x = 1$ and $x = 2$ respectively.

9. Find the length of the loop of the curve $9 y^2 = 3 x^2 + x^3$.

89. Area of a surface of revolution. A surface of revolution is a surface generated by the revolution of a plane curve around an axis in its plane. Let the curve AB (Fig. 111) revolve about OH as an axis. To find the area of the surface generated, assume $n - 1$ points, $P_1, P_2, P_3, \cdots, P_{n-1}$, between A and B and connect each pair of consecutive points by a straight line. These lines are omitted in the figure since they are so nearly coincident with the arcs. The surface generated by AB is then defined as the limit of the sum of the areas of the surfaces generated by the n chords $AP_1, P_1P_2, P_2P_3, \cdots, P_{n-1}B$ as n increases without limit and the length of each chord approaches zero as a limit.

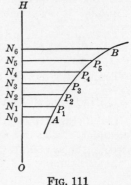

Fig. 111

Each chord generates the lateral surface of a frustum of a right circular cone, the area of which may be found by elementary geometry.

Draw the lines AN_0, P_1N_1, P_2N_2, $\cdots$ perpendicular to OH, and place

$$N_0A = r_0, \quad N_1P_1 = r_1, \quad N_2P_2 = r_2, \cdots, \quad N_nB = r_n.$$

Then the frustum of the cone generated by P_iP_{i+1} has for the radius of the upper base $N_{i+1}P_{i+1} = r_{i+1}$, and for the radius of the lower base $N_iP_i = r_i$, and for its slant height P_iP_{i+1}. Its lateral area is therefore equal to

$$2\,\pi\left(\frac{r_i + r_{i+1}}{2}\right)P_iP_{i+1}.$$

But $r_{i+1} = r_i + \Delta r_i.$

Therefore the lateral area of the frustum of the cone equals

$$2\,\pi\left(r_i + \frac{\Delta r_i}{2}\right)P_iP_{i+1}.$$

Now P_iP_{i+1} differs from ds (§ 88) by an infinitesimal of higher order. The lateral area of the frustum is therefore an infinitesimal which differs from

$$2\,\pi r_i ds$$

by an infinitesimal of higher order. Hence, if we represent the required area by S, we have $dS = 2\,\pi r ds$, whence

$$S = 2\,\pi\int r\,ds.$$

To evaluate the integral it is necessary to express r and ds in terms of the same variable and supply the limits of integration.

Example. Find the area of the surface of revolution generated by revolving about OX the portion of the parabola $y^2 = kx$ between the points for which $x = 0$ and $x = a$ respectively.

Let B (Fig. 112) be the point of the parabola for which $x = a$; the required surface is generated by the arc OB.

As in Example 1, § 88, we find

$$ds = \sqrt{1 + \frac{k^2}{4\,y^2}}\,dx = \frac{\sqrt{4\,y^2 + k^2}}{2\,y}\,dx$$
$$= \frac{\sqrt{4\,kx + k^2}}{2\,y}\,dx.$$

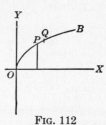

FIG. 112

If PQ is the arc represented by ds, then r of the formula is the y for the point P.

Hence

$$dS = 2\,\pi y \cdot \frac{\sqrt{4\,kx + k^2}}{2\,y}\,dx$$

$$= \pi\sqrt{4\,kx + k^2}\,dx,$$

and

$$S = \pi \int_0^a \sqrt{4\,kx + k^2}\,dx$$

$$= \pi \left[\frac{1}{6\,k}(4\,kx + k^2)^{\frac{3}{2}}\right]_0^a$$

$$= \frac{\pi}{6\,k}\,[(4\,ka + k^2)^{\frac{3}{2}} - k^3].$$

EXERCISES

1. Find the area of a zone of height h on a sphere of radius a.

2. Find the area of the surface of the ring formed by revolving a circle of radius a about an axis in its plane b units from the center ($b > a$).

3. Find the area of the surface formed by revolving the curve $x^{\frac{2}{3}} + y^{\frac{2}{3}} = a^{\frac{2}{3}}$ about OY.

4. Find the area of the curved surface of the catenoid formed by revolving about OX the portion of the catenary $y = \frac{a}{2}\left(e^{\frac{x}{a}} + e^{-\frac{x}{a}}\right)$ between $x = -h$ and $x = h$.

5. Find the area of the surface formed by revolving about the tangent at its lowest point the portion of the catenary $y = \frac{a}{2}\left(e^{\frac{x}{a}} + e^{-\frac{x}{a}}\right)$ between $x = -h$ and $x = h$.

6. Find the area of the curved surface formed by revolving about OY the portion of the parabola $y^2 = kx$ between $y = 0$ and $y = k$.

7. Find the area of the surface formed by revolving about OX an arch of the cycloid $x = a(\phi - \sin \phi)$, $y = a(1 - \cos \phi)$.

8. Find the area of the surface formed by revolving an arch of the cycloid $x = a(\phi - \sin \phi)$, $y = a(1 - \cos \phi)$ about the tangent at its highest point.

9. Find the area of the surface formed by revolving the lemniscate $r^2 = 2\,a^2 \cos 2\,\theta$ about the initial line.

10. Find the area of the surface formed by revolving the lemniscate $r^2 = 2\,a^2 \cos 2\,\theta$ about the line $\theta = 90°$.

90. Work. By definition the work done in moving a body against a constant force is equal to the force multiplied by the distance through which the body is moved. If the foot is taken as the unit of distance and the pound is taken as the unit of force, the unit of measure of work is called a *foot-pound*. Thus the work done in lifting a weight of 25 lb. through a distance of 50 ft. is 1250 ft.-lb.

Suppose now that a body is moved along OX (Fig. 113) from $A(x = a)$ to $B(x = b)$ against a force which is not constant but is a function of x, expressed by
$f(x)$. Let the line AB be divided
into intervals each equal to dx,
and let one of these intervals

$$\overline{O \quad A \qquad\qquad M\,N \qquad B}\ X$$

Fig. 113

be MN, where $OM = x$. Then the force at the point M is $f(x)$, and if the force were constantly equal to $f(x)$ throughout the interval MN, the work done in moving the body through MN would be $f(x)dx$. This expression therefore represents approximately the work actually done, and the approximation becomes more and more nearly exact as MN is taken smaller and smaller. The work done in moving from A to B is the limit of the sum of the terms $f(x)dx$ computed for all the intervals between A and B. Hence we have

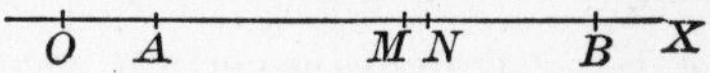

$$dW = f(x)dx$$

and

$$W = \int_a^b f(x)\,dx.$$

Example. The force which resists the stretching of a spring is proportional to the amount the spring has been already stretched. For a certain spring this force is known to be 10 lb. when the spring has been stretched $\frac{1}{2}$ in. Find the work done in stretching the spring 1 in. from its natural (unstretched) length.

If F is the force required to stretch the spring through a distance x, we have, from the statement of the problem,

$$F = kx;$$

and since $F = 10$ lb. when $x = \frac{1}{24}$ ft., we have $k = 240$. Therefore $F = 240\, x$.

Reasoning as in the text, we have

$$W = \int_0^{\frac{1}{12}} 240\, x\, dx = \tfrac{5}{6}\ \text{ft.-lb.}$$

1. The law of force is $F = 3\,s - 5$, where s is the distance. Find the work done upon a mass in moving it from a point where $F = 1$ to a point where $F = 25$.

2. A positive charge m of electricity is fixed at O. The repulsion on a unit charge at a distance x from O is $\dfrac{m}{x^2}$. Find the work done in bringing a unit charge from infinity to a distance a from O.

3. Assuming that the force required to stretch a wire from the length a to the length $a + x$ is proportional to $\dfrac{x}{a}$, and that a force of 1 lb. stretches a certain wire 48 in. in length to a length .04 in. greater, find the work done in stretching that wire from 48 in. to 80 in.

4. A block slides along a straight line from O against a resistance equal to $\dfrac{ka^2}{x^2 + a^2}$, where k and a are constants and x is the distance of the block from O at any time. Find the work done in moving the block from a distance a to a distance $a\sqrt{3}$ from O.

5. A cylindrical tank 10 ft. high and 10 ft. in diameter stands upon the roof of a building 50 ft. high. Find the work done in pumping the tank full of water from the level of the ground, through a pipe to the bottom of the tank.

6. The section of a bowl made by any plane through its axis is a parabolic segment of height 3 ft. and base 4 ft. How much work is necessary to pump all the water out of the bowl if it is originally full?

7. A body moves in a straight line according to the formula $x = ct^2$, where x is the distance traversed in a time t. If the resistance of the air is proportional to the square of the velocity, find the work done against the resistance of the air as the body moves from $x = 0$ to $x = a$.

8. A particle is moving along the ellipse $x = a \cos kt$, $y = b \sin kt$ against a force which resists with a magnitude directly equal to the speed of the particle. Find the work done by the particle in moving along the arc of the ellipse in the first quadrant.

9. Assuming that above the surface of the earth the force of the earth's attraction varies inversely as the square of the distance from the earth's center, find the work done in moving a weight of w pounds from the surface of the earth to a distance a miles above the surface.

10. A piston is free to slide in a cylinder of cross section S. The force acting on the piston is pS, where p is the pressure of the gas in the cylinder and is 7.8 lb. per square inch when the volume v is 2.6 cu. in. Find the work done as the volume changes from 3 cu. in. to 6 cu. in., according as the law connecting p and v is (1) $pv = k$ or (2) $pv^{1.4} = k$. $W = \int p \, dv = \int \frac{k}{v} \, dv$

91. Center of gravity. It is shown in mechanics that the center of gravity of n particles of masses $m_1, m_2, \cdots, m_n$ lying in a plane at points whose coördinates are $(x_1, y_1), (x_2, y_2), \cdots, (x_n, y_n)$ respectively is given by the formulas

$$\bar{x} = \frac{m_1 x_1 + m_2 x_2 + \cdots + m_n x_n}{m_1 + m_2 + \cdots + m_n},$$
$$\bar{y} = \frac{m_1 y_1 + m_2 y_2 + \cdots + m_n y_n}{m_1 + m_2 + \cdots + m_n}. \tag{1}$$

This is the point through which the resultant of the weights of the particles always passes, no matter how the particles are placed with respect to the direction of the earth's attraction.

We now wish to extend formulas (1) so that they may be applied to physical bodies in which the number of particles may be said to be infinite. For that purpose we divide the body into n elementary portions so small that the mass of each may be considered as concentrated at a point (x, y). Let the mass of each element be dm. If all the dimensions of dm are infinitesimal, it is immaterial at which point (x, y) within it we consider the mass as concentrated (§ 84). We have then to replace the m's of formula (1) by dm and to take the limit of the sums involved in (1) as the number n is indefinitely increased and the elements of mass become indefinitely small. There result the general formulas

$$\bar{x} = \frac{\int x \, dm}{\int dm}, \qquad \bar{y} = \frac{\int y \, dm}{\int dm}. \tag{2}$$

The integral $\int dm$ is the total mass of the body, and, if this mass is denoted by M, formulas (2) may be written in the form

$$M\bar{x} = \int x \, dm, \qquad M\bar{y} = \int y \, dm. \tag{3}$$

In applying formulas (3) it is necessary to evaluate the two integrals $\int x\,dm$ and $\int y\,dm$, but if M can be found by elementary methods without integration, its value may be written down immediately.

We will first apply these formulas to the case of a slender wire so fine and so placed that it may be represented by a plane curve. More strictly speaking, the curve may be taken as the mathematical line which runs through the center of the physical wire. Let the curve be divided into elements of length ds. Then

$$dm = \rho\,ds,$$

where ρ is a constant equal to the mass of the wire per unit length. If this is substituted in (3), the constant ρ may be taken out of the integrals and canceled, and the result may be written in the form

$$s\bar{x} = \int x\,ds, \qquad s\bar{y} = \int y\,ds, \tag{4}$$

where s on the left of the equations is the total length of the curve. These formulas give the *center of gravity of a plane curve*.

Example 1. Find the center of gravity of one fourth of the circumference of a circle of radius a.

Here we know that the total length is $\frac{1}{2}\pi a$; so that, from (4), we have

$$\tfrac{1}{2}\pi a\bar{x} = \int x\,ds, \qquad \tfrac{1}{2}\pi a\bar{y} = \int y\,ds.$$

To integrate, it is convenient to introduce the central angle ϕ (Fig. 114); whence

$$x = a\cos\phi, \; y = a\sin\phi, \; ds = a\,d\phi.$$

Then

$$\tfrac{1}{2}\pi a\bar{x} = \int_0^{\frac{\pi}{2}} a^2\cos\phi\,d\phi,$$

$$\tfrac{1}{2}\pi a\bar{y} = \int_0^{\frac{\pi}{2}} a^2\sin\phi\,d\phi;$$

whence

$$\bar{x} = \frac{2\,a}{\pi}, \qquad \bar{y} = \frac{2\,a}{\pi}.$$

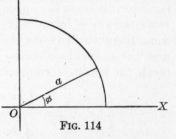

FIG. 114

Consider now a solid of revolution formed by revolving the plane area (Fig. 115) $ABCD$ about OY as an axis. It is assumed that the equation of the curve CD is given. It is evident from symmetry that the center of gravity of the solid lies on OY, so that we have to find only $\bar{y}$.

Let the solid be divided into thin slices perpendicular to OY, as was done in § 25, and let each slice be divided into elements of mass dm. Let the summation of $y\,dm$ first take place over one of the slices. In this summation y is constant, and the result of the summation is therefore y times the mass of the slice. It is therefore $\rho y(\pi x^2 dy)$, where ρ is the density which we assume to be constant. We have now to extend the summation over all the slices. This gives the result

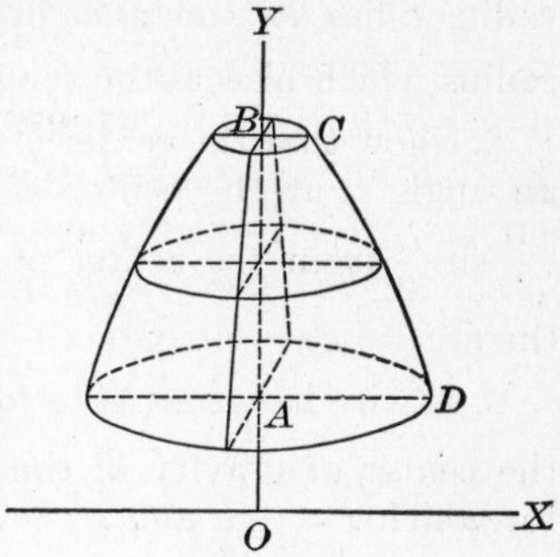

$$\rho \int_a^b \pi x^2 y\, dy, \qquad (5)$$

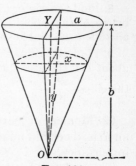

FIG. 115

where $OA = a$ and $OB = b$.

The mass M of the body is ρV, where V is the total volume. Substituting these values in formula (3) and dividing out ρ, we have the formula

$$V\bar{y} = \int_a^b \pi x^2 y\, dy. \qquad (6)$$

It is to be noticed that this result is what we obtain if we interpret dm in (3) as the mass of the slice and consider it concentrated at the middle point of one base of the slice.

Example 2. Find the center of gravity of a right circular cone of altitude b and radius a (Fig. 116).

This is a solid of revolution formed by revolving a right triangle about OY. However, the equation of a straight line need not be used, as similar triangles are simpler.

We have $\dfrac{x}{y} = \dfrac{a}{b}$; whence $x = \dfrac{a}{b} y$. The volume V is known to be $\frac{1}{3}\pi a^2 b$. Therefore, from (6), we have

FIG. 116

$$\tfrac{1}{3}\pi a^2 b\, \bar{y} = \int_0^b \frac{\pi a^2}{b^2} y^3 dy = \frac{\pi a^2 b^2}{4};$$

whence

$$\bar{y} = \tfrac{3}{4} b.$$

1. Show that the center of gravity of a semicircumference of radius a lies at a distance of $\dfrac{2\,a}{\pi}$ from the center of the circle on the radius which bisects the semicircumference.

2. Show that the center of gravity of a circular arc which subtends an angle α at the center of a circle of radius a lies at a distance $\dfrac{2\,a}{\alpha}\sin\dfrac{\alpha}{2}$ from the center of the circle on the radius which bisects the arc.

3. A wire hangs so as to form the catenary $y = \dfrac{a}{2}\left(e^{\frac{x}{a}} + e^{-\frac{x}{a}}\right)$. Find the center of gravity of the piece of the curve between the points for which $x = -\,a$ and $x = a$.

4. Find the center of gravity of the arc of the cycloid $x = a(\phi - \sin\phi)$, $y = a(1 - \cos\phi)$ between the first two sharp points.

5. Find the center of gravity of a solid hemisphere.

6. Find the center of gravity of the segment cut from a solid sphere of radius a by two parallel planes distant, respectively, h_1 and $h_2 (h_2 > h_1)$ from the center of the sphere.

7. Find the center of gravity of a solid formed by revolving about its altitude a parabolic segment of base b and altitude a.

8. Find the center of gravity of the upper half of the solid formed by revolving about its base a parabolic segment of base b and altitude a, so placed that its base is vertical.

9. Find the center of gravity of the solid formed by revolving about OX the area bounded by OX, OY, and the first quadrant of the ellipse $\dfrac{x^2}{9} + \dfrac{y^2}{4} = 1$.

92. Moment of inertia. When a rigid body is rotating about an axis, a certain quantity called the *moment of inertia* is of great importance.

This is defined as follows: The moment of inertia of a particle about an axis is the product of its mass and the square of its distance from the axis. The moment of inertia of a number of particles about the same axis is the sum of the moments of inertia of the separate particles about that axis. From these definitions we may derive the moment of inertia of a body.

Let the body be divided into elements of mass dm. Let R be the distance of any point in the element from the axis about which we wish the moment of inertia. Then the moment of inertia of the element is approximately

$$R^2 dm.$$

We say "approximately" because not all points of the element are exactly a distance R from the axis, as R is the distance of some one point in the element. However, the smaller the element the more nearly can it be regarded as concentrated at one point, and the limit of the sum of all the elements, as their size approaches zero and their number increases without limit, is the moment of inertia of the body. By § 84 it is immaterial which point of dm is taken at the distance R from the axis. Hence if I represents the moment of inertia of the body,

$$dI = R^2 dm,$$

and
$$I = \int R^2 dm. \tag{1}$$

Consider now a thin plate which can be considered as a plane area with a mass. Let the surface of the plate be referred to coördinate axes and let it be required to find the moments of inertia about OY and OX. These moments of inertia will be denoted by I_y and I_x respectively.

To determine I_y we may divide the surface of the plate into elements of area dA, taking for dA a vertical strip as in (1), § 86, so that
$$dA = (y_2 - y_1)dx.$$

Then
$$dm = \rho(y_2 - y_1)dx,$$

where ρ is the amount of mass per unit area of the plate.

Now all the points of the strip are approximately at the distance x from OY, and hence x may be taken as R for the whole strip. Therefore the moment of inertia of the strip about OY is its mass multiplied by x^2. Hence, denoting the moment of inertia of the strip about OY by dI_y, we have

$$dI_y = \rho x^2 (y_2 - y_1)dx.$$

Since I_y is the limit of the sum of these differentials, we have

$$I_y = \rho \int x^2(y_2 - y_1)dx. \tag{2}$$

Similarly, if we want I_x, we may divide the area into strips parallel to OX of mass $\rho(x_2 - x_1)dy$. Each point of the strip may be regarded as at a distance y from OX, and, reasoning as before, we have

$$dI_x = \rho y^2(x_2 - x_1)dy$$

and

$$I_x = \rho \int y^2(x_2 - x_1)dy. \tag{3}$$

If we place $\rho = 1$ in (2) and (3), the resulting I_y and I_x are called the moments of inertia of the plane area about OY and OX respectively.

Example 1. Find the moment of inertia of a rectangle of dimensions a and b about the side of length b.

Let the rectangle be placed as in Fig. 117.

Draw the element of area

$$MN = dA = b\,dx.$$

Then, since each point of MN is approximately at the distance x from OY, we have

$$dI_y = bx^2\,dx$$

and $I_y = \int_0^a bx^2\,dx = \tfrac{1}{3}\,a^3b.$

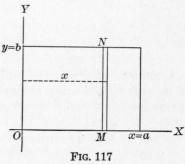

Fig. 117

This is the moment of inertia of the area. If we want the moment of inertia of a plate, we must multiply the result by ρ. But in that case the total mass M of the plate is ρab. Whence $\rho = \dfrac{M}{ab}$ and

$$I_y = \tfrac{1}{3}\,Ma^2.$$

Example 2. Find the moment of inertia of the quadrant of an ellipse $\dfrac{x^2}{a^2} + \dfrac{y^2}{b^2} = 1$ $(a > b)$ about its major axis.

We draw a strip parallel to OX (Fig. 118). Its area is

$$x\,dy = \frac{a}{b}\sqrt{b^2 - y^2}\,dy.$$

Since each point of the strip is approximately at a distance y from OX,

$$dI_x = y^2 x \, dy = \frac{a}{b} y^2 \sqrt{b^2 - y^2} \, dy,$$

and hence
$$I_x = \frac{a}{b} \int_0^b y^2 \sqrt{b^2 - y^2} \, dy$$

$$= \frac{\pi a b^3}{16}.$$

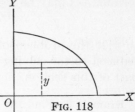

FIG. 118

This is the moment of inertia of the area. To find the moment of inertia of a thin plate, we must multiply by ρ. The area of the quadrant is $\frac{\pi a b}{4}$ (Example 1, § 86). Hence, if M is the total mass of the plate, $M = \frac{\rho \pi a b}{4}$. Hence, for the plate,

$$I = \tfrac{1}{4} M b^2.$$

The *polar moment of inertia* of a plane area is defined as the moment of inertia of the area about an axis perpendicular to its plane. This may also be called conveniently the moment of inertia with respect to the point in which the axis cuts the plane of the area, for the distance of an element from the axis is simply its distance from that point. Thus we may speak, for example, of the polar moment of inertia with respect to an axis through the origin perpendicular to the plane of an area, or, more concisely, of the polar moment with respect to the origin.

If the area is divided into elements dm, and one point in the element has the coördinates (x, y), the distance of that point from the origin is $\sqrt{x^2 + y^2}$. That is, in (1), if we place $R^2 = x^2 + y^2$, we shall have the formula for the polar moment of inertia with respect to the origin. Denoting this by I_0, we have

$$I_0 = \int (x^2 + y^2) \, dm. \tag{4}$$

This integral may be split up into two integrals, giving

$$I_0 = \int x^2 \, dm + \int y^2 \, dm. \tag{5}$$

The first integral in (5) is the moment of inertia about OY and has been denoted by I_y; the second integral is the moment of inertia about OX and has been denoted by I_x. Therefore formula (4) may be written as

$$I_0 = I_y + I_x, \tag{6}$$

so that the problem of finding the moment of inertia may be reduced to the solving of two problems of the type of the first part of this section.

Example 3. Find the polar moment of inertia of an ellipse with respect to the origin.

In Example 2 we found I_x for a quadrant of the ellipse. For the entire ellipse it is four times as great, since moments of inertia are added by definition. Hence $I_x = \frac{1}{4} \pi a b^3$.

By a similar calculation $I_y = \frac{1}{4} \pi a^3 b$.

Therefore $I_0 = \frac{1}{4} \pi a b (a^2 + b^2)$.

If the area is replaced by a plate of mass M, this result gives

$$I_0 = \frac{1}{4} M (a^2 + b^2).$$

Example 4. Required the polar moment of inertia of a circle of radius a about its center.

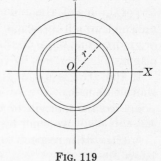

FIG. 119

This problem may be solved by the method of Example 3. It is more convenient to divide the circle into circular rings of radius r and width dr (Fig. 119). The area of one of these is $2 \pi r\, dr$, and since each point is approximately at the distance r from 0, we have

$$dI_0 = 2 \pi r^3\, dr$$

and $I_0 = 2 \pi \int_0^a r^3\, dr = \frac{1}{2} \pi a^4$.

If M is the mass of a circular plate, this result multiplied by ρ reduces to

$$I_0 = \frac{1}{2} M a^2.$$

It is evident from symmetry that for the circle $I_x = I_y$. Hence

$$I_0 = I_x + I_y = 2 I_x.$$

Therefore $I_x = \frac{1}{4} M a^2$,

which is the moment of inertia of a circle about any diameter.

The moment of inertia of a solid of revolution about the axis of revolution is the sum of the moments of inertia of the circular slices about the same axis, that is, of the polar moments of inertia of the circular slices about their centers. If the axis of revolution is OY, the radius of any circular section perpendicular to OY is x and its thickness is dy. Its mass is therefore $\rho\pi x^2\,dy$; and therefore, by Example 4, its moment of inertia about OY is $\frac{1}{2}\rho\pi x^4\,dy$. The total moment of inertia of the solid is therefore

$$I_y = \tfrac{1}{2}\,\rho\pi\int x^4\,dy.$$

Example 5. Find the moment of inertia of a circular cone about its axis.

Take the cone as in Example 2, § 91. Then we have

$$I_y = \frac{1}{2}\,\rho\pi\int_0^b \frac{a^4}{b^4}y^4\,dy = \frac{1}{10}\,\rho\pi a^4 b.$$

But if M is the mass of the cone, we have $M = \frac{1}{3}\,\rho\pi a^2 b$.

Therefore $\qquad\qquad I_y = \tfrac{3}{10}\,Ma^2.$

EXERCISES

1. Find the moment of inertia of a rectangle of base b and altitude a about a line through its center parallel to its base.

2. Find the moment of inertia of a triangle of base b and altitude a about a line through its vertex parallel to its base.

3. Find the moment of inertia of a triangle of base b and altitude a about its base.

4. Find the moment of inertia of an ellipse about its minor axis and also about its major axis.

5. Find the moment of inertia of a trapezoid about its lower base, taking the lower base as b, the upper base as a, and the altitude as h.

6. Find the moment of inertia about its base of a parabolic segment of base b and altitude a.

7. Find the polar moment of inertia about its center of a rectangle of base b and altitude a.

8. Find the polar moment of inertia about its center of a circular ring, the outer radius being r_2 and the inner radius r_1.

9. Find the polar moment of inertia of a right triangle of sides a and b about the vertex of the right angle.

10. Find the moment of inertia about its axis of a right circular cylinder of height h and radius r.

11. Find the moment of inertia of a solid sphere of radius a about any diameter.

12. A paraboloid of revolution is formed by revolving the parabola $x^2 = 4\,y$ about OY. Find the moment of inertia about OY of the solid bounded by this surface and the planes formed by revolving about OY the lines $y = 1$ and $y = 5$.

93. Attraction. Two particles of matter of masses m_1 and m_2 respectively, separated by a distance r, attract each other with a force equal to $k\dfrac{m_1 m_2}{r^2}$. The same law holds for the attraction of two electric masses or of two magnetic poles. In all cases k is a constant which depends upon the units used.

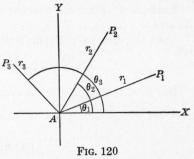

FIG. 120

Consider now n particles of masses $m_1, m_2, m_3, \cdots, m_n$ lying in a plane at the points $P_1, P_2, P_3, \cdots, P_n$ (Fig. 120). Let it be required to find their attraction upon a particle of unit mass situated at a point A in their plane.

Let the distances AP_1, AP_2, $\cdots$, AP_n be denoted by r_1, $r_2, \cdots, r_n$. The attractions of the individual particles are

$$k\frac{m_1}{r_1^2}, \quad k\frac{m_2}{r_2^2}, \quad \cdots, \quad k\frac{m_n}{r_n^2},$$

but these attractions cannot be added directly, since they are not parallel forces. To find their resultant we will resolve each into components along two perpendicular axes AX and AY respectively. If we denote the angle XAP_i by θ_i, we have as the sum of the components along AX,

$$X = k\,\frac{m_1}{r_1^2}\cos\theta_1 + k\,\frac{m_2}{r_2^2}\cos\theta_2 + \cdots + k\,\frac{m_n}{r_n^2}\cos\theta_n,$$

and for the sum of the components along AY,

$$Y = k\,\frac{m_1}{r_1^2}\sin\theta_1 + k\,\frac{m_2}{r_2^2}\sin\theta_2 + \cdots + k\,\frac{m_n}{r_n^2}\sin\theta_n.$$

The resultant attraction is then

$$R = \sqrt{X^2 + Y^2}$$

and acts in a direction which makes the angle $\tan^{-1}\dfrac{Y}{X}$ with AX.

Let it now be required to find the attraction of a solid of mass m upon a particle of unit mass situated at a point A. Let the solid be divided into n elements, the mass of each of which may be denoted by Δm, and let P_i be a point at which the mass of any one element may be considered as concentrated. Then the attraction of this element on the particle at A is $k\dfrac{\Delta m}{r_i^2}$, where $r_i = AP_i$, and its component in the direction of AX is $\dfrac{\Delta m}{r_i^2}\cos\theta_i$, where θ_i is the angle between the directions AX and AP_i. Also the component in the direction of AY is $k\dfrac{\Delta m}{r_i^2}\sin\theta_i$. Hence we have

$$X = \operatorname*{Lim}_{n\to\infty}\sum_{i=1}^{i=n} k\,\frac{\cos\theta_i}{r_i^2}\,\Delta m = k\int\frac{\cos\theta}{r^2}dm,$$

$$Y = \operatorname*{Lim}_{n\to\infty}\sum_{i=1}^{i=n} k\,\frac{\sin\theta_i}{r_i^2}\,\Delta m = k\int\frac{\sin\theta}{r^2}\,dm.$$

Example. Find the attraction of a uniform wire of length l and mass M on a particle of unit mass situated in a straight line perpendicular to one end of the wire and at a distance a from it.

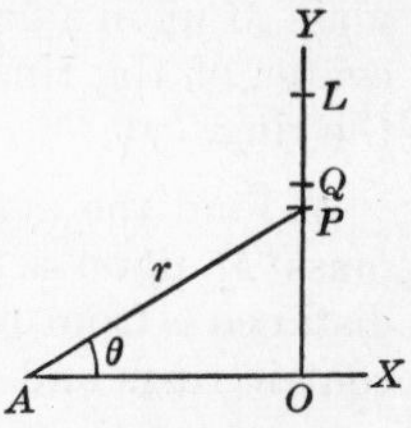

Let the wire OL (Fig. 121) lie in the axis of y with one end at the origin and let the particle of unit mass be at A on the axis of x where $AO = a$.

Divide OL into elements of length dy one of which is PQ, where $OP = y$. Then if ρ is the mass per unit length of the wire, $dm = \rho\,dy$. Draw AP. Then $AP = r = \sqrt{a^2 + y^2}$, $\theta = OAP$, $\cos\theta = \dfrac{a}{\sqrt{a^2 + y^2}}$, $\sin\theta = \dfrac{y}{\sqrt{a^2 + y^2}}$. Hence the formulas become

FIG. 121

$$X = \rho k \int_0^l \frac{a\,dy}{(a^2 + y^2)^{\frac{3}{2}}},$$

$$Y = \rho k \int_0^l \frac{y\,dy}{(a^2 + y^2)^{\frac{3}{2}}}.$$

To integrate, it is convenient to express y in terms of θ. Then $y = a \tan \theta$, and

$$X = \frac{\rho k}{a} \int_0^\alpha \cos \theta \, d\theta = \frac{\rho k}{a} \sin \alpha = \frac{Mk}{al} \sin \alpha,$$

$$Y = \frac{\rho k}{a} \int_0^\alpha \sin \theta \, d\theta = \frac{\rho k}{a} (1 - \cos \alpha) = \frac{Mk}{al} (1 - \cos \alpha),$$

where $\alpha = OAL$, and $M = l\rho$.

If R is the resultant of X and Y, and β the angle the resultant makes with OX,

$$R = \sqrt{X^2 + Y^2} = \frac{2\,Mk}{al} \sin \frac{1}{2}\, \alpha,$$

and

$$\beta = \tan^{-1} \frac{Y}{X} = \tan^{-1} \frac{1 - \cos \alpha}{\sin \alpha} = \frac{1}{2}\, \alpha.$$

EXERCISES

1. Find the attraction of a uniform straight wire of length l and mass M upon a particle of unit mass situated in the line of direction of the wire at a distance c from one end.

2. A particle of unit mass is situated at a perpendicular distance c from the center of a straight homogeneous wire of mass M and length l. Find the force of attraction of the wire.

3. Find the attraction of a uniform circular ring of radius a and mass M upon a particle of unit mass situated at a distance c from the center of the ring in a straight line perpendicular to the plane of the ring.

4. Find the attraction of a uniform circular disk of radius a and mass M upon a particle of unit mass situated at a perpendicular distance c from the center of the disk. (Divide the disk into concentric rings and use the result of Ex. 3.)

5. Find the attraction of a uniform right circular cylinder with mass M, radius of its base a, and length l upon a particle of unit mass situated in the axis of the cylinder produced, at a distance c from one end. (Divide the cylinder into parallel disks and use the result of Ex. 4.)

6. Find the attraction of a homogeneous hemisphere of radius a and mass M on a particle of unit mass in the straight line perpendicular to the base at its center and at a distance a from the base in the direction away from the hemisphere.

7. The top of a homogeneous right circular cylinder of radius a is cut away into the form of a spherical surface of radius b $(b > a)$, the center of which coincides with the center of the base of the cylinder. Find the attraction of the remaining portion of the cylinder on a particle of unit mass at the middle point of its base.

8. A solid of revolution of mass M is formed by revolving about OY as axis the area bounded by the curve $y^3 = x^2$ and the line $y = 3$. Find the attraction of this solid on a particle of unit mass at the origin of coördinates.

GENERAL EXERCISES

1. Find the area of the sector of the ellipse $16\,x^2 + 25\,y^2 = 400$ cut out of the first quadrant by the axis of x and the line $15\,y - 16\,x = 0$.

2. Find the area bounded on the right by the circle $x^2 + y^2 = 12$ and on the left by the curve $y^2 = x^3$.

3. Find the total area of the loop of the curve $ax^2 = y^2(a + y)$.

4. Find the total area bounded by the curves $27\,y^2 = 16\,x^3$ and $y^2 = 8(5 - x)$.

5. Find the area bounded by the curve $x^2y^2 + a^2b^2 = a^2y^2$ and its asymptotes.

6. Find the area bounded by the curve $y^2(x^2 + a^2) = a^2x^2$ and its asymptotes.

7. Find the area bounded by the curve $x = a \cos \theta$, $y = b \sin^3\theta$.

8. Find the area inclosed by the curve $x = a \cos^3\theta$, $y = a \sin^3\theta$.

9. Find the area of a loop of the curve $r^2 = a^2 \sin n\theta$.

10. Find the area inclosed by the curve $r = \dfrac{4}{1 - \cos \theta}$ and the curve $r = \dfrac{4}{1 + \cos \theta}$.

11. Find the area bounded by the circles $r = a \cos \theta$ and $r = a \sin \theta$.

12. Find the area in the first quadrant between the first and the second turns of the logarithmic spiral $r = e^{a\theta}$.

13. Find the total area inside the curve $r = a \sin 2\,\theta$ and outside the circle $r = \dfrac{a}{2}$.

14. Find the area bounded on the outside by the large loop of the curve $r = 2 + \sin \dfrac{\theta}{2}$ and on the inside by the small loop of the same curve.

15. Find the area of the segment of the cardioid $r = a(1 + \cos \theta)$ cut off by a straight line perpendicular to the initial line at a distance $\frac{3}{4} a$ from the origin O.

16. Find the area cut off from the lemniscate $r^2 = 2 a^2 \cos 2 \theta$ by the straight line $r \cos \theta = \dfrac{a \sqrt{3}}{2}$.

17. Two parabolas have a common vertex and a common axis, but lie in perpendicular planes. An ellipse moves with its plane perpendicular to the axis and with the ends of its axes on the parabolas. Find the volume generated when the ellipse has moved a distance h from the common vertex of the parabolas.

18. Find the volume of the solid formed by revolving about the line $x = 2$ the figure bounded by the parabola $y^2 = 8 x$ and the line $2 x - 1 = 0$.

19. Find the volume of the solid generated by revolving about OY the area in the first quadrant bounded by the axis of x and the curves $y^2 = 4 ax$ and $y^2 = 4 a^2 - 4 ax$.

20. Find the volume of the solid generated by revolving about the line $y + a = 0$ as axis the area bounded by the curve $x^{\frac{1}{2}} + y^{\frac{1}{2}} = a^{\frac{1}{2}}$ and the axes of x and y.

21. The plane sections of a certain solid made by planes perpendicular to OX are squares with the ends of one of the diagonals of each square lying on the curve $x^{\frac{2}{3}} + y^{\frac{2}{3}} = a^{\frac{2}{3}}$. Find its volume.

22. Find the volume formed by revolving about the line $x = 2$ the plane figure bounded by the curve $y^2 = 4(2 - x)$ and the axis of y.

23. The sections of a solid made by planes perpendicular to OY are circles with one diameter extending from the curve $y^2 = 6 x$ to the curve $y^2 = 6 - 3 x$. Find the volume of the solid between the points of intersection of the curves.

24. A right circular cylinder of radius a is intersected by two planes, the first of which is perpendicular to the axis of the cylinder and the second of which makes an angle θ with the first. Find the volume of the portion of the cylinder included between these two planes if their line of intersection is tangent to the circle cut from the cylinder by the first plane.

25. The cross section of a horizontal pipe is in the form of a semicircle of 4 in. radius, the diameter of the semicircle being at the top and horizontal. The pipe receives water from a roof 40 ft. above the top of the pipe. If the conductor leading from the roof to the pipe is full, what is the pressure on a board closing the end of the pipe?

26. A horizontal gutter is U-shaped, a semicircle of radius 4 in. surmounted by a rectangle 8 in. wide by 4 in. deep. If the gutter is full of water and a board is placed across the end, how much pressure is exerted on the board?

27. The vertical end of an oil tank, 4 ft. tall and 6 ft. broad at its widest point, is made up of two parabolic segments with their bases horizontal and coincident. Find the total pressure on the end when the tank is full of oil which weighs 45 lb. per cubic foot.

28. The gasoline tank of an automobile is in the form of a horizontal cylinder the ends of which are plane ellipses 20 in. high and 10 in. broad. Assuming w as the weight of a cubic inch of gasoline, find the pressure on one end of the tank when the gasoline is 15 in. deep.

29. Show that if y is a linear function of x, the mean value of y with respect to x is equal to one half the sum of the first and the last value of y in the interval over which the average is taken.

30. Find the mean width of the part of the curve $y = \dfrac{8\,a^3}{x^2 + 4\,a^2}$ above the line $y = a$.

31. An ellipsoid of revolution is formed by revolving the ellipse $9\,x^2 + 16\,y^2 = 144$ about its minor axis. In this ellipsoid is inscribed a series of cones of revolution with their respective vertices at one end of the minor axis of the ellipse and their bases cutting off equal distances on the minor axis. Find the mean volume of these cones.

32. In a sphere of radius a a series of right circular cones is inscribed with their bases perpendicular to a given diameter of the sphere and so placed that they cut off arcs of equal length on any circle of the sphere made by a plane through the given diameter. Find the mean volume of these cones.

33. A series of rectangles are inscribed in the ellipse $\dfrac{x^2}{a^2} + \dfrac{y^2}{b^2} = 1$, $(a > b)$, with their sides parallel respectively to the major and the minor axes of the ellipse. If the sides perpendicular to the minor axis cut off equal distances on that axis, find the mean area of the rectangles.

34. A particle describes a simple harmonic motion defined by the equation $s = a \sin kt$. Show that the mean kinetic energy $\left(\dfrac{mv^2}{2}\right)$ during a quarter vibration is half the maximum kinetic energy, if the average is taken with respect to the time.

35. In the motion defined in Ex. 34 what will be the ratio of the mean kinetic energy during a quarter vibration to the maximum kinetic energy, if the average is taken with respect to the space traversed in a quarter vibration?

36. A quantity of steam expands according to the law $pv^{0.8} = 1800$, p being the pressure in pounds per square foot. Find the average pressure as the volume v increases from 1 cu. ft. to 4 cu. ft.

37. Find the total length of the curve $x^{\frac{2}{3}} + y^{\frac{2}{3}} = a^{\frac{2}{3}}$.

38. Find the length of the curve

$$x = a \cos \phi + a\phi \sin \phi, \qquad y = a \sin \phi - a\phi \cos \phi,$$

from $\phi = 0$ to $\phi = 4\pi$.

39. A given area is inside the curve $r = a \cos \theta$ and outside the curve $r = a(1 - \cos \theta)$. Find the length of the boundary of this area.

40. Find the length of the loop of the curve $3y^2 = x^2 - x^3$.

41. Find the total length of the curve $x = a \cos^3 \phi$, $y = b \sin^3 \phi$.

42. Find the length of the curve

$$x = 2a \cos \phi - a \cos 2\phi, \quad y = 2a \sin \phi - a \sin 2\phi$$

between the points for which $\phi = 0$ and $\phi = 2\pi$.

43. Show that the length of the logarithmic spiral $r = e^{a\theta}$ between any two points is proportional to the difference of the radius vectors of the points.

44. Find the total length of the curve $r = a \sin^3 \dfrac{\theta}{3}$.

45. Find the surface area of the prolate spheroid formed by revolving an ellipse about its major axis.

46. Find the surface area of the oblate spheroid formed by revolving an ellipse about its minor axis.

47. Find the area of the surface formed by revolving the curve $x = a \cos^3 \phi$, $y = a \sin^3 \phi$ about OX.

48. Find the area of the surface formed by revolving about the line $x = a$ the portion of the curve $x = a \cos^3 \phi$, $y = a \sin^3 \phi$ which is at the right of OY.

49. Find the area of the surface formed by revolving about the initial line the cardioid $r = a(1 + \cos \theta)$.

50. If a center of force attracts with a magnitude equal to $\dfrac{k}{x^{\frac{5}{3}}}$, where x is the distance of the body from the center, how much work will be done in moving the body in a straight line away from the center from a distance a to a distance $8a$?

51. A body is moved along a straight line toward a center of force which repels with a magnitude equal to kx when the body is at a distance x from the center. How much work will be done in moving the body from a distance $2\,a$ to a distance a from the center?

52. A central force attracts a body at a distance x from the center by an amount $\dfrac{k}{x^3}$. Find the work done in moving the body directly away from the center from a distance a to the distance $2\,a$.

53. A bag containing originally 80 lb. of sand is lifted through a vertical distance of 8 ft. If the sand leaks out at such a rate that while the bag is being lifted the number of pounds of sand lost is equal to a constant times the square of the number of feet through which the bag has been lifted, and a total of 20 lb. of sand is lost during the lifting, find the number of foot-pounds of work done in lifting the bag.

54. Find the foot-pounds of work done in lifting to a height of 20 ft. above the top of the tank all the water contained in a horizontal cylindrical tank 10 ft. long and 2 ft. in radius, the tank being full at the outset.

55. Assuming that below the surface of the earth the force of the earth's attraction varies directly as the distance from the earth's center, find the work done in moving a weight of w pounds from a point a miles below the surface of the earth to the surface.

56. A wire carrying an electric current of magnitude C is bent into a circle of radius a. The force exerted by the current upon a unit magnetic pole at a distance x from the center of the circle in a straight line perpendicular to the plane of the circle is known to be $\dfrac{2\,\pi C a^2}{(a^2 + x^2)^{\frac{3}{2}}}$. Find the work done in bringing a unit magnetic pole from infinity to the center of the circle along the line just mentioned.

57. Find the center of gravity of the arc of the curve $x^{\frac{2}{3}} + y^{\frac{2}{3}} = a^{\frac{2}{3}}$ which is above the axis of x.

58. A wire is bent into a curve of the form $9\,y^2 = x^3$. Find the center of gravity of the portion of the wire between the two points for which $x = 5$ respectively.

59. Find the center of gravity of the upper arc of the curve $9\,ay^2 - x(x - 3\,a)^2 = 0$ between the ordinates $x = 0$ and $x = 3\,a$.

60. Find the center of gravity of the solid formed by revolving about OY the plane figure bounded by the parabola $y^2 = kx$, the axis of y. and the line $y = k$.

61. Find the center of gravity of the solid formed by revolving about OY the surface bounded by the hyperbola $\dfrac{x^2}{a^2} - \dfrac{y^2}{b^2} = 1$ and the lines $y = 0$ and $y = b$.

62. Find the moment of inertia of a parallelogram of altitude a and base b about its base as an axis.

63. Find the moment of inertia of a plane circular ring, the inner radius and the outer radius of which are respectively 3 in. and 5 in., about a diameter of the ring as an axis.

64. Find the moment of inertia about its axis of a hollow right circular cylinder of mass M, its inner radius being r_1, its outer radius r_2, and its height h.

65. A ring is cut from a spherical shell, whose inner and outer radii are, respectively, 5 ft. and 6 ft., by two parallel planes on the same side of the center and distant 1 ft. and 3 ft. respectively from the center. Find the moment of inertia of this ring about its axis.

66. The radius of the upper base and the radius of the lower base of the frustum of a right circular cone are, respectively, r_1 and r_2. Find its moment of inertia about its axis.

67. Find the moment of inertia about OX of the volume formed by revolving about OX the area bounded by $y = 4\,x^2$, $x = 1$, and the axis of x.

68. Find the moment of inertia about OY of the solid formed by revolving about OY the area bounded by the curve $x^2 = y^3$ and the lines $y = 1$ and $y = 3$.

69. Find the attraction of a homogeneous straight wire of infinite length and mass ρ per unit length on a particle of unit mass at a perpendicular distance c from wire.

70. Find the attraction of a uniform straight wire of length l and mass M upon a particle of unit mass situated at a perpendicular distance c from the wire and so that lines drawn from the particle to the ends of the wire inclose an angle α.

71. Find the attraction of a wire of length l and mass M on another parallel bar of the same length and mass so placed that the lines connecting the ends of the two bars are perpendicular to the bars and of length c.

72. A ring of mass M is cut from a homogeneous spherical shell, the inner radius and the outer radius of which are, respectively, 4 ft. and 5 ft., by two parallel planes on the same side of the center of the shell and distant 1 ft. and 3 ft. respectively from the center.

Find the attraction of this ring on a particle of unit mass which is situated at the center of the shell.

73. A homogeneous solid of mass M is bounded by a right circular cone of vertical angle 90° and a spherical surface of radius 2 ft., the center of the spherical surface being at the vertex of the cone. Find the attraction of this solid on a particle of unit mass at the vertex of the cone.

74. Show that the attraction of a segment of one base, cut from a homogeneous sphere of radius a, on a particle of unit mass at its vertex is $2\pi hk\rho\left(1 - \frac{1}{3}\sqrt{\frac{2\,h}{a}}\right)$, where ρ is the density of the sphere and h is the height of the segment.

75. The vertex of a right circular cone of vertical angle $2\,\alpha$ is at the center of a homogeneous spherical shell, the inner radius and the outer radius of which are, respectively, a_1 and a_2. Find the attraction of the portion of the shell outside the cone on a particle of unit mass at the center of the shell.

CHAPTER XII

REPEATED INTEGRATION

94. Double integrals. The symbol

$$\int_a^b \int_{y_1}^{y_2} f(x, y)dx\,dy, \tag{1}$$

in which a and b are constants and y_1 and y_2 are either constants or functions of x, indicates that two integrations are to be carried out in succession. The first integral to be evaluated is

$$\int_{y_1}^{y_2} f(x, y)dx\,dy,$$

where x and dx are to be held constant. The result is a function of x only, multiplied by dx; let us say, for convenience, $F(x)dx$.

The second integral to be evaluated is, then,

$$\int_a^b F(x)dx,$$

which is of the familiar type.

Similarly, the symbol

$$\int_a^b \int_{x_1}^{x_2} f(x, y)dy\,dx, \tag{2}$$

where a and b are constants and x_1 and x_2 are either constants or functions of y, indicates first the integration

$$\int_{x_1}^{x_2} f(x, y)dy\,dx,$$

in which y and dy are handled as constants, and afterwards integration with respect to y between the limits a and b.

Example 1. Evaluate $\int_0^3 \int_0^2 xy\,dx\,dy.$

The first integration is

$$\int_0^2 xy\,dx\,dy = \left[\tfrac{1}{2}\,xy^2dx\right]_0^2 = 2\,x\,dx.$$

The second integration is

$$\int_0^3 2\,x\,dx = \left[x^2\right]_0^3 = 9.$$

Example 2. Evaluate $\int_0^1 \int_{1-x}^{1-x^2} (x^2 + y^2)dx\,dy.$

The first integration is

$$\int_{1-x}^{1-x^2}(x^2 + y^2)dx\,dy = \left[(x^2y + \tfrac{1}{3}\,y^3)dx\right]_{1-x}^{1-x^2} = (x - 2\,x^2 + \tfrac{4}{3}\,x^3 - \tfrac{1}{3}x^6)dx.$$

The second integration is

$$\int_0^1 (x - 2\,x^2 + \tfrac{4}{3}\,x^3 - \tfrac{1}{3}\,x^6)dx = \tfrac{5}{42}.$$

Example 3. Evaluate $\int_0^{2\,a} \int_0^{\frac{y^2}{4\,a}} y^2dy\,dx.$

The first integration is

$$\int_0^{\frac{y^2}{4\,a}} y^2\,dy\,dx = \left[y^2\,x\,dy\right]_0^{\frac{y^2}{4\,a}} = \frac{y^4}{4\,a}\,dy.$$

The second integration is

$$\int_0^{2\,a} \frac{y^4}{4\,a}\,dy = \left[\frac{y^5}{20\,a}\right]_0^{2\,a} = \frac{8}{5}\,a^4.$$

A definite integral in one variable has been shown to be the limit of a sum, from which we infer that formula (1) involves first the determination of the limit of a sum with respect to y, and then the determination of the limit of a sum with respect to x. The application of the double integral comes from its interpretation as the limit of a double summation.

How such forms arise in practice will be illustrated in the following sections. In the next section, by means of an application to area, the method by which the limits of integration are found is explained. This should be read with care since the same principles are applied in all subsequent sections.

EXERCISES

Find the values of the following integrals:

1. $\int_1^3 \int_y^{y^2} \dfrac{y}{x^3}\, dy\, dx.$

7. $\int_0^{\sqrt{2}} \int_0^x \dfrac{y\, dx\, dy}{\sqrt{x^2 + y^2}}.$

2. $\int_1^2 \int_0^{\frac{1}{y}} xy^2\, dy\, dx.$

8. $\int_0^\pi \int_0^{4\cos x} \dfrac{dx\, dy}{\sqrt{y + 4}}.$

3. $\int_2^4 \int_{\frac{1}{x}}^{\frac{1}{x^2}} xy\, dx\, dy.$

9. $\int_0^{\frac{\pi}{3}} \int_0^{\sin 3\theta} r\, d\theta\, dr.$

4. $\int_0^{\frac{\pi}{2}} \int_0^{x^2} \cos \dfrac{y}{x}\, dx\, dy.$

10. $\int_0^\pi \int_0^{a\sin\theta} \dfrac{r\, d\theta\, dr}{\sqrt{a^2 - r^2}}.$

5. $\int_0^1 \int_0^{x^2} \dfrac{dx\, dy}{\sqrt{x^2 - y^2}}.$

11. $\int_0^{\frac{\pi}{2}} \int_0^{a\sin\theta} r\cos\theta\, d\theta\, dr.$

6. $\int_1^4 \int_0^x \dfrac{dx\, dy}{y^2 + x^2}.$

12. $\int_0^{\frac{\pi}{2}} \int_0^{a\cos\theta} r^2 \cos\theta\, d\theta\, dr.$

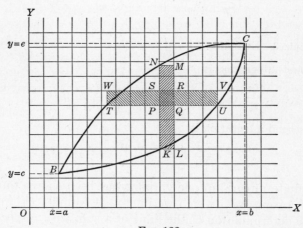

Fig. 122

95. Area as a double integral. Let it be required to find an area (Fig. 122) which is bounded below by the curve

$$y = f_1(x) \tag{1}$$

and above by the curve $\qquad y = f_2(x), \tag{2}$

which intersect at the points $B(a, c)$ and $C(b, e)$. It is essential in Fig. 122 that any straight line parallel to OY between the lines

$x = a$ and $x = b$ intersect each of the curves (1) and (2) in one and only one point. We shall call y_1 the value of y from equation (1) and y_2 the value of y from equation (2); hence $y_2 > y_1$.

Let the plane be divided into rectangles by straight lines parallel to OX and OY respectively. Then the area of any such rectangle is
$$dA = dx\,dy, \tag{3}$$
where dx is the distance between two consecutive lines parallel to OY, and where dy is the distance between two consecutive lines parallel to OX. The sum of the rectangles which are either wholly or partially within the required area is an approximation to the required area, but only an approximation, because the rectangles extend partially outside that area. We assume as evident, however, that the sum thus found becomes more nearly equal to the required area as the number of rectangles becomes larger and dx and dy become smaller. Hence we say that the required area is the limit of the sum of the terms $dx\,dy$.

This summation must be so carried out as to include every rectangle once and only once. To do this systematically we begin with any rectangle in the interior, such as $PQRS$, and add first those rectangles which lie in the vertical strip with it. That is, we take the limit of the sum of $dx\,dy$, with x and dx held constant and y varying from $y_1 = f_1(x)$ to $y_2 = f_2(x)$. This is indicated by the symbol

$$\int_{y_1}^{y_2} dx\,dy = (y_2 - y_1)dx = [f_2(x) - f_1(x)]\,dx. \tag{4}$$

This is the area of the strip $KLMN$.

We are now to take the limit of the sum of all such strips as $dx \to 0$ and x varies from a to b. We have then

$$A = \int_a^b (y_2 - y_1)dx = \int_a^b [f_2(x) - f_1(x)]\,dx. \tag{5}$$

If we put together what we have done we see that we have

$$A = \int_a^b \int_{y_1}^{y_2} dx\,dy. \tag{6}$$

This discussion enables us to express the area as a double integral. It does not, however, give us any more convenient way to compute the area than that used in Chapter XI, for the result (4) of the first integration is simply what may be written down at once for the area of a vertical strip taken as the element of area, as in (1), § 86.

Let us now also assume that any straight line parallel to OX between the lines $y = c$ and $y = e$ intersects each of the boundary curves in but a single point. In this case we may proceed as follows:

Let the equation of the boundary curve on the left of the area be written in the form
$$x = F_1(y), \tag{7}$$

and the equation of the boundary curve on the right of the area be written in the form
$$x = F_2(y). \tag{8}$$

Denote by x_1, the value of x from equation (7), and by x_2, the value of x from equation (8); then $x_2 > x_1$.

We may now make our first summation with respect to x, holding y and dy constant. The result is the area of the horizontal strip $TUVW$ and is indicated by the symbol
$$\int_{x_1}^{x_2} dy\, dx = (x_2 - x_1)dy = [F_2(y) - F_1(y)]\, dy. \tag{9}$$

We now take the limit of the sum of all these strips as $dy \to 0$ and y varies from c to e. We have then
$$A = \int_c^e (x_2 - x_1)dy = \int_c^e [F_2(y) - F_1(y)]dy. \tag{10}$$

If we put together what has been done we see that we have
$$A = \int_c^e \int_{x_1}^{x_2} dy\, dx. \tag{11}$$

The area has now been expressed as a double integral with the order of integration the reverse of that in (6). We noted that the use of (6) gives a no more convenient method of determining area than the use of the vertical strip of area (1), § 86. In like manner, the use of (11) gives a no more convenient method of determining area than the use of the horizontal strip of area (3), § 86.

It should not be assumed that it is always possible to express a required area as one double integral, using either order of integration. For example, consider the area $BCDE$ (Fig. 123) which is bounded below by the curve $y = f_1(x)$, above by the curve $y = f_2(x)$, on the left by the line $x = a$, and on the right by the line $x = b$. As every straight line parallel to OY between the lines $x = a$ and $x = b$ cuts each of the boundary curves $y = f_1(x)$ and $y = f_2(x)$ in but a single point, it is evident that we can express the area by one double integral of the form $\iint dx\,dy$ as in our previous discussion.

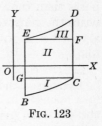

FIG. 123

Suppose, however, that we try to make the first integration with respect to x. Draw the straight lines CG and EF parallel to OX, dividing the area into three parts, I, II, and III, as noted in the figure. In I, the result of the first integration is the area of a horizontal strip extending from the line $x = a$ on the left to the curve $y = f_1(x)$ on the right; in II, the result of the first integration is the area of a horizontal strip extending from the line $x = a$ on the left to the line $x = b$ on the right; and in III, the result of the first integration is the area of a horizontal strip extending from the curve $y = f_2(x)$ on the left to the line $x = b$ on the right. Hence the limits of integration are different according as the strip formed by the first integration is in I, II, or III; it follows that it will require three double integrals of the form $\iint dy\,dx$ to express the area $BCDE$.

As another example, suppose we have to find the area $BCDE$ (Fig. 124), bounded on the left by the curve $x = f_1(y)$, on the right by the curve $x = f_2(y)$, below by the line $y = c$, and above by the line $y = e$. Drawing the straight lines EF and DG parallel to OY, and examining Fig. 124 as we examined Fig. 123, we conclude that the area $BCDE$ may be expressed by one double integral of the form $\iint dy\,dx$, but that it will require three double integrals of the form $\iint dx\,dy$ to express the same area.

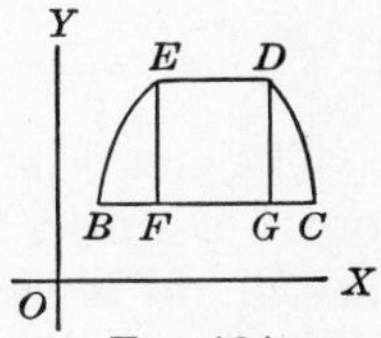

FIG. 124

It is to be noted that the above diagrams do not cover all possible cases, but that the fundamental aim is to include all the elements $dx\,dy$ in the summation. In order to accomplish this purpose it may be necessary to divide the area into more parts than those in the cases considered. In all cases we may write the general formula

$$A = \iint dx\,dy = \iint dy\,dx.$$

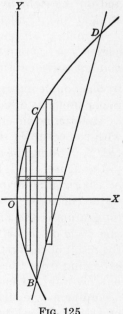

FIG. 125

Example. Find by double integration the area bounded by the parabola $y^2 = 16\,x$ and the line $y = 4\,x - 8$ (Fig. 125).

The boundary lines intersect at the points $B(1, -4)$ and $D(4, 8)$.

Drawing in an element of area

$$dA = dx\,dy,$$

we see that if the first integration is made with respect to x all the resulting horizontal strips will be alike in that they extend from the parabola on the left to the straight line on the right; hence for the first integration with respect to x the lower limit, derived from the equation of the parabola, is always $\dfrac{y^2}{16}$, and the upper limit, derived from the equation of the straight line, is always $2 + \dfrac{y}{4}$.

To sum up all the horizontal strips, evidently y varies from -4 to 8. Hence

$$A = \int_{-4}^{8} \int_{\frac{y^2}{16}}^{2 + \frac{y}{4}} dy\,dx$$

$$= \int_{-4}^{8} \left(2 + \frac{y}{4} - \frac{y^2}{16}\right) dy$$

$$= \left[2\,y + \frac{y^2}{8} - \frac{y^3}{48}\right]_{-4}^{8} = 18.$$

Suppose, however, we wish to make the first integration with respect to y. We see that the limits of integration with respect to y depend on whether the resulting vertical strip is to the left or to the right of the straight line BC which is drawn parallel to OY and hence has the equation $x = 1$; accordingly two double integrals will be required to find the total area.

Considering first the area to the left of BC, which we will denote by A_1, we see that the limits of integration with respect to y are $-4\sqrt{x}$ and $4\sqrt{x}$, as from the equation of the parabola the equation of OB is $y = -4\sqrt{x}$ and the equation of OCD is $y = 4\sqrt{x}$. Finally, the limits of integration with respect to x are 0 and 1. Hence

$$A_1 = \int_0^1 \int_{-4\sqrt{x}}^{4\sqrt{x}} dx\, dy$$
$$= \int_0^1 8\sqrt{x}\, dx = \left[\tfrac{16}{3} x^{\frac{3}{2}}\right]_0^1 = \tfrac{16}{3}.$$

Denoting the area to the right of BC by A_2, we see that the limits of integration with respect to y are $4x - 8$ from the equation of the straight line and $4\sqrt{x}$ from the equation of the parabola. Finally, the limits of integration with respect to x are 1 and 4. Hence

$$A_2 = \int_1^4 \int_{4x-8}^{4\sqrt{x}} dx\, dy$$
$$= \int_1^4 (4\sqrt{x} - 4x + 8)\, dx$$
$$= \left[\tfrac{8}{3} x^{\frac{3}{2}} - 2x^2 + 8x\right]_1^4 = \tfrac{38}{3}.$$

Finally, the required area is $\tfrac{16}{3} + \tfrac{38}{3}$, which is 18, as was found by the other solution.

Consider a similar problem in polar coördinates. Let an area, as in Fig. 126, be bounded by two curves $r_1 = f_1(\theta)$ and $r_2 = f_2(\theta)$, and let the values of θ corresponding to the points B and C be θ_1 and θ_2 respectively. We assume that $r_1 < r_2$ for all values of θ between θ_1 and θ_2. The plane may be divided into four-sided figures by circles with centers at O and straight lines radiating from O. Let the angle between two consecutive radii be $d\theta$ and the distance between two consecutive circles be dr. We want first the area of one of the quadrilaterals, such as $PQRS$. Here $OP = r$, $PQ = dr$, and the angle $POS = d\theta$. By geometry the area of the sector $POS = \tfrac{1}{2} r^2 d\theta$ and the area of the sector $QOR = \tfrac{1}{2}(r + dr)^2 d\theta$; therefore $PQRS = \tfrac{1}{2}(r + dr)^2 d\theta - \tfrac{1}{2} r^2 d\theta$ $= r\, dr\, d\theta + \tfrac{1}{2}(dr)^2 d\theta = \left(r + \dfrac{dr}{2}\right) dr\, d\theta$. Now as dr and $d\theta$ approach zero as a limit it is evident that the area $PQRS$ is of the form

$(r + \epsilon)dr\,d\theta$, where ϵ is an infinitesimal. Hence $PQRS$ differs from $r\,d\theta\,dr$ by an infinitesimal of higher order (§ 84), and it may

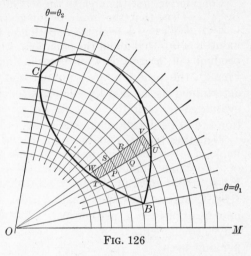

FIG. 126

be shown by a discussion similar to that of § 84 that this infinitesimal does not affect the limit of the sum of the expression, and we are therefore justified in writing as the differential of area

$$dA = r\,d\theta\,dr. \quad (12)$$

Referring to Fig. 126, we see that $r\,d\theta$ is the length of the side PS of the area $PQRS$ and dr is the length of the side PQ.

The required area is the limit of the sum of the differentials of area (12). To find it we first take the limit of the sum of the quadrilaterals, such as $PQRS$, which lie in the same sector UOV. That is, we integrate $r\,d\theta\,dr$, holding θ and $d\theta$ constant and allowing r to vary from r_1 to r_2. We have

$$\int_{r_1}^{r_2} r\,d\theta\,dr = \tfrac{1}{2}\,(r_2{}^2 - r_1{}^2)\,d\theta, \quad (13)$$

which is the area of the strip $TUVW$.

Finally, we take the limit of the sum of the areas of all such strips in the required area and have

$$A = \int_{\theta_1}^{\theta_2} \tfrac{1}{2}(r_2{}^2 - r_1{}^2)\,d\theta. \quad (14)$$

If we put together what we have done, we may write

$$A = \int_{\theta_1}^{\theta_2} \int_{r_1}^{r_2} r\,d\theta\,dr. \quad (15)$$

It is clear that this formula leads to nothing which might not be obtained by (5), § 86, but it is convenient sometimes to have the expression (15).

In connection with a plane area we may consider the integral

$$\iint f(x, y)\,dx\,dy \qquad (16)$$

Here $dx\,dy = dA$ as before, while $f(x, y)$ is a function whose value is computed at some point (x, y) of the element $dx\,dy$. The product $f(x, y)dx\,dy$ is then formed for each element of area. Finally, the products are summed and the limit of the sum is determined as dx and dy each approaches zero. The result is evaluated by a double integration where the limits of integration are to be determined, exactly as in finding the area.

The integral

$$\iint f(r, \theta)\,r\,d\theta\,dr \qquad (17)$$

has a similar meaning in polar coördinates.

96. Center of gravity of a plane area. Formulas (3), § 91, may now be applied to a plane area. Let the area be divided in any way into elements of area dA. Then if ρ is the amount of mass per unit area, $dm = \rho\,dA$, $\qquad M = \rho A$.

By substitution in (3), § 91, we have

$$A\overline{x} = \int x\,dA, \quad A\overline{y} = \int y\,dA. \qquad (1)$$

If we use Cartesian coördinates we may take $dA = dx\,dy$, and if the area considered is of the general form of Fig. 122, we have, using the notation of § 95,

$$A\overline{x} = \int_a^b \int_{y_1}^{y_2} x\,dx\,dy, \quad A\overline{y} = \int_a^b \int_{y_1}^{y_2} y\,dx\,dy. \qquad (2)$$

Making the first integration in each of the formulas (2), we have

$$A\overline{x} = \int_a^b x(y_2 - y_1)dx,$$
$$A\overline{y} = \int_a^b \tfrac{1}{2}(y_2{}^2 - y_1{}^2)dx = \int_a^b \tfrac{1}{2}(y_2 + y_1)(y_2 - y_1)dx \qquad (3)$$

These results may be interpreted as follows: The area of the vertical strip in Fig. 122 is $(y_2 - y_1)dx$ and the middle point of its left-hand edge is $(x, \tfrac{1}{2}(y_2 + y_1))$. Hence in (1) we may take

dA as the area of a vertical strip, regard its mass as concentrated at the middle point of its left-hand edge, and complete the work by a single integration.

Example 1. Find the center of gravity of the area bounded by the parabola $y^2 = kx$, the axis of x, and the ordinate through the point (a, b) of the parabola (Fig. 127).

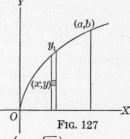

We shall denote the ordinate of any point on the parabola by y_1 to distinguish it from the ordinate of the point (x, y) at which the element dA is concentrated.

We will solve the problem first by taking dA as the vertical strip of the figure. Then $dA = y_1dx = \sqrt{kx}\,dx$ and the middle

FIG. 127

point of its left-hand edge is $\left(x, \dfrac{y_1}{2}\right)$, which is $\left(x, \dfrac{\sqrt{kx}}{2}\right)$. Hence

$$A\bar{x} = \int_0^a x\sqrt{kx}\,dx = \tfrac{2}{5}\,k^{\frac{1}{2}}a^{\frac{5}{2}},$$

$$A\bar{y} = \int_0^a \frac{\sqrt{kx}}{2}\sqrt{kx}\,dx = \frac{ka^2}{4}.$$

But, from the equation of the curve, $k = \dfrac{b^2}{a}$, and, by Exercise 4, p. 76, $A = \tfrac{2}{3}\,ab$. Therefore

$$\bar{x} = \tfrac{3}{5}\,a, \quad \bar{y} = \tfrac{3}{8}\,b.$$

Or we may solve the problem by taking as dA the small shaded rectangle of dimension dx and dy in Fig. 127. Then $dA = dx\,dy$ and the point of concentration (x, y) may be taken as the lower left-hand corner of the rectangle. Then we have, since $y_1 = \sqrt{kx}$,

$$A\bar{x} = \int_0^a \int_0^{y_1} x\,dx\,dy = \int_0^a x\sqrt{kx}\,dx = \tfrac{2}{5}\,k^{\frac{1}{2}}a^{\frac{5}{2}},$$

$$A\bar{y} = \int_0^a \int_0^{y_1} y\,dx\,dy = \int_0^a \frac{kx}{2}\,dx = \frac{ka^2}{4},$$

as before. It is to be noted that the results of the first integrations in this method of solution are the integrals which we wrote down at once in the first method of solution.

If we have an area bounded by curves in polar coördinates, we may put $dA = r\,d\theta\,dr$ in (1). We have then to place $x = r\cos\theta$, $y = r\sin\theta$ and (1) becomes

$$A\bar{x} = \iint r^2 \cos\theta\,d\theta\,dr, \qquad A\bar{y} = \iint r^2 \sin\theta\,d\theta\,dr. \qquad (4)$$

Example 2. Find the center of gravity of a sextant of a circle of radius a.

To solve this problem it is convenient to place the sextant so that the axis of x bisects it (Fig. 128) and to use polar coördinates.

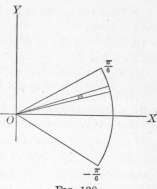

From the symmetry of the figure the center of gravity lies on OX, so that we may write at once $\overline{y} = 0$. To find $\overline{x}$ take an element of area $r \, d\theta \, dr$ in polar coördinates and place $x = r \cos \theta$. We have then, from (4),

$$A\overline{x} = \int_{-\frac{\pi}{6}}^{\frac{\pi}{6}} \int_0^a r^2 \cos \theta \, d\theta \, dr,$$

where $A = \frac{1}{6} \pi a^2$, one sixth the area of a circle. In the first integration θ and $d\theta$ are constant, and the summation takes place along a line radiating from O with r varying from 0 to a. The angle θ then

Fig. 128

varies from $-\dfrac{\pi}{6}$ to $\dfrac{\pi}{6}$, and thus the entire area is covered. The solution is as follows:

$$\tfrac{1}{6} \pi a^2 \overline{x} = \int_{-\frac{\pi}{6}}^{\frac{\pi}{6}} \tfrac{1}{3} a^3 \cos \theta \, d\theta = \tfrac{1}{3} a^3 ;$$

whence
$$\overline{x} = \frac{2 \, a}{\pi}.$$

EXERCISES

1. Find the center of gravity of a parabolic segment of base b and altitude a.

2. Find the center of gravity of a quadrant of the area of a circle.

3. Find the center of gravity of a triangle.

4. Find the center of gravity of the area bounded by the curve $y = \sin x$ and the axis of x between $x = 0$ and $x = \pi$.

5. Find the center of gravity of the plane area bounded by the two parabolas $y^2 = 12 \, x$ and $x^2 = 12 \, y$.

6. Find the center of gravity of a figure which is composed of a rectangle of base $2 \, a$ and altitude b surmounted by a semicircle of radius a.

7. Find the center of gravity of the area bounded by the first arch of the cycloid (§ 51) and the axis of x.

8. Show that the center of gravity of a sector of a circle lies at a distance $\frac{4}{3}\frac{a}{\alpha}\sin\frac{\alpha}{2}$ from the vertex of the sector on a line bisecting the angle of the sector, where α is the angle and a the radius.

9. Find the center of gravity of the area bounded by the cardioid $r = a(1 + \cos\theta)$.

10. Find the center of gravity of the area bounded by the curve $r = 2\cos\theta + 4$.

11. Find the center of gravity of the area inside the curve $r = a\cos\theta$ and outside the curve $r = a(1 - \cos\theta)$.

97. Center of gravity of a composite body. In finding the center of gravity of a body the following theorem is often useful:

If a body of mass M is composed of several parts of masses $M_1, M_2, \cdots, M_n$, and if the centers of gravity of these parts are respectively $(\bar{x}_1, \bar{y}_1), (\bar{x}_2, \bar{y}_2), \cdots, (\bar{x}_n, \bar{y}_n)$, then the center of gravity of the composite body is given by the formulas

$$M\bar{x} = M_1\bar{x}_1 + M_2\bar{x}_2 + \cdots + M_n\bar{x}_n,$$
$$M\bar{y} = M_1\bar{y}_1 + M_2\bar{y}_2 + \cdots + M_n\bar{y}_n. \tag{1}$$

We shall prove the theorem for the $\bar{x}$ coördinate. The proof for $\bar{y}$ is the same.

By (3), § 91, we have, for the original body,

$$M\bar{x} = \int x\, dm, \tag{2}$$

where the integration is to be taken over all the partial masses $M_1, M_2, \cdots, M_n$ into which the body is divided. Hence formula (2) can be written

$$M\bar{x} = \int x_1\, dm_1 + \int x_2\, dm_2 + \cdots + \int x_n\, dm_n, \tag{3}$$

where the subscripts indicate that the integration in each case is restricted to one of the several bodies.

But we have also
$$M_1\bar{x}_1 = \int x_1\, dm_1,$$

$$M_2\bar{x}_2 = \int x_2\, dm_2, \tag{4}$$

$$\cdots \cdots \cdots$$

$$M_n\bar{x}_n = \int x_n\, dm_n,$$

and, by substitution in (3), the theorem is proved.

Example. Find the center of gravity of an area bounded by two circles one of which is completely inside the other.

Let the two circles be placed as in Fig. 129, where the center of the larger circle of radius a is at the origin, and the center of the smaller circle of radius b is on the axis of x at a distance c from the origin.

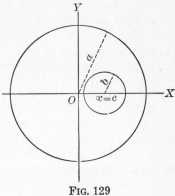

The area which can be considered as composed of two parts is that of the larger circle, the two parts being, first, the smaller circle and, second, the irregular ring whose center of gravity we wish to find. Now the center of gravity of a circle is known to be at its center. Therefore, in the formula of the theorem, we know $(\overline{x}, \overline{y})$, which is on the left of the equation, to be $(0, 0)$, and $(\overline{x}_1, \overline{y}_1)$ to be $(c, 0)$, and wish to find $(\overline{x}_2, \overline{y}_2)$.

FIG. 129

Since we are dealing with areas, we take the masses to be equal to the areas, and have, accordingly, $M = \pi a^2$ (the mass of the larger circle), $M_1 = \pi b^2$ (the mass of the smaller circle), and $M_2 = \pi (a^2 - b^2)$ (the mass of the ring). Substituting in the formula, we have

$$\pi a^2 \cdot 0 = \pi b^2 c + \pi (a^2 - b^2)\overline{x}_2 ;$$

whence, by solving for $\overline{x}_2$, $\overline{x}_2 = -\dfrac{b^2 c}{a^2 - b^2}.$

It is unnecessary to find $\overline{y}_2$, since, by symmetry, the center of gravity lies on OX.

EXERCISES

1. Prove that if a mass M_2 with center of gravity $(\overline{x}_2, \overline{y}_2)$ is cut from a mass M_1 with center of gravity $(\overline{x}_1, \overline{y}_1)$, the center of gravity of the remaining mass is

$$\overline{x} = \frac{M_1 \overline{x}_1 - M_2 \overline{x}_2}{M_1 - M_2}, \quad \overline{y} = \frac{M_1 \overline{y}_1 - M_2 \overline{y}_2}{M_1 - M_2}.$$

2. Two circles of radii r_1 and r_2 are tangent externally. Find their center of gravity.

3. Find the center of gravity of a hemispherical shell bounded by two concentric hemispheres of radii r_1 and r_2. *use result of prob. 5 p 384*

4. Place $r_2 = r_1 + \Delta r$ in Ex. 3, let Δr approach zero, and thus find the center of gravity of a hemispherical surface.

5. Find the center of gravity of a hollow right circular cone bounded by two parallel conical surfaces of altitudes h_1 and h_2 respectively and with their bases in the same plane.

6. Place $h_2 = h_1 + \Delta h$ in Ex. 5, let Δh approach zero, and thus find the center of gravity of a conical surface.

7. Find the center of gravity of a carpenter's square, each arm of which is 18 in. on its outer edge and 3 in. wide.

8. From a square of edge 8 in. a quadrant of a circle is cut out, the center of the quadrant being at a corner of the square and the radius of the quadrant being 4 in. Find the center of gravity of the figure remaining.

9. Two iron balls, of radius 4 in. and 6 in. respectively, are connected by an iron rod of length 1 in. Assuming that the rod is a cylinder of radius 1 in., find the center of gravity of the system.

10. A cubical pedestal of side 4 ft. is surmounted by a sphere of radius 2 ft. Find the center of gravity of the system, assuming that the sphere rests on the middle point of the top of the pedestal.

98. Theorems. The following theorems involving the center of gravity may often be used to advantage in finding pressures, volumes of solids of revolution, or areas of surfaces of revolution.

1. *The total pressure on a plane surface immersed in liquid in a vertical position is equal to the area of the surface multiplied by the pressure at its center of gravity.*

Take any area of any shape, as in Fig. 130. Construct coördinate axes so that the axis of x is in the surface of the liquid and the axis of y is measured downward, and divide the area into elements of area $dA = dx\,dy$. Then, if such an element is at the depth y, the pressure on it is $wy\,dx\,dy$, and the total pressure P is the

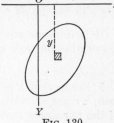

FIG. 130

limit of the sum of the pressures on all the elements as the elements are made to approach zero in size. Hence

$$P = \int\int wy\,dx\,dy = w\int\int y\,dx\,dy. \tag{1}$$

Moreover, from § 96, we have

$$A\bar{y} = \int\int y\,dx\,dy. \tag{2}$$

By comparison of (1) and (2) we have

$$P = w\bar{y}A.$$

But $w\bar{y}$ is the pressure at the center of gravity, and the theorem is proved.

Example 1. A circular bulkhead which closes the outlet of a reservoir has a radius 3 ft., and its center is 12 ft. below the surface of the water. Find the total pressure on it.

Here $A = 9\pi$ and the depth of the center of gravity is 12. Therefore

$$P = 108\,\pi w = \tfrac{27}{8}\,\pi \text{ tons} = 10.6 \text{ tons.}$$

2. The volume generated by revolving a plane area about an axis in its plane not intersecting the area is equal to the area of the figure multiplied by the circumference of the circle described by its center of gravity.

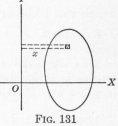

Let the plane area be taken in the plane XOY and let OY be the axis of revolution (Fig. 131). Each element of area $dx\,dy$ will generate a cylindrical shell of inner radius x, thickness dx, and altitude dy. The volume of this shell is $2\pi x\,dx\,dy$, by (10), § 86, and the volume of the whole solid of revolution is the limit of the sum of the volumes of these shells. Hence

$$V = 2\pi \iint x\,dx\,dy. \qquad (3)$$

FIG. 131

By § 96, $\qquad A\bar{x} = \iint x\,dx\,dy; \qquad (4)$

and, by comparison of (3) and (4), we have

$$V = 2\pi\bar{x}A,$$

which was to be proved.

Example 2. Find the volume of the ring solid formed by revolving about an axis in its plane a circle of radius a whose center is at a distance c from the axis, where $c > a$.

We know that $A = \pi a^2$ and that the center of gravity of the circle is at the center of the circle and therefore describes a circumference of length $2\pi c$. Therefore

$$V = 2\pi^2 a^2 c.$$

3. *The area generated by revolving a plane curve about an axis in its plane not intersecting the curve is equal to the length of the curve multiplied by the circumference of the circle described by its center of gravity.*

If S is the area of the surface formed by revolving a plane curve about OY, then, by § 89,

$$S = 2 \pi \int x\, ds. \tag{5}$$

Moreover, by (4), § 91, we have

$$s\overline{x} = \int x\, ds; \tag{6}$$

and comparing the two equations (5) and (6), we have

$$S = 2 \pi s\overline{x},$$

which was to be proved.

Example 3. Find the area of the ring surface described in Example 2.

We know that $s = 2 \pi a$ and that the center of gravity of a circumference is at its center and therefore describes a circumference of length $2 \pi c$. Therefore

$$S = 4 \pi^2 ac.$$

Theorems 2 and 3 are known as the *theorems of Pappus.*

EXERCISES

1. Find by the theorems of Pappus the volume and the surface of a sphere.

2. Find by the theorems of Pappus the volume and the lateral surface of a right circular cone.

3. Find by the theorems of Pappus the volume generated by revolving a parabolic segment about its altitude.

4. Find by the theorems of Pappus the volume generated by revolving a parabolic segment about its base.

5. Find by the theorems of Pappus the volume generated by revolving a parabolic segment about the tangent at its vertex.

6. Find the volume and the surface generated by revolving a square of side a about an axis in its plane perpendicular to one of its diagonals and at a distance $b \left(b > \dfrac{a}{\sqrt{2}} \right)$ from its center.

7. Find the volume and the area generated by revolving a right triangle with legs a and b about an axis in its plane parallel to the leg of length a on the opposite side from the hypotenuse and at a distance c from the vertex of the right angle.

8. A circular water main has a diameter of 4 ft. One end is closed by a bulkhead, and the other is connected with a reservoir in which the surface of the water is 18 ft. above the center of the bulkhead. Find the pressure on the bulkhead.

9. Find the pressure on an ellipse of semiaxes a and b completely submerged, if the center of the ellipse is c units below the surface of the liquid.

10. Find the pressure on a semiellipse of semiaxes a and b $(a > b)$ submerged with the major axis in the surface of the liquid and the minor axis vertical.

11. Find the pressure on a parabolic segment submerged with the base horizontal, the axis vertical, the vertex above the base, and the vertex c units below the surface of the liquid.

12. What is the effect on the pressure on a submerged vertical area in a reservoir if the level of the water in the reservoir is raised by c feet?

13. Find the center of gravity of an area of a semicircle by the theorems of Pappus.

14. Find the center of gravity of a semicircumference by the theorems of Pappus.

99. Moment of inertia of a plane area. The moment of inertia of a plane area may be expressed as a double integral. Let the area be divided into elements of area $dx\,dy$. Then $dm = \rho\,dx\,dy$, where ρ is the amount of mass per unit of area. Let (x, y) be any point of the element of area. By the theorem of § 84, which is easily extended to the case of a double integral, it is immaterial which point of $dx\,dy$ is taken as the point (x, y). The mass dm is at a distance x from OY. Its moment of inertia about OY is therefore $\rho x^2 dx\,dy$, by the definition of § 92. The moment of inertia of the area about OY is the limit of the sum of the moments of inertia of the elements as dx and dy approach zero. Therefore, placing $\rho = 1$, we have

$$I_y = \iint x^2\,dx\,dy. \tag{1}$$

Similarly, the element $dx\,dy$ is at a distance y from OX, and therefore

$$I_x = \iint y^2\,dx\,dy. \tag{2}$$

Again, each element is at a distance $\sqrt{x^2 + y^2}$ from O. Its polar moment of inertia about O is therefore $(x^2 + y^2)dx\,dy$, and the polar moment of the whole area is

$$I_0 = \iint (x^2 + y^2)dx\,dy. \tag{3}$$

In evaluating these integrals the integration may be carried out in either order. It is usually convenient to integrate (1) with respect to y first. Then, if the area and limits are as in Fig. 122, § 95, we have

$$I_y = \int_a^b x^2(y_2 - y_1)dx,$$

which agrees with (2), § 92.

On the other hand, it is usually convenient to integrate (2) first with respect to x. We then have, with the notation of (10), § 95,

$$I_x = \int_c^e y^2(x_2 - x_1)dy,$$

which agrees with (3), § 92.

In evaluating (3) it is often convenient to separate I_0 into the sum of two integrals and integrate the two in different orders. We have then, in agreement with (6), § 92,

$$I_0 = \iint x^2\,dx\,dy + \iint y^2\,dy\,dx = I_y + I_x. \tag{4}$$

If polar coördinates are used, the element of area is $r\,d\theta\,dr$ and the distance of a point in an element from the origin is r. Therefore

$$I_0 = \iint r^3\,d\theta\,dr. \tag{5}$$

In practice it is usually convenient to integrate first with respect to r, holding θ constant. This is, in fact, to find the polar moment of inertia of a sector with vertex at O.

Example. Find the polar moment of inertia of a circle with respect to a point on its circumference.

Let the circle be placed as in Fig. 132. Its equation is then ((2), § 61) $r = 2\,a\cos\theta$, where a is the radius. If we take any element $r\,d\theta\,dr$ and find I_0 for all elements which lie in the same sector with it, we have to add the elements $r^3\,d\theta\,dr$, with r ranging from 0 to r_1, where r_1 is the value of r on the circle; and therefore $r_1 = 2\,a\cos\theta$. We have

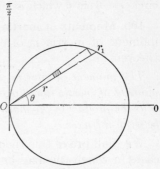

FIG. 132

$$\int_0^{r_1} r^3\,d\theta\,dr = \tfrac{1}{4}\,r_1{}^4\,d\theta = 4\,a^4\cos^4\theta\,d\theta.$$

We have finally to sum these quantities, with θ ranging from $-\dfrac{\pi}{2}$ to $+\dfrac{\pi}{2}$.

We have
$$I_0 = \int_{\frac{\pi}{2}}^{\frac{\pi}{2}} 4\,a^4\cos^4\theta\,d\theta = \tfrac{3}{2}\,\pi a^4.$$

If M is the mass of a circular plate, this result, multiplied by ρ, gives
$$I_0 = \tfrac{3}{2}\,M a^2.$$

EXERCISES

1. Find the polar moment of inertia about the origin of the area bounded by the hyperbola $xy = 4$ and the straight line $x + y - 5 = 0$.

2. Find the moment of inertia about OY of the area bounded above by the circle $x^2 + y^2 = 128$ and below by the parabola $x^2 = 8\,y$.

3. Find the moment of inertia about OY of the area bounded by $y = \dfrac{8}{x^2 + 4}$ and $x^2 = 4\,y$.

4. Find the polar moment of inertia about the pole of the entire area bounded by the curve $r^2 = a^2 \sin 3\,\theta$.

5. Find the polar moment of inertia about the pole of the area bounded by the cardioid $r = a(1 + \cos\theta)$.

6. Find the polar moment of inertia about O of the total area bounded by the curve $r = a(1 + \cos 2\,\theta)$.

7. Find the polar moment of inertia about O of the total area bounded by the curve $r = a(1 + 2\sin\theta)$.

8. Find the polar moment of inertia about O of that part of the area inside the curve $r = 4 + 2\cos\theta$ which is outside the circle $r = 4$.

9. Find the polar moment of inertia about O of the area inside the curve $r = a \sin \theta$ and outside the curve $r = a(1 - \sin \theta)$.

10. Find the polar moment of inertia about O of that part of the circle $r = 6 \sin \theta$ which is outside the circle $r = 3$.

100. Moments of inertia about parallel axes. The finding of a moment of inertia is often simplified by use of the following theorem:

The moment of inertia of a body about an axis is equal to its moment of inertia about a parallel axis through its center of gravity plus the product of the mass of the body by the square of the distance between the axes.

We shall prove this theorem only for a plane area, in the two cases in which the axes lie in the plane of the figure or are perpendicular to that plane. We shall also consider the mass of the area as equal to the area, as in § 92.

CASE I. *When the axes lie in the plane of the figure.*

Let the area be placed as in Fig. 133, where the center of gravity $(\overline{x}, \overline{y})$ is taken as the origin $(0, 0)$ and where the axis of y is taken parallel to the axis LK, about which we wish to find the moment of inertia. Let x be the distance of an element $dx\,dy$ from OY, and x_1 its distance from LK. Then, if I_g is the moment of inertia about OY, and I_l the moment of inertia about LK, we have

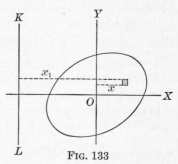

FIG. 133

$$I_g = \iint x^2 \, dx \, dy, \qquad I_l = \iint x_1{}^2 \, dx \, dy. \qquad (1)$$

Moreover, if a is the distance between OY and LK, we have

$$x_1 = x + a; \qquad (2)$$

so that, by substituting from (2) in the second equation of (1), we have

$$I_l = \iint x^2 \, dx \, dy + 2\,a \iint x \, dx \, dy + a^2 \iint dx \, dy. \qquad (3)$$

Now, by § 95, $\iint dx \, dy = A$; by § 96, $\iint x \, dx \, dy = A\overline{x} = 0$, since by hypothesis $\bar{x} = 0$; and, by (1), the first integral on the right hand of (3) is I_g. Therefore (3) can be written

$$I_l = I_g + a^2 A, \tag{4}$$

which proves the theorem for this case.

CASE II. *When the axes are perpendicular to the plane of the figure.*

We have to do now with polar moments of inertia. Let the area be placed as in Fig. 134, where the center of gravity is taken as the origin, and P is any point about which we wish the polar moment of inertia. Let I_g be the polar moment of inertia about O, and I_p the polar moment of inertia about P. Draw through P axes PX' and PY' parallel to the axes of coördinates OX and OY. Let I_x and I_y be the moments of inertia about OX and OY respectively, and let $I_{x'}$ and $I_{y'}$ be the moments of inertia about PX' and PY'. Then, by (4), § 99,

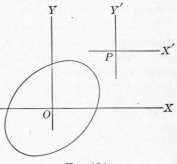

FIG. 134

$$\begin{aligned} I_g &= I_x + I_y, \\ I_p &= I_{x'} + I_{y'}. \end{aligned} \tag{5}$$

Moreover, if (a, b) are the coördinates of P, we have, by Case I,

$$I_{x'} = I_x + b^2 A, \quad I_{y'} = I_y + a^2 A. \tag{6}$$

Therefore, from (5), we have

$$I_p = I_g + (a^2 + b^2)A, \tag{7}$$

which proves the theorem for this case also.

The student may easily prove that the theorem is true also for the moment of inertia of any solid of revolution about an axis parallel to the axis of revolution of the solid.

Example. Find the polar moment of inertia of a circle with respect to a point on the circumference.

The center of gravity of a circle is at its center, and the distance of any point on its circumference from its center is a. By Ex. 4, § 92, the polar moment of inertia of a circle about its center is $\frac{1}{2}\pi a^4$. Therefore, by the above theorem,

$$I_p = \tfrac{1}{2}\pi a^4 + a^2(\pi a^2) = \tfrac{3}{2}\pi a^4.$$

This result agrees with the example in § 99, where the required moment of inertia was found directly.

EXERCISES

1. Find the moment of inertia of a circle about a tangent.

2. From a square of side 10 a circular hole of radius 4 is cut, the center of the circle being at the center of the square. Find the moment of inertia of the resulting figure about a side of the square.

3. Find the polar moment of inertia about a corner of the square of the figure in Ex. 2.

4. From a circle of radius 8 in. a square of side 2 in. is cut out, the center of the square being 3 in. from the center of the circle. Find the polar moment of inertia of the resulting figure about the center of the circle.

5. From a circle of radius a is cut a circle of radius $\dfrac{a}{2}$ tangent to the larger circle. Find the moment of inertia of the remaining figure about the line through the centers of the two circles.

6. Find the moment of inertia of the figure in Ex. 5 about a line through the center of the larger circle perpendicular to the line of centers of the two circles and in the plane of the circles.

7. Find the polar moment of inertia about one of its outer corners of a picture frame bounded by two rectangles, the outer one being of dimensions 9 ft. by 12 ft., and the inner one of dimensions 6 ft. by 9 ft.

8. Find the moment of inertia about one of its outer edges of a carpenter's square of which the outer edges are 15 in. and the inner edges 12 in.

p. 290
no. 1

9. Find the moment of inertia of a hollow cylindrical column of outer radius r_2 and inner radius r_1 about an element of the inner cylinder.

10. Find the moment of inertia of the hollow column of Ex. 9 about an element of the outer cylinder.

101. Space coördinates. In the preceding pages we have become familiar with two methods of fixing the position of a point in a plane, namely, by Cartesian coördinates (x, y) and by polar coördinates (r, θ). If, now, any plane has been thus supplied with a coördinate system, and, starting from a point in that plane, we measure another distance, called z, at right angles to the plane, we can reach any point in space. The quantity z will be considered positive if measured in one direction and negative if measured in the other. We have, accordingly, two systems of space coördinates.

1. *Cartesian coördinates.* We take any plane, as XOY, in which are already drawn a pair of coördinate axes, OX and OY, at right angles with each other. Perpendicular to this plane at the origin we draw a third axis OZ (Fig. 135). If P is any point of space, we draw PM parallel to OZ, meeting the plane XOY at M, and from M draw a line parallel to OY, meeting OX at L. Then for the point $P(x, y, z)$, $OL = x$, $LM = y$, and $MP = z$. It is to be noticed that the three axes determine

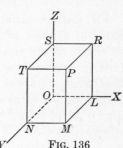

Fig. 135

three planes, XOY, YOZ, and ZOX, called the coördinate planes, and that we may just as readily draw the line from P perpendicular to either the plane YOZ or ZOX and then complete the construction as above.

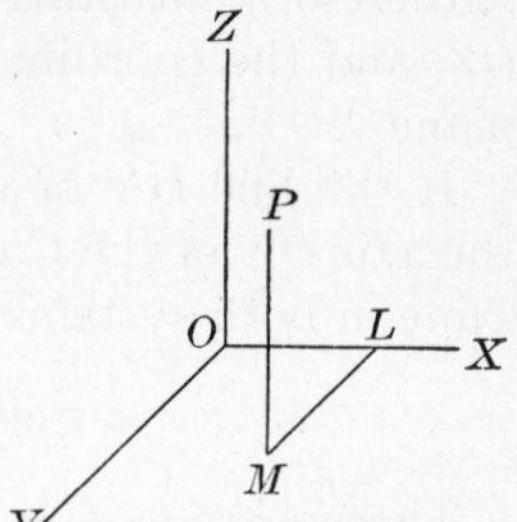

These possibilities are shown in Fig. 136, where it is seen that $x = OL = NM = SR = TP$, with similar sets of values for y and z.

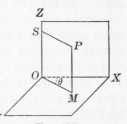

Fig. 136

2. *Cylindrical coördinates.* Let XOY be any plane in which a fixed point O is the origin of a system of polar coördinates, and OX is the initial line of that system (Fig. 137). Let OZ be an axis perpendicular to the plane XOY at O. If P is any point in space, we draw from P a straight line parallel to OZ until it meets the plane XOY at M. Then, if the polar coördinates of M in the plane XOY are $r = OM$, $\theta = XOM$, and we denote the distance MP by z, the cylindrical coördinates of P are (r, θ, z).

Fig. 137

It is evident that the axes OX and OZ determine a fixed plane, and that the angle θ is the plane angle of the dihedral angle between that fixed plane and the plane through OZ and the point P. If SP is drawn in the latter plane perpendicular to OZ, it is evident that $OM = SP = r$ and $OS = MP = z$. The coördinate r, therefore, measures the distance of the point P from the axis OZ, and the coördinate z measures the distance of P from the plane XOY.

If the line OX of the cylindrical coördinates is the same as the axis OX of the Cartesian coördinates, and the axis OZ is the same in both systems, it is evident, from (1), § 60, that

$$x = r \cos \theta, \qquad y = r \sin \theta, \qquad z = z. \tag{1}$$

These are formulas by which we may pass from one system to the other. It is convenient to notice especially that

$$r^2 = x^2 + y^2. \tag{2}$$

102. Certain surfaces. A single equation between the coördinates of a point in space represents a surface. We shall give examples of the equations of certain surfaces which are important in applications. In this connection it should be noticed that when we speak of the equation of a sphere we mean the equation of a spherical surface, and when we speak of the volume of a sphere we mean the volume of the solid bounded by a spherical surface. The word *sphere*, then, indicates a surface or a solid, according to the context. Similarly, the word *cone* is used to denote either a conical surface indefinite in extent or a solid bounded by a conical surface and a plane base. It is in the former sense that we speak of the equation of a cone, and in the latter sense that we speak of the volume of a cone. In the same way the word *cylinder* may denote either a cylindrical surface or a solid bounded by a cylindrical surface and two plane bases. This double use of these words makes no confusion in practice, as the context always indicates the proper meaning in any particular case.

1. *Cylinders.* Consider first a right circular cylinder with its axis along OZ (Fig. 138). From any point P of the surface of the cylinder draw PS perpendicular to OZ. Then SP is always equal to a, the radius of the cylinder. Therefore, for all points on the surface,

$$r = a, \qquad (1)$$

which is the equation of the cylinder in cylindrical coördinates. Changed to Cartesian coördinates, equation (1) becomes

$$x^2 + y^2 = a^2. \qquad (2)$$

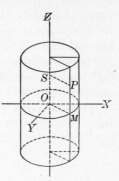

Fig. 138

More generally, any equation in x and y only, or in r and θ only, represents a cylinder with its elements parallel to OZ. In fact, either of these equations, if interpreted in the plane XOY, represents a curve; but if a straight line is drawn from any point in this curve perpendicular to the plane XOY, and P is any point on this line, the coördinates of P also satisfy the equation, since z is not involved in the equation. Hence the line lies entirely in the surface. Accordingly, the surface is a cylindrical surface with its elements parallel to OZ and with the given equation as the equation of the right section of the surface made by the plane XOY. As examples, the equation $y^2 = 4\,x$ represents a cylinder whose right section is a parabola, and the equation $r = a \sin 3\,\theta$ represents a cylinder whose right section is a rose of three leaves (Fig. 84, § 60).

Similarly, a Cartesian equation in y and z alone is the equation of a cylinder with its elements parallel to OX, and a Cartesian equation in z and x alone is the equation of a cylinder with its elements parallel to OY.

2. *Surfaces of revolution.* Consider any surface of revolution with OZ as the axis of revolution (Fig. 139). Take P any point on the surface and pass a plane through P and OZ, cutting the surface in the curve CD. In this plane draw OR perpendicular to OZ; we may now regard OR and OZ as a pair of rectangular axes in this plane. Draw the

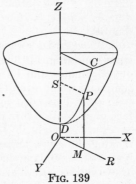

Fig. 139

straight lines SP and MP perpendicular, respectively, to OZ and OR. Then $SP = r$, $MP = z$, and we may write down the equation of the curve CD in the plane ROZ in the form

$$z = f(r), \qquad (3)$$

exactly as $y = f(x)$ is the equation of a curve in the plane XOY. But z and r in (3) are also the cylindrical coördinates of any point P of the curve CD in space of three dimensions, and CD is the same curve in all sections of the surface made by planes passing through OZ. Therefore equation (3) is true for all points P in the surface and is the equation of the surface in cylindrical coördinates. Hence we have the following theorem :

An equation of the form $z = f(r)$ in cylindrical coördinates always represents a surface of revolution with OZ as the axis of revolution.

The shape of the surface may be inferred by constructing a pair of rectangular axes OZ and OR in a plane and drawing in that plane the plane curve having $z = f(r)$ as its equation.

If the equation of the surface of revolution in Cartesian coördinates is desired, it may be found by placing $r = \sqrt{x^2 + y^2}$, according to (2), § 101.

When the plane POZ coincides with the plane XOZ, r is equal to x, and equation (3) becomes, for that section,

$$z = f(x). \tag{4}$$

Hence we have the following theorem :

The equation of a surface of revolution formed by revolving about OZ any curve in the plane XOZ may be found in cylindrical coördinates by writing r for x in the equation of the curve.

For example, the equation of the surface formed by revolving the parabola $z^2 = 4x$ about OZ as an axis is $z^2 = 4r$ in cylindrical coördinates, and $z^4 = 16(x^2 + y^2)$ in Cartesian coördinates.

3. *Right circular cone.* Consider any right circular cone (Fig. 140) with its vertex at the origin of coördinates and its axis along OZ. Let α be the angle which each element of the cone makes with OZ. This cone may be regarded as a surface of revolution formed by revolving about OZ as axis a straight line passing through O and making the given angle α with OZ. We accordingly take any plane through OZ and in that plane draw the axis OR. This plane cuts the cone in the element OA, a straight line making the angle α with OZ, and hence having the equation

$$r = z \tan \alpha. \tag{5}$$

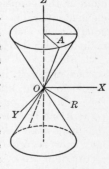

FIG 140

Hence, interpreted in space of three dimensions, (5) is the equation of the cone in cylindrical coördinates.

Replacing r by $\sqrt{x^2 + y^2}$ and simplifying, we have

$$x^2 + y^2 - z^2 \tan^2 \alpha = 0, \qquad (6)$$

as the equation of the cone in Cartesian coördinates.

As explained above, we have here used the word *cone* in the sense of a conical surface. If the cone is a solid with its altitude h and the radius of its base a, then $\tan \alpha = \dfrac{a}{h}$. In this case equation (5) or (6) is that of the curved surface of the cone only.

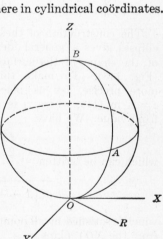

4. *Sphere with center at origin.* Consider any sphere (Fig. 141) with its center at the origin of coördinates and its radius equal to a. We shall derive the equation of the sphere by regarding it as a surface of revolution formed by revolving about OZ as axis a circle of radius a with its center at O. Let ROZ be any plane through OZ. The equation of the circle ABC cut out of the sphere by this plane is, by § 28,

$$r^2 + z^2 = a^2. \qquad (7)$$

Fig. 141

Hence, interpreted in space of three dimensions, (7) is the equation of the sphere in cylindrical coördinates.

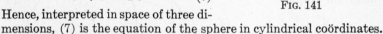

Replacing r by $\sqrt{x^2 + y^2}$, we obtain

$$x^2 + y^2 + z^2 = a^2 \qquad (8)$$

as the equation of the sphere in Cartesian coördinates.

5. *Sphere tangent at origin to a coördinate plane.* Consider a sphere of radius a, tangent to the plane XOY at O (Fig. 142). Regarding this sphere as a surface of revolution formed by revolving a circle of radius a about its diameter OZ as axis, we pass any plane ROZ through OZ. This plane cuts the sphere in a circle, one half of which, OAB, is shown in the figure. The coördinates of the center of this circle are $z = a$, $r = 0$; hence its equation is, by § 28,

Fig. 142

$$(r - 0)^2 + (z - a)^2 = a^2,$$

which reduces to

$$r^2 + z^2 - 2 az = 0. \qquad (9)$$

Considered in space of three dimensions, (9) is the equation of the sphere in cylindrical coördinates.

Replacing r by $\sqrt{x^2 + y^2}$, we have

$$x^2 + y^2 + z^2 - 2\,az = 0 \tag{10}$$

as the equation of the sphere in Cartesian coördinates.

6. *Ellipsoid.* Consider the surface defined by the equation

$$\frac{x^2}{a^2} + \frac{y^2}{b^2} + \frac{z^2}{c^2} = 1. \tag{11}$$

If we place $z = 0$, we get the points on the surface which lie in the XOY plane. These points satisfy the equation

$$\frac{x^2}{a^2} + \frac{y^2}{b^2} = 1 \tag{12}$$

and therefore form an ellipse.

Similarly, the points in the ZOX plane lie on the ellipse

$$\frac{x^2}{a^2} + \frac{z^2}{c^2} = 1, \tag{13}$$

and those in the YOZ plane lie on the ellipse

$$\frac{y^2}{b^2} + \frac{z^2}{c^2} = 1. \tag{14}$$

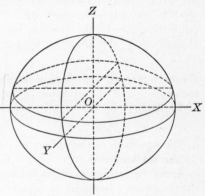

FIG. 143

The construction of these ellipses gives a general idea of the shape of the surface (Fig. 143). To make this more precise, let us place $z = z_1$ in (11), where z_1 is a fixed value. We have

$$\frac{x^2}{a^2} + \frac{y^2}{b^2} = 1 - \frac{z_1^2}{c^2}, \tag{15}$$

which can be written

$$\frac{x^2}{a^2\left(1 - \frac{z_1^2}{c^2}\right)} + \frac{y^2}{b^2\left(1 - \frac{z_1^2}{c^2}\right)} = 1, \tag{16}$$

which is satisfied by all points which lie in the plane at the distance z_1 from the XOY plane.

As long as $z_1^2 < c^2$, equation (16) represents an ellipse with semi-axes $a\sqrt{1 - \frac{z_1^2}{c^2}}$ and $b\sqrt{1 - \frac{z_1^2}{c^2}}$. By taking a sufficient number of these sections we may construct the ellipsoid with as much exactness as desired.

If $z_1{}^2 = c^2$ in (16), the axes of the ellipse reduce to zero, and we have a point. If $z_1{}^2 > c^2$, the axes are imaginary, and there is no section.

7. *Elliptic paraboloid.* Consider the surface

$$\frac{z}{c} = \frac{x^2}{a^2} + \frac{y^2}{b^2},\tag{17}$$

where we shall assume, for definiteness, that c is positive.

If we place $z = 0$, we get

$$\frac{x^2}{a^2} + \frac{y^2}{b^2} = 0,\tag{18}$$

which is satisfied in real quantities only by $x = 0$ and $y = 0$. Therefore the XOY plane simply touches the surface at the origin.

If we place $z = c$, we get the ellipse

$$\frac{x^2}{a^2} + \frac{y^2}{b^2} = 1,\tag{19}$$

which lies in the plane c units distant from the XOY plane.

If we place $y = 0$, we get the parabola

$$z = \frac{c}{a^2}\, x^2;\tag{20}$$

and if we place $x = 0$, we get the parabola

$$z = \frac{c}{b^2}\, y^2.\tag{21}$$

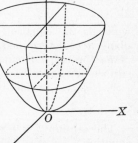

Fig. 144

The sections (19), (20), and (21) determine the general outline of surface. For more detail we place $z = z_1$ and find the ellipse

$$\frac{x^2}{\dfrac{a^2 z_1}{c}} + \frac{y^2}{\dfrac{b^2 z_1}{c}} = 1,\tag{22}$$

so that all sections parallel to the XOY plane and above it are ellipses (Fig. 144).

8. *Elliptic cone.* Consider the surface

$$\frac{x^2}{a^2} + \frac{y^2}{b^2} - \frac{z^2}{c^2} = 0.\tag{23}$$

Proceeding as in 7, we find that the section $z = 0$ is simply the origin and that the section $z = c$ is the ellipse

$$\frac{x^2}{a^2} + \frac{y^2}{b^2} = 1.\tag{24}$$

If we place $x = 0$, we get the two straight lines

$$y = \pm \frac{b}{c} z, \qquad (25)$$

and if we place $y = 0$, we get the two straight lines

$$x = \pm \frac{a}{c} z. \qquad (26)$$

The sections we have found suggest a cone with an elliptic base. To prove that the surface really is a cone, we change equation (23) to cylindrical coördinates, obtaining

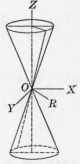

$$\left(\frac{\cos^2 \theta}{a^2} + \frac{\sin^2 \theta}{b^2} \right) r^2 = \frac{z^2}{c^2}. \qquad (27)$$

Now if θ is held constant in (27), the coefficient of r^2 is constant, and the equation may be written

$$r = \pm kz, \qquad (28)$$

FIG. 145

which is the equation of two straight lines in the plane ROZ determined by $\theta = $ constant. Hence any plane through OZ cuts the surface in two straight lines, and the surface is a cone (Fig. 145).

9. *Plane.* Consider the surface

$$Ax + By + Cz + D = 0. \qquad (29)$$

The section $z = 0$ is the straight line KH (Fig. 146) with the equation

$$Ax + By + D = 0, \qquad (30)$$

the section $y = 0$ is the straight line LH with the equation

$$Ax + Cz + D = 0, \qquad (31)$$

and the section $x = 0$ is the straight line LK with the equation

$$By + Cz + D = 0. \qquad (32)$$

The two lines (31) and (32) intersect OZ in the point $L\left(0, 0, -\frac{D}{C}\right)$, unless

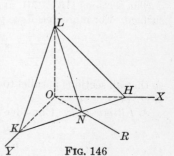

FIG. 146

$C = 0$. Assuming for the present that C is not zero, we change equation (29) to cylindrical coördinates, obtaining

$$(A \cos \theta + B \sin \theta) r + Cz + D = 0. \qquad (33)$$

This is the equation of a straight line LN in the plane $\theta = $ constant. It passes through the point L, which has the cylindrical coördinates $r = 0$, $z = -\dfrac{D}{C}$; and it meets the plane $z = 0$ in a point which lies on KH, since KH contains all the points of the surface which lie in the plane $z = 0$. Hence the surface is covered by straight lines which pass through L and meet KH. The locus of such lines is clearly a plane.

We have assumed that C in (29) is not zero. If $C = 0$, equation (29) is

$$Ax + By + D = 0. \tag{34}$$

The point L does not exist, since the lines corresponding to HL and KL are now parallel. But, by 1, equation (34) represents a plane parallel to OZ intersecting XOY in the line whose equation is (34). Therefore we have the following theorem:

Any equation of the first degree in x, y, z represents a plane.

EXERCISES

Describe each of the following surfaces:

1. $y^2 - 2y - 4x = 0$.
2. $y(z - 2) = 4$.
3. $4x^2 + 9y^2 = 12z - 24$.
4. $4x^2 + 9y^2 + 36z^2 - 8x - 32 = 0$.
5. $x^2 + y^2 + z^2 + 2Fx + 2Gy + 2Hz + C = 0$.
6. $\dfrac{x^2}{a^2} + \dfrac{y^2}{b^2} - \dfrac{(z - h)}{c} = 0$.
7. $\dfrac{x^2}{a^2} + \dfrac{y^2}{b^2} - \dfrac{(z - h)^2}{c^2} = 0$.
8. $Az + By + C = 0$.
9. $Az + Br + C = 0$. *Cone*
10. $\dfrac{x^2}{a^2} + \dfrac{y^2}{b^2} - \dfrac{z^2}{c^2} = 1$.
11. $\dfrac{x^2}{a^2} - \dfrac{y^2}{b^2} - \dfrac{z^2}{c^2} = 1$.
12. $r = a \cos \theta$.
13. $r^2 = a^2 \cos 2\theta$.
14. $r^2 + z^2 + 2z - 3 = 0$. *sphere*
15. $z^2 - 3r = 0$.
16. $6z^2 + 4r^2 = 24$.
17. $6z^2 - 4r^2 = 12$.

18. Find the equation of the surface formed by revolving about OZ as axis the parabola $z^2 = 14x$.

19. Find the equation of the oblate spheroid formed by revolving an ellipse about its minor axis.

20. Find the equation of the prolate spheroid formed by revolving an ellipse about its major axis.

103. Volume. Starting from any point (x, y, z) in space, we may draw lines of length dx, dy, and dz in directions parallel to OX, OY, and OZ respectively, and on these lines as edges construct a rectangular parallelepiped. The volume of this figure we call the element of volume dV and have

$$dV = dx\,dy\,dz. \tag{1}$$

For cylindrical coördinates we construct an element of volume whose base is $r\,d\theta\,dr$ ((12), § 95), the element of plane area in polar coördinates, and whose altitude is dz. This figure has for its volume dV the product of its base by its altitude, and we have
$$dV = r\,d\theta\,dr\,dz. \tag{2}$$

The two elements of volume dV given in (1) and (2) are not equal to each other, since they refer to differently shaped figures. Each is to be used in its appropriate place. To find the volume of any solid we divide it into elements of one of these types.

To do this in Cartesian coördinates, note that the x-coördinate of any point will determine a plane parallel to the plane YOZ and x units from it, and that similar planes correspond to the values of y and z. We may, accordingly, divide any required volume into elements of volume as follows:

Pass planes through the volume parallel to YOZ and dx units apart. The result is to divide the required volume into slices of thickness dx, one of which is shown in Fig. 147. Secondly, pass

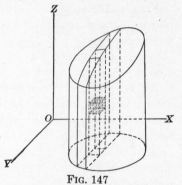

Fig. 147

planes through the volume parallel to XOZ and dy units apart, with the result that each slice is divided into columns of cross section $dx\,dy$. One such column is shown in Fig. 147.

Finally, pass planes through the required volume parallel to XOY and dz units apart, with the result that each column is divided into rectangular parallelepipeds of dimensions dx, dy, and dz. One of these is shown in Fig. 147.

It is to be noted that the order followed in the above explanation is not fixed and that, in fact, the choice of beginning with either x or y or z, and the subsequent order, depend upon the particular volume considered.

A similar construction may be made for cylindrical coördinates. In this case the coördinate θ determines a plane through OZ. We accordingly divide the volume by means of planes through OZ, each pair of adjacent planes making the angle $d\theta$ with each other. The result is a set of wedge-shaped slices, one of which is shown in Fig. 148.

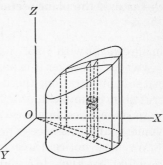

The coördinate r determines a cylinder with OZ as its axis. We accordingly divide each slice into columns with cross section $r\,d\theta\,dr$ by means of cylinders with radii differing by dr. One such column is shown in Fig. 148.

FIG. 148

Finally, these columns are divided into elements of volume by planes parallel to XOY at a distance dz apart. One such element is shown in Fig. 148.

When the volume has been divided in either of these ways, it is evident that some of the elements will extend outside the boundary surfaces of the solid. The sum of all the elements that are either completely or partially in the volume will be approximately the volume of the solid, and this approximation becomes better as the size of each element becomes smaller. In fact, the volume is the limit of the sum of the elements. The determination of this limit involves in principle three integrations, and we write

$$V = \iiint dx\,dy\,dz \qquad (3)$$

or

$$V = \iiint r\,d\theta\,dr\,dz. \qquad (4)$$

In carrying out the integrations we may, in some cases, find it convenient first to hold z and dz constant. We shall then be taking the limit of the sum of the elements which lie in a plane parallel to the XOY plane. We may indicate this by writing (3) or (4) in the form

$$V = \int dz \iint dx\,dy \quad \text{or} \quad V = \int dz \iint r\,d\theta\,dr. \tag{5}$$

But, by § 95, $\iint dx\,dy = A$ and $\iint r\,d\theta\,dr = A$, where A is the area of the plane section at a distance z from XOY. Hence (5) is

$$V = \int A\,dz, \tag{6}$$

in agreement with § 25.

Hence, whenever it is possible to find A by elementary means without integration, the use of (6) is preferable. This is illustrated in Example 1.

In some cases, however, this method of evaluation is not convenient, and it is necessary to carry out three integrations.

We may notice three types of volumes. The first is represented by Figs. 147 and 148, where the required volume is bounded below by the plane XOY, above by a surface whose equation is given, and laterally by a right cylinder whose equation is given. If we first integrate with respect to z, taking as a lower limit $z = 0$ and as an upper limit the value of z from the equation of the upper surface, we have the volume of a column parallel to OZ. All such columns as lie in the given cylinder are to be summed and the limits of the last integrations are to be determined by the equation of the cylinder, or of its intersection with the plane XOY, exactly as in the case of any double integral.

The above type of volume may be modified by taking as the lower boundary not the plane $z = 0$ but any surface whose equation is known. The student may easily imagine such a surface drawn in Fig. 147 or Fig. 148. The volume required is bounded above and below by given surfaces and laterally by a given cylinder. We may first integrate with respect to z, taking as a lower limit the value of z given by the equation of the lower surface. In other respects the work proceeds as before.

Again, we may have the case of a volume which is completely bounded by two surfaces, one above and one below. This may be considered a special case of the preceding where the lateral surface has shrunk to zero. It is then necessary to find the equation of the surrounding cylinder, since only the equations of the two surfaces are given. This may be done by eliminating z from the equations of the two surfaces. The resulting equation certainly represents a cylinder since it contains no z (1, § 102), and it passes through the curve of intersection of the two given surfaces since it is satisfied by the coördinates of any point whose coördinates satisfy the two equations simultaneously. The equation of the cylinder having been found, the work proceeds as before.

We have considered in the foregoing the case in which integration with respect to z is first performed. This is not always the most convenient thing to do. In case it is more convenient to integrate first with respect to some other variable, the student should fix the limits in accordance with the principles which underlie the above discussion.

Example 1. Find the volume of the ellipsoid $\dfrac{x^2}{a^2} + \dfrac{y^2}{b^2} + \dfrac{z^2}{c^2} = 1$.

By 16, § 102, the section made by a plane parallel to XOY is an ellipse with semiaxes $a\sqrt{1 - \dfrac{z^2}{c^2}}$ and $b\sqrt{1 - \dfrac{z^2}{c^2}}$. Therefore, by Example 1, § 86, its area is $\pi ab\left(1 - \dfrac{z^2}{c^2}\right)$. Hence we use formula (6) and have

$$V = \pi ab \int_{-c}^{c}\left(1 - \frac{z^2}{c^2}\right) dz = \frac{4}{3}\,\pi abc.$$

Example 2. Find the volume bounded above by the sphere $x^2 + y^2 + z^2 = 5$ and below by the paraboloid $x^2 + y^2 = 4\,z$ (Fig. 149).

As these are surfaces of revolution, this example may be solved by formula (6) as in Example 1, but in so doing we need two integrations, one for the sphere and the other for the paraboloid. We shall solve the example, however, by the other method in order to illustrate that method.

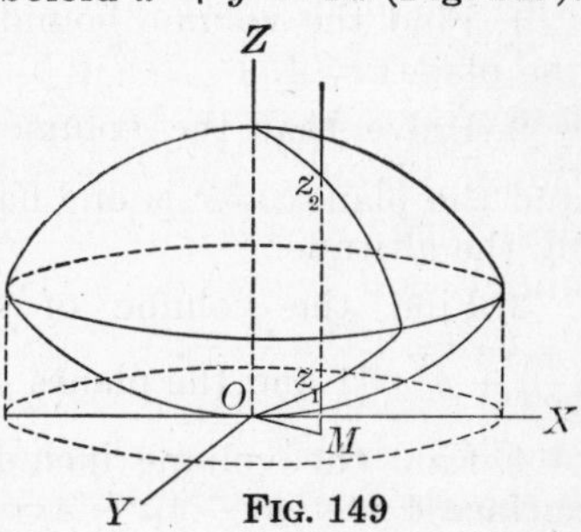

We first reduce our equations to cylindrical coördinates, obtaining, respectively,

FIG. 149

$$r^2 + z^2 = 5 \tag{1}$$

and

$$r^2 = 4\,z. \tag{2}$$

Eliminating z between the two equations, we have $r = 2$. Therefore the required volume lies entirely in the cylinder $r = 2$.

We now imagine the element $r\, d\theta\, dr\, dz$ inside the volume and, holding r, θ, $d\theta$, dr constant, we take the sum of all the elements obtained by varying z inside the volume. These elements obviously extend from $z = z_1$ in the lower boundary to $z = z_2$ in the upper boundary. From (2), $z_1 = \dfrac{r^2}{4}$ and, from (1), $z_2 = \sqrt{5 - r^2}$. The first integration is therefore

$$r\, d\theta\, dr \int_{\frac{r^2}{4}}^{\sqrt{5-r^2}} dz = \left[r\sqrt{5 - r^2} - \frac{r^3}{4} \right] d\theta\, dr,$$

which is the volume of a column with cross section $r\, d\theta\, dr$.

We must now allow θ and r to vary so as to include all the columns which lie in the cylinder $r = 2$.

If we hold θ constant, r varies from 0 to 2. The second integration is therefore

$$d\theta \int_0^2 \left[r\sqrt{5 - r^2} - \frac{r^3}{4} \right] dr = \left(\frac{5\sqrt{5}}{3} - \frac{4}{3} \right) d\theta.$$

Finally, θ must vary from 0 to 2π, and the third integration is

$$\left(\frac{5\sqrt{5}}{3} - \frac{4}{3} \right) \int_0^{2\pi} d\theta = \frac{2\pi}{3} (5\sqrt{5} - 4).$$

If we put together what we have done, we have

$$V = \int_0^{2\pi} \int_0^2 \int_{\frac{r^2}{4}}^{\sqrt{5-r^2}} r\, d\theta\, dr\, dz = \frac{2\pi}{3} (5\sqrt{5} - 4).$$

EXERCISES

1. Find the volume bounded by the paraboloid $z = x^2 + y^2$ and the plane $z = 4$.

2. Prove that the volume bounded by the surface $\dfrac{z}{c} = \dfrac{x^2}{a^2} + \dfrac{y^2}{b^2}$ and the plane $z = c$ is one half the product of the area of the base by the altitude.

3. Find the volume of the solid bounded by the cylinder $\left(\dfrac{x}{2} \right)^{\frac{1}{2}} + y^{\frac{1}{2}} = 1$ and the planes $y = 0$, $z = 0$, and $z = x$.

4. Find the volume included between the XOY plane and the surface $4x^2 + y^2 - 4z - 4 = 0$.

5. Find the volume bounded above by the cylinder $y^2 = a^2 - az$, below by the plane $z = 0$, and laterally by the cylinder $x^2 + y^2 = a^2$.

6. Find the volume of the paraboloid $x^2 + y^2 = z$ cut off by the plane $z = x$.

7. Find the volume cut from the sphere $r^2 + z^2 = a^2$ by the cylinder $r = a \cos \theta$.

8. Find the volume bounded below by the paraboloid $r^2 = az$ and above by the sphere $r^2 + z^2 - 2\,az = 0$.

9. The curve $az^2 = x^3$ is revolved about the axis of z to form a surface. Find the volume included between this surface and the surface $r = a$.

10. Find the volume of the surface bounded by the plane $z = 0$, the cylinder $y^2 = a^2 - az$, and the cylinder $r^2 = a^2 \cos 2\,\theta$.

104. Center of gravity of a solid. The center of gravity of a solid has three coördinates, $\bar{x}$, $\bar{y}$, $\bar{z}$, which are defined by the equations

$$M\bar{x} = \int x\,dm, \quad M\bar{y} = \int y\,dm, \quad M\bar{z} = \int z\,dm, \qquad (1)$$

where M is the total mass of the body, dm is the mass of one of the elements into which the solid may be divided, and x, y, and z are the coördinates of the point at which the element dm may be regarded as concentrated. The derivation of these formulas is the same as that in § 91.

When dm is expressed in terms of space coördinates, the integrals become triple integrals, and the limits of integration are to be substituted so as to include the whole solid.

We place $dm = \rho\,dV$, where ρ is the density. If ρ is constant, it may be placed outside the integral signs and canceled from the equations. Formulas (1) then become

$$V\bar{x} = \int x\,dV, \quad V\bar{y} = \int y\,dV, \quad V\bar{z} = \int z\,dV. \qquad (2)$$

Example. Find the center of gravity of a body bounded below by one nappe of a right circular cone of vertical angle $2\,\alpha$ and above by a sphere of radius a, the center of the sphere being at the vertex of the cone.

If the center of the sphere is taken as the origin of coördinates and the axis of the cone as the axis of z, it is evident from the symmetry of the solid that $\bar{x} = \bar{y} = 0$. To find $\bar{z}$ we shall use cylindrical coördinates, the equations of the sphere and the cone being, respectively,

$$r^2 + z^2 = a^2 \quad \text{and} \quad r = z \tan \alpha.$$

By eliminating z the surfaces are found to intersect on the cylinder $r = a \sin \alpha$.

$$V = \int_0^{2\pi} \int_0^{a \sin \alpha} \int_{r \operatorname{ctn} \alpha}^{\sqrt{a^2 - r^2}} r \, d\theta \, dr \, dz = \tfrac{2}{3} \pi a^3 (1 - \cos \alpha)$$

and $\quad \int z \, dV = \int_0^{2\pi} \int_0^{a \sin \alpha} \int_{r \operatorname{ctn} \alpha}^{\sqrt{a^2 - r^2}} rz \, d\theta \, dr \, dz = \tfrac{1}{4} \pi a^4 \sin^2 \alpha.$

Therefore, from (2), $\quad \bar{z} = \tfrac{3}{8} a(1 + \cos \alpha)$.

EXERCISES

1. Find the center of gravity of the pyramid bounded by the coordinate planes and the plane $\dfrac{x}{a} + \dfrac{y}{b} + \dfrac{z}{c} = 1$.

2. Find the center of gravity of the first octant of the solid bounded by the cylinders $x^2 + z^2 = a^2$ and $x^2 + y^2 = a^2$.

3. Find the center of gravity of the solid bounded by the paraboloid $\dfrac{z}{c} = \dfrac{x^2}{a^2} + \dfrac{y^2}{b^2}$ and the planes $x = 0$, $y = 0$, $z = c$.

4. Find the center of gravity of a body in the form of an octant of the ellipsoid $\dfrac{x^2}{a^2} + \dfrac{y^2}{b^2} + \dfrac{z^2}{c^2} = 1$.

5. A ring is cut from a spherical shell, the inner radius and the outer radius of which are, respectively, 4 ft. and 5 ft., by two parallel planes on the same side of the center of the shell and distant 1 ft. and 3 ft., respectively, from the center. Find the center of gravity of this ring.

6. Find the center of gravity of the first octant of the solid bounded below by the paraboloid $az = r^2$ and above by the right circular cone $z + r = 2a$.

7. Find the center of gravity of the first octant of the solid bounded below by the cone $z = r$ and above by the sphere $r^2 + z^2 = 1$.

8. Find the center of gravity of a solid bounded by the surfaces $z = 0$, $r^2 + z^2 = b^2$, and $r = a(a < b)$.

105. Moment of inertia of a solid. If a solid body is divided into elements of volume dV, the moment of inertia of the solid about any axis is

$$I = \int R^2 \rho \, dV = \rho \int R^2 \, dV, \tag{1}$$

where R is the distance of any point of the element from the axis, and ρ is the density of the solid, which we have assumed to be constant and therefore have been able to place before the integral sign. If M is the total mass of the solid, ρ may be determined from the formula $M = \rho V$.

If the moment of inertia about OZ, which we shall call I_z, is required, then in cylindrical coördinates $R = r$ and $dV = r\,d\theta\,dr\,dz$, so that (1) becomes

$$I_z = \rho \iiint r^3\,d\theta\,dr\,dz. \tag{2}$$

If we use Cartesian coördinates to determine I_z, we have $R^2 = x^2 + y^2$ and $dV = dx\,dy\,dz$, so that

$$I_z = \rho \iiint (x^2 + y^2)dx\,dy\,dz. \tag{3}$$

Similarly, if I_y and I_x are the moments of inertia about OY and OX respectively, we have

$$I_y = \rho \iiint (x^2 + z^2)dx\,dy\,dz, \quad I_x = \rho \iiint (y^2 + z^2)dx\,dy\,dz. \tag{4}$$

In evaluating (2) it is sometimes convenient to integrate with respect to z last. We indicate this by the formula

$$I_z = \rho \int dz \iint r^3\,d\theta\,dr. \tag{5}$$

But $\iint r^3\,d\theta\,dr$ is, by (5), § 99, the polar moment of inertia of a plane section perpendicular to OZ about the point in which OZ intersects the plane section. Consequently, if this polar moment is known, the evaluation of (5) reduces to a single integration. This has already been illustrated in the case of solids of revolution.

A similar result is obtained by considering (3). In fact, the ease with which a moment of inertia is found depends upon a proper choice of Cartesian or cylindrical coördinates and, after that choice has been made, upon the order in which the integrations are carried out.

Equation (3) may be written in the form

$$I_z = \rho \iiint x^2\,dx\,dy\,dz + \rho \iiint y^2\,dx\,dy\,dz, \tag{6}$$

and the order of integration in the two integrals need not be the same. Similar forms are derived from (4).

The theorem of § 100 holds for solids. This is easily proved by the methods used in that section.

Example. Find the moment of inertia about OZ of a cylindrical solid of altitude h whose base is one loop of the curve $r = a \sin 3\theta$.

The base of this cylinder is shown in Fig. 84, § 60. We have, from formula (2),

$$I_z = \rho \int_0^{\frac{\pi}{3}} \int_0^{a \sin 3\theta} \int_0^h r^3 \, d\theta \, dr \, dz,$$

where the limits are obtained as follows:

First, holding r, θ, $d\theta$, dr constant, we allow z to vary from the lower base $z = 0$ to the upper base $z = h$, and integrate. The result $\rho h r^3 \, d\theta \, dr$ is the moment of inertia of a column such as is shown in Fig. 148. We next hold θ and $d\theta$ constant and allow r to vary from its value at the origin to its value on the curve $r = a \sin 3\theta$, and integrate. The result $\frac{1}{4} \rho h \, a^4 \sin^4 3\theta \, d\theta$ is the moment of inertia of a slice as shown in Fig. 148. Finally, we sum the moments of inertia of all these slices while allowing θ to vary from its smallest value 0 to its largest value $\frac{\pi}{3}$. The result is $\frac{1}{32} \rho h a^4 \pi$.

The volume of the cylinder may be computed from the formula

$$V = \int_0^{\frac{\pi}{3}} \int_0^{a \sin 3\theta} \int_0^h r \, d\theta \, dr \, dz = \frac{1}{12} h a^2 \pi.$$

Therefore $\qquad M = \frac{1}{12} \rho h a^2 \pi \quad$ and $\quad I_z = \frac{3}{8} M a^2.$

EXERCISES

1. Find the moment of inertia about OZ of the solid bounded by the surfaces $z = 0$, $z = 2$, $x = 1$, and $y^2 = x^3$.

2. Find the moment of inertia about OZ of a solid bounded by the paraboloid $\frac{z}{c} = \frac{x^2}{a^2} + \frac{y^2}{b^2}$ and the plane $z = c$.

3. Find the moment of inertia about its axis of a right elliptic cylinder of height h, the major and the minor axis of its base being, respectively, $2a$ and $2b$.

4. Find the moment of inertia about OZ of the ellipsoid

$$\frac{x^2}{a^2} + \frac{y^2}{b^2} + \frac{z^2}{c^2} = 1.$$

5. Find the moment of inertia about OZ of the portion of the sphere $r^2 + z^2 = a^2$ cut out by the plane $z = 0$ and the cylinder $r = a \cos\theta$.

6. Find the moment of inertia about OZ of the solid bounded by the surfaces $r = a \cos\theta$, $z = 0$, $z = 2$.

7. Find the moment of inertia about OZ of the solid bounded below by the plane $z = 0$, above by the paraboloid $az = r^2$, and included in the cylinder with base a loop of the curve $r = a \cos 2\theta$ and with elements parallel to OZ.

8. Find the moment of inertia about OX of the solid bounded by the plane $z = 0$ and the surface $\dfrac{x^2}{a^2} + \dfrac{y^2}{b^2} = 1 - \dfrac{z}{c}$.

9. Find the moment of inertia of a right circular cone of radius a and height h about any diameter of its base as an axis.

10. Find the moment of inertia of a right circular cone of height h and radius a about an axis perpendicular to the axis of the cone at its vertex.

11. Find the moment of inertia of a right circular cylinder of height h and radius a about a diameter of its base.

12. A solid is in the form of a right circular cone, the altitude and radius of base being each equal to a. Find its moment of inertia about an axis which is perpendicular to the axis of the cone at a point distant $2\,a$ from the base of the cone and a from the vertex.

GENERAL EXERCISES

1. Find the center of gravity of the area in the first quadrant bounded by the curve $9\,y = x^3$ and the line $y = x$.

2. Find the center of gravity of the area in the first quadrant bounded by the curves $y = 8 - 2\,x^2$, $y = 4\,x^2$, and the axis of y.

3. Find the center of gravity of the area bounded by the curves $8\,y = x^3$ and $y = \dfrac{4}{x^2}$, the axis of x, and the line $x = 4$.

4. Find the center of gravity of the area bounded by the axes of x and y and the curve $x = a \cos^3\phi$, $y = a \sin^3\phi$.

5. Find the center of gravity of the area in the first quadrant bounded by the ellipse $\dfrac{x^2}{a^2} + \dfrac{y^2}{b^2} = 1\,(a > b)$, the circle $x^2 + y^2 = a^2$, and the axis of y.

6. Find the center of gravity of the area bounded below by the parabola $x^2 = 6\,y$ and above by the circle $x^2 + y^2 = 72$.

7. Find the center of gravity of the area bounded on the right by the curve $r = 2 + \cos 2\,\theta$ and on the left by the circle $r = 2$.

8. Find the center of gravity of that part of the area inside the curve $r = 3 + 2 \cos \theta$ which is outside the circle $r = 3$.

9. Find the center of gravity of the area bounded by the large loop of the curve $r = a\left(2 + \sin \dfrac{\theta}{2}\right)$.

10. Find the center of gravity of the area included in one loop of the curve $r = a \cos 2\,\theta$.

11. Find the center of gravity of the segment of a circle of radius a cut off by a straight line b units from the center.

12. Find the center of gravity of an area in the form of a semicircle of radius a surmounted by an equilateral triangle having one of its sides coinciding with the diameter of the semicircle.

13. Find the center of gravity of an area in the form of a rectangle of dimensions a and b surmounted by an equilateral triangle one side of which coincides with a side of the rectangle which is b units long.

14. From a rectangle 8 ft. long and 6 ft. broad a semicircle of diameter 6 ft. is cut, the diameter of the semicircle coinciding with one end of the rectangle. Find the center of gravity of the remaining portion of the rectangle.

15. Find the center of gravity of a plate in the form of one half of a circular ring the inner and the outer radii of which are respectively r_1 and r_2.

16. Find the center of gravity of a plate in the form of a T-square 10 in. across the top and 12 in. tall, the width of the upright and that of the top being each 2 in.

17. From a plate in the form of a regular hexagon 6 in. on a side one of the six equilateral triangles into which it may be divided is removed. Find the center of gravity of the portion left.

18. Find the center of gravity of the figure formed by cutting out of a circle of radius 8 in. a square hole 2 in. on a side, the center of the square being 3 in. from the center of the circle.

19. Find the center of gravity of a plate, in the form of the ellipse $\dfrac{x^2}{a^2} + \dfrac{y^2}{b^2} = 1$ $(a > b)$, in which there is a circular hole of radius c, the center of the hole being on the major axis of the ellipse at a distance d from its center.

20. A square, $6\sqrt{2}$ in. on a side, has a corner cut off by a straight line joining the middle points of two adjacent sides. Find the center of gravity of the remaining area.

21. Find the polar moment of inertia about the origin of the area bounded by the curves $y = x^2$ and $y = 2 - x^2$.

22. Find the moment of inertia about OX of the smaller area bounded by the curves $x^2 + y^2 = 36$ and $y^2 = x^3$.

23. Find the polar moment of inertia about the origin of the area of one loop of the lemniscate $r^2 = 2\,a^2 \cos 2\,\theta$.

24. Find the polar moment of inertia about O of the area bounded by the curve $r = 2(1 - \cos \theta)$.

25. Find the polar moment of inertia about O of the total area bounded by the curve $r^2 = a^2 \sin \theta$.

26. Find the polar moment of inertia about O of the area bounded by the large loop of the curve $r = 2 + \sin \dfrac{\theta}{2}$.

27. Find the polar moment of inertia about the pole of that area of the circle $r = a$ which is not included in the curve $r = a \sin 2\,\theta$.

28. Find the moment of inertia of a circular ring of inner radius r_1 and outer radius r_2 about a tangent to the outer circle.

29. A square plate 10 in. on a side has a square hole 5 in. on a side cut in it, the center of the hole being at the center of the plate and its sides parallel to the sides of the plate. Find the moment of inertia of the plate about a line through its center parallel to one side.

30. Find the moment of inertia of the plate of Ex. 29 about one of the outer sides.

31. Find the moment of inertia of the plate of Ex. 29 about one side of the hole.

32. Find the moment of inertia of the plate of Ex. 29 about one of its diagonals.

33. A square plate 8 in. on a side has a circular hole 4 in. in diameter cut in it, the center of the hole coinciding with the center of the square. Find the moment of inertia of the plate about a line passing through its center parallel to one side.

34. Find the moment of inertia of the plate of Ex. 33 about a diagonal of the square.

35. Find the polar moment of inertia of the plate of Ex. 33 about its center.

36. Find the moment of inertia of a semicircle about a tangent parallel to its diameter.

37. All sections of a given right cylinder made by planes parallel to the plane XOY are ellipses with major axis 10 in. long and minor axis 8 in. long. Find the equation of this cylinder.

38. Show that the surface $z = a - \sqrt{x^2 + y^2}$ is a cone of revolution, and locate its vertex and axis.

39. Find the equation of the surface formed by revolving a hyperbola about its transverse axis.

40. Find the equation of the surface formed by revolving a hyperbola about its conjugate axis.

41. Derive the equation of the ring surface formed by revolving the ellipse $\dfrac{(x-a)^2}{b^2} + \dfrac{z^2}{c^2} = 1$ $(a > b)$ about OZ as axis.

42. Find the equation of the surface formed by revolving the curve $z = \dfrac{8\,a^3}{x^2 + 4\,a^2}$ about OZ as axis.

43. Find the equation of the curved surface of a right circular cone of altitude 10 ft. and radius 4 ft.

44. Find the volume bounded by the surface $x^{\frac{2}{3}} + y^{\frac{2}{3}} + z^{\frac{2}{3}} = a^{\frac{2}{3}}$ by making use of the area bounded by the curve $x^{\frac{2}{3}} + y^{\frac{2}{3}} = a^{\frac{2}{3}}$.

45. Find the volume bounded by the surfaces $x^2 = 4 - z$ and $z = x^2 + y^2$.

46. Find the volume of the solid bounded by the paraboloid $2\,z = x^2 + y^2$ and the plane $z = x + 1$.

47. Find the volume bounded by the plane XOY, the cylinder $x^2 + y^2 - 2\,ax = 0$, and the right circular cone having its vertex at O, its axis coincident with OZ, and its vertical angle equal to 90°.

48. Find the volume bounded by the surfaces $r^2 = bz$, $z = 0$, and $r = a \cos \theta$.

49. Find the volume of the portion of the sphere, of radius a and with its center at the origin of coördinates, included in the cylinder having for its base one loop of the curve $r^2 = a^2 \cos 2\,\theta$.

50. Find the volume of the solid bounded by the plane $z = 0$, the cylinder $y^2 = a^2 - az$, and the cylinder $r = a \cos \theta$.

51. Find the volume of the portion of the cylinder, included between the planes $z = 0$ and $z = x$, having its elements parallel to OZ and for its base that loop of the curve $r = a \cos 2\,\theta$ which is bisected by OX.

52. Find the center of gravity of the solid bounded below by the plane $z = 0$, above by the cone $z + r = 2\,a$, and laterally by the cylinder $r = a \cos \theta$.

53. Find the center of gravity of the volume bounded below by the upper nappe of the cone $r = 2\,z - 2$ and above by the surface $r^2 + z^2 = 25$.

54. Find the moment of inertia about OX of a solid bounded by the paraboloid $z = r^2$ and the plane $z = 2$.

55. Find the moment of inertia about OZ of the volume bounded below by the surface $z = r$ and above by the surface $r^2 = a(2\,a - z)$.

56. Find the moment of inertia about its axis of a cylindrical post of density 3, diameter 2, and total length 6, the top of the post being rounded off into the shape of a paraboloid whose altitude is equal to the diameter of its base.

57. Find the moment of inertia about OX of the volume bounded by the surface $r = 4\,z^2$ and the plane $z = 1$.

58. A solid is in the form of a hemispherical shell the inner radius and the outer radius of which are, respectively, r_1 and r_2. Find its moment of inertia about any diameter of the base of the shell as an axis.

59. An anchor ring of mass M is bounded by the surface generated by revolving a circle of radius a about an axis in its plane distant b ($b > a$) from its center. Find the moment of inertia of this anchor ring about its axis.

60. Find the moment of inertia of the elliptic cylinder $\dfrac{x^2}{a^2} + \dfrac{y^2}{b^2} = 1$ ($a > b$), its height being h, about the major axis of its base.

61. Find the center of gravity of the solid bounded by the cylinder $r = 2\,a \cos \theta$, the cone $z = r$, and the plane $z = 0$.

62. Find the moment of inertia about OZ of the solid of Ex. 61.

63. Find the volume of the cylinder having for its base one loop of the curve $r = 2\,a \cos 2\,\theta$, between the cone $z = 2\,r$ and the plane $z = 0$.

64. Find the center of gravity of the solid of Ex. 63.

65. Find the moment of inertia about OZ of the solid of Ex. 63.

66. Find the volume bounded by the planes $z = 0$ and $z = x + 2\,a$ and the cylinder having for its base the particular loop of the curve $r = a \cos 2\,\theta$ which is bisected by the initial line.

67. Find the moment of inertia about OZ of the solid of Ex. 66.

68. Find the volume of the cylinder $r = 2\,a \cos \theta$ included between the planes $z = 0$ and $z = 2\,x + a$.

69. Find the moment of inertia about OZ of the solid of Ex. 68.

70. Through a spherical shell, of which the inner radius and the outer radius are, respectively, r_1 and r_2, a circular hole of radius a ($a < r_1$) is bored, the axis of the hole coinciding with a diameter of the shell. Find the moment of inertia of the ring thus formed about the axis of the hole.

TABLE OF INTEGRALS

I. Fundamental Forms

1. $\displaystyle\int c\,du = c\int du.$

2. $\displaystyle\int (du + dv + dw + \cdots) = \int du + \int dv + \int dw + \cdots.$

3. $\displaystyle\int u\,dv = uv - \int v\,du.$

4. $\displaystyle\int u^n du = \frac{u^{n+1}}{n+1}.\quad (n \neq -1)$

5. $\displaystyle\int \frac{du}{u} = \ln u.$

6. $\displaystyle\int \frac{du}{u^2 + a^2} = \frac{1}{a}\tan^{-1}\frac{u}{a}.$

7. $\displaystyle\int \frac{du}{u^2 - a^2} = \frac{1}{2a}\ln\frac{u-a}{u+a}.$

8. $\displaystyle\int \frac{du}{\sqrt{a^2 - u^2}} = \sin^{-1}\frac{u}{a}.$

9. $\displaystyle\int \frac{du}{\sqrt{u^2 \pm a^2}} = \ln\left(u + \sqrt{u^2 \pm a^2}\right).$

10. $\displaystyle\int \sin u\,du = -\cos u.$

11. $\displaystyle\int \cos u\,du = \sin u.$

12. $\displaystyle\int \tan u\,du = -\ln \cos u.$

13. $\displaystyle\int \operatorname{ctn} u\,du = \ln \sin u.$

14. $\displaystyle\int \sec u\,du = \ln(\sec u + \tan u).$

15. $\displaystyle\int \csc u\,du = \ln(\csc u - \operatorname{ctn} u).$

16. $\displaystyle\int \sec^2 u\,du = \tan u.$

17. $\displaystyle\int \csc^2 u\,du = -\operatorname{ctn} u.$

18. $\displaystyle\int \sec u \tan u\,du = \sec u.$

19. $\displaystyle\int \csc u \operatorname{ctn} u\,du = -\csc u.$

20. $\displaystyle\int e^u du = e^u.$

21. $\displaystyle\int a^u du = \frac{a^u}{\ln a}.$

II. Expressions involving $\sqrt{a + bx}$

22. $\displaystyle\int \sqrt{a + bx}\, dx = \frac{2}{3\,b}\,(a + bx)^{\frac{3}{2}}.$

23. $\displaystyle\int x\,\sqrt{a + bx}\, dx = -\frac{2(2\,a - 3\,bx)}{15\,b^2}\,(a + bx)^{\frac{3}{2}}.$

24. $\displaystyle\int x^n\,\sqrt{a + bx}\, dx = \frac{2\,x^n(a + bx)^{\frac{3}{2}}}{(2\,n + 3)b}$
$$-\frac{2\,an}{(2\,n + 3)b}\int x^{n-1}\,\sqrt{a + bx}\, dx. \quad (2\,n + 3 \neq 0)$$

25. $\displaystyle\int \frac{dx}{\sqrt{a + bx}} = \frac{2}{b}\,\sqrt{a + bx}.$

26. $\displaystyle\int \frac{x\,dx}{\sqrt{a + bx}} = -\frac{2(2\,a - bx)}{3\,b^2}\,\sqrt{a + bx}.$

27. $\displaystyle\int \frac{x^n\,dx}{\sqrt{a + bx}} = \frac{2\,x^n\,\sqrt{a + bx}}{(2\,n + 1)b}$
$$-\frac{2\,an}{(2\,n + 1)b}\int \frac{x^{n-1}\,dx}{\sqrt{a + bx}}. \quad (2\,n + 1 \neq 0)$$

28. $\displaystyle\int \frac{dx}{x\,\sqrt{a + bx}} = \frac{1}{\sqrt{a}}\ln \frac{\sqrt{a + bx} - \sqrt{a}}{\sqrt{a + bx} + \sqrt{a}} \quad (a > 0)$
$$= \frac{2}{\sqrt{-a}}\tan^{-1}\sqrt{\frac{a + bx}{-a}}. \quad (a < 0)$$

29. $\displaystyle\int \frac{dx}{x^n\,\sqrt{a + bx}} = -\frac{\sqrt{a + bx}}{(n - 1)ax^{n-1}}$
$$-\frac{(2\,n - 3)b}{2(n - 1)a}\int \frac{dx}{x^{n-1}\,\sqrt{a + bx}}. \quad (n \neq 1)$$

III. Expressions involving $\sqrt{a^2 - x^2}$

30. $\displaystyle\int \sqrt{a^2 - x^2}\, dx = \frac{x}{2}\sqrt{a^2 - x^2} + \frac{a^2}{2}\sin^{-1}\frac{x}{a}.$

31. $\displaystyle\int x\,\sqrt{a^2 - x^2}\, dx = -\tfrac{1}{3}(a^2 - x^2)^{\frac{3}{2}}.$

32. $\displaystyle\int x^2\,\sqrt{a^2 - x^2}\, dx = -\frac{x}{4}(a^2 - x^2)^{\frac{3}{2}} + \frac{a^2}{8}x\,\sqrt{a^2 - x^2} + \frac{a^4}{8}\sin^{-1}\frac{x}{a}.$

33. $\displaystyle\int x^n \sqrt{a^2 - x^2}\, dx = -\frac{x^{n-1}(a^2 - x^2)^{\frac{3}{2}}}{n+2}$
$$+ \frac{(n-1)a^2}{n+2}\int x^{n-2}\sqrt{a^2 - x^2}\, dx. \quad (n+2 \neq 0)$$

34. $\displaystyle\int \frac{dx}{\sqrt{a^2 - x^2}} = \sin^{-1}\frac{x}{a}.$

35. $\displaystyle\int \frac{x\, dx}{\sqrt{a^2 - x^2}} = -\sqrt{a^2 - x^2}.$

36. $\displaystyle\int \frac{x^2\, dx}{\sqrt{a^2 - x^2}} = -\frac{x}{2}\sqrt{a^2 - x^2} + \frac{a^2}{2}\sin^{-1}\frac{x}{a}.$

37. $\displaystyle\int \frac{x^n dx}{\sqrt{a^2 - x^2}} = -\frac{x^{n-1}\sqrt{a^2 - x^2}}{n}$
$$+ \frac{(n-1)a^2}{n}\int \frac{x^{n-2}\, dx}{\sqrt{a^2 - x^2}}. \quad (n \neq 0)$$

38. $\displaystyle\int \frac{dx}{x\sqrt{a^2 - x^2}} = -\frac{1}{a}\ln\frac{a + \sqrt{a^2 - x^2}}{x}.$

39. $\displaystyle\int \frac{dx}{x^n \sqrt{a^2 - x^2}} = -\frac{\sqrt{a^2 - x^2}}{(n-1)a^2 x^{n-1}}$
$$+ \frac{n-2}{(n-1)a^2}\int \frac{dx}{x^{n-2}\sqrt{a^2 - x^2}}. \quad (n \neq 1)$$

IV. Expressions involving $\sqrt{x^2 \pm a^2}$

40. $\displaystyle\int \sqrt{x^2 \pm a^2}\, dx = \frac{x}{2}\sqrt{x^2 \pm a^2} \pm \frac{a^2}{2}\ln(x + \sqrt{x^2 \pm a^2}).$

41. $\displaystyle\int x\sqrt{x^2 \pm a^2}\, dx = \frac{1}{3}(x^2 \pm a^2)^{\frac{3}{2}}.$

42. $\displaystyle\int x^2 \sqrt{x^2 \pm a^2}\, dx = \frac{x}{4}(x^2 \pm a^2)^{\frac{3}{2}} \mp \frac{a^2}{8}x\sqrt{x^2 \pm a^2}$
$$- \frac{a^4}{8}\ln(x + \sqrt{x^2 \pm a^2}).$$

43. $\displaystyle\int x^n \sqrt{x^2 \pm a^2}\, dx = \frac{x^{n-1}(x^2 \pm a^2)^{\frac{3}{2}}}{n+2}$
$$\mp \frac{(n-1)a^2}{n+2}\int x^{n-2}\sqrt{x^2 \pm a^2}\, dx. \quad (n+2 \neq 0)$$

44. $\displaystyle\int \frac{dx}{\sqrt{x^2 \pm a^2}} = \ln\left(x + \sqrt{x^2 \pm a^2}\right).$

45. $\displaystyle\int \frac{x\,dx}{\sqrt{x^2 \pm a^2}} = \sqrt{x^2 \pm a^2}.$

46. $\displaystyle\int \frac{x^2\,dx}{\sqrt{x^2 \pm a^2}} = \frac{x}{2}\sqrt{x^2 \pm a^2} \mp \frac{a^2}{2}\ln\left(x + \sqrt{x^2 \pm a^2}\right).$

47. $\displaystyle\int \frac{x^n\,dx}{\sqrt{x^2 \pm a^2}} = \frac{x^{n-1}\sqrt{x^2 \pm a^2}}{n}$
$$\mp \frac{(n-1)a^2}{n}\int \frac{x^{n-2}\,dx}{\sqrt{x^2 \pm a^2}}. \quad (n \neq 0)$$

48. $\displaystyle\int \frac{dx}{x\sqrt{x^2 + a^2}} = -\frac{1}{a}\ln \frac{a + \sqrt{x^2 + a^2}}{x}.$

49. $\displaystyle\int \frac{dx}{x\sqrt{x^2 - a^2}} = \frac{1}{a}\cos^{-1}\frac{a}{x}.$

50. $\displaystyle\int \frac{dx}{x^n\sqrt{x^2 \pm a^2}} = \mp \frac{\sqrt{x^2 \pm a^2}}{(n-1)a^2 x^{n-1}}$
$$\mp \frac{n-2}{(n-1)a^2}\int \frac{dx}{x^{n-2}\sqrt{x^2 \pm a^2}}. \quad (n \neq 1)$$

V. Expressions involving $\sqrt{ax^2 + bx + c}$

Reduce to expressions involving $\sqrt{a^2 - u^2}$ or $\sqrt{u^2 \pm a^2}$.

VI. Trigonometric Expressions

51. $\displaystyle\int \sin ax\,dx = -\frac{1}{a}\cos ax.$

52. $\displaystyle\int \sin^2 ax\,dx = \frac{x}{2} - \frac{\sin 2\,ax}{4\,a}.$

53. $\displaystyle\int \sin^3 ax\,dx = -\frac{1}{a}\cos ax + \frac{1}{3\,a}\cos^3 ax.$

54. $\displaystyle\int \sin^4 ax\,dx = \frac{3}{8}x - \frac{1}{4\,a}\sin 2\,ax + \frac{1}{32\,a}\sin 4\,ax.$

55. $\displaystyle\int \sin^n ax\,dx = -\frac{1}{na}\sin^{n-1} ax \cos ax + \frac{n-1}{n}\int \sin^{n-2} ax\,dx.$

56. $\int \cos ax\, dx = \dfrac{1}{a} \sin ax.$

57. $\int \cos^2 ax\, dx = \dfrac{x}{2} + \dfrac{\sin 2\,ax}{4\,a}.$

58. $\int \cos^3 ax\, dx = \dfrac{1}{a} \sin ax - \dfrac{1}{3\,a} \sin^3 ax.$

59. $\int \cos^4 ax\, dx = \dfrac{3}{8}\, x + \dfrac{1}{4\,a} \sin 2\,ax + \dfrac{1}{32\,a} \sin 4\,ax.$

60. $\int \cos^n ax\, dx = \dfrac{1}{na} \cos^{n-1} ax \sin ax + \dfrac{n-1}{n} \int \cos^{n-2} ax\, dx.$

61. $\int \sin^n ax \cos ax\, dx = \dfrac{\sin^{n+1} ax}{(n+1)a}.$ $\qquad\qquad (n+1 \neq 0)$

62. $\int \cos^n ax \sin ax\, dx = -\dfrac{\cos^{n+1} ax}{(n+1)a}.$ $\qquad\qquad (n+1 \neq 0)$

63. $\int \tan ax\, dx = -\dfrac{1}{a} \ln \cos ax.$

64. $\int \tan^n ax\, dx = \dfrac{1}{(n-1)a} \tan^{n-1} ax - \int \tan^{n-2} ax\, dx.\ (n \neq 1)$

65. $\int \operatorname{ctn} ax\, dx = \dfrac{1}{a} \ln \sin ax.$

66. $\int \operatorname{ctn}^n ax\, dx = -\dfrac{1}{(n-1)a} \operatorname{ctn}^{n-1} ax - \int \operatorname{ctn}^{n-2} ax\, dx.\ (n \neq 1)$

67. $\int \sin^m ax \cos^n ax\, dx = \dfrac{\sin^{m+1} ax \cos^{n-1} ax}{(m+n)a}$

$\qquad + \dfrac{n-1}{m+n} \int \sin^m ax \cos^{n-2} ax\, dx.$ $\qquad (m+n \neq 0)$

68. $\int \sin^m ax \cos^n ax\, dx = -\dfrac{\sin^{m+1} ax \cos^{n+1} ax}{(n+1)a}$

$\qquad + \dfrac{m+n+2}{n+1} \int \sin^m ax \cos^{n+2} ax\, dx.$ $\qquad (n \neq -1)$

69. $\int \sin^m ax \cos^n ax\, dx = -\dfrac{\sin^{m-1} ax \cos^{n+1} ax}{(m+n)a}$

$\qquad + \dfrac{m-1}{m+n} \int \sin^{m-2} ax \cos^n ax\, dx.$ $\qquad (m+n \neq 0)$

70. $\displaystyle\int \sin^m ax \cos^n ax\, dx = \frac{\sin^{m+1} ax \cos^{n+1} ax}{(m+1)a}$

$$+ \frac{m+n+2}{m+1} \int \sin^{m+2} ax \cos^n ax\, dx. \qquad (m \neq -1)$$

VII. Miscellaneous Expressions

71. $\displaystyle\int x^n e^{ax}\, dx = \frac{x^n}{a} e^{ax} - \frac{n}{a} \int x^{n-1} e^{ax}\, dx.$

72. $\displaystyle\int e^{ax} \sin bx\, dx = \frac{e^{ax}(a \sin bx - b \cos bx)}{a^2 + b^2}.$

73. $\displaystyle\int e^{ax} \cos bx\, dx = \frac{e^{ax}(a \cos bx + b \sin bx)}{a^2 + b^2}.$

74. $\displaystyle\int \sin^{-1} ax\, dx = x \sin^{-1} ax + \frac{1}{a} \sqrt{1 - a^2 x^2}.$

75. $\displaystyle\int x^n \sin^{-1} ax\, dx = \frac{x^{n+1}}{n+1} \sin^{-1} ax - \frac{a}{n+1} \int \frac{x^{n+1}\, dx}{\sqrt{1 - a^2 x^2}}.$
$$(n \neq -1)$$

76. $\displaystyle\int \ln x\, dx = x \ln x - x.$

77. $\displaystyle\int x^n \ln x\, dx = \frac{x^{n+1}}{n+1} \ln x - \frac{x^{n+1}}{(n+1)^2}. \qquad (n \neq -1)$

78. $\displaystyle\int x^n \sin ax\, dx = -\frac{x^n}{a} \cos ax + \frac{n}{a} \int x^{n-1} \cos ax\, dx.$

79. $\displaystyle\int x^n \cos ax\, dx = \frac{x^n}{a} \sin ax - \frac{n}{a} \int x^{n-1} \sin ax\, dx.$

ANSWERS

[The answers to some problems are intentionally omitted.]

CHAPTER I

Page 4 (§ 2)

1. $26\frac{2}{5}$. 3. 164 ft. per sec. 5. 2.51. 7. 158.

2. $6\frac{34}{53}$. 4. 157. 6. $146\frac{2}{3}$. 8. 471.2.

Page 7 (§ 3)

1. 128 ft. per sec. 2. 160 ft. per sec. 3. 96 ft. per sec.

4. 84 ft. per sec. 5. 104 ft. per sec.

Page 8 (§ 3)

6. 42 ft. per sec. 7. 6 ft. per sec.

Page 9 (§ 4)

2. $6t + 4$. 3. $t + 2$. 4. $3t^2$. 5. $6t^2 + 1$. 6. $t^2 + t$. 7. $3t^2 + 3$.

Page 11 (§ 5)

1. 37; 8.

2. 5 ft. per sec.; $5\dfrac{\text{ft.}}{\text{sec.}^2}$.

4. 60; 37.

5. 21 ft. per sec.; $19\dfrac{\text{ft.}}{\text{sec.}^2}$.

6. $9\dfrac{\text{ft.}}{\text{sec.}^2}$; $13\dfrac{\text{ft.}}{\text{sec.}^2}$; $11\dfrac{\text{ft.}}{\text{sec.}^2}$.

Page 12 (§ 5)

7. $5\dfrac{\text{ft.}}{\text{sec.}^2}$; $33\dfrac{\text{ft.}}{\text{sec.}^2}$; $17\dfrac{\text{ft.}}{\text{sec.}^2}$. 8. 48 ft.; 20 ft. per sec.; $4\dfrac{\text{ft.}}{\text{sec.}^2}$.

10. (a) 72 ft.; (b) 18 ft. per sec., 58 ft. per sec.; (c) $14\dfrac{\text{ft.}}{\text{sec.}^2}$, $26\dfrac{\text{ft.}}{\text{sec.}^2}$.

Page 14 (§ 6)

1. $\dfrac{C}{2\pi}$. 2. $4\pi r^2$. 3. $8\pi r$. 4. $3x^2$, $x = $ length of edge. 5. $6\pi r^2$. 6. 18.

Page 15 (§ 6)

7. 2π.

8. $\dfrac{x\sqrt{3}}{2}$, $x = $ length of side.

9. mv.

10. $12\pi - \pi h^2$, $h = $ altitude.

11. $L_0(a + 2bt)$.

12. $\dfrac{3\pi h^2}{8}$, $h = $ total height.

13. $4\pi(t^2 + 12t + 36)$, $t = $ thickness.

353

CHAPTER II

Page 19 (§ 7)

　　1. $5(2x+1)$. 　　　　**2.** $9x^2 - 2x$. 　　　　**3.** $4x^3 - 2$.

4. $-\dfrac{2}{x^3}$. 　**5.** $3x^2 + \dfrac{1}{x^2}$. 　**6.** $-\dfrac{2}{(x+4)^2}$. 　**7.** $\dfrac{4}{(x+2)^2}$. 　**8.** $\dfrac{1-x^2}{(x^2+1)^2}$.

Page 22 (§ 9)

　1. Increasing if $x > 3$; decreasing if $x < 3$.
　2. Increasing if $x > -\tfrac{2}{3}$; decreasing if $x < -\tfrac{2}{3}$.
　3. Increasing if $x < \tfrac{3}{4}$; decreasing if $x > \tfrac{3}{4}$.
　4. Increasing if $x > -1$; decreasing if $x < -1$.
　5. Increasing if $x < 2$ or $x > 4$; decreasing if $2 < x < 4$.
　6. Increasing if $x < -1$ or $x > 3$; decreasing if $-1 < x < 3$.
　7. Increasing if $x < 0$ or $x > \tfrac{4}{3}$; decreasing if $0 < x < \tfrac{4}{3}$.
　8. Increasing if $-3 < x < \tfrac{1}{3}$; decreasing if $x < -3$ or $x > \tfrac{1}{3}$.
　9. Always increasing.
　10. Increasing if $x < -1$ or $0 < x < 1$; decreasing if $-1 < x < 0$ or $x > 1$.
　11. Increasing if $x > \tfrac{3}{2}$; decreasing if $x < \tfrac{3}{2}$.
　12. Increasing if $x < -\tfrac{3}{2}$ or $-1 < x < \tfrac{3}{2}$; decreasing if $-\tfrac{3}{2} < x < -1$ or $x > \tfrac{3}{2}$.

Page 25 (§ 10)

　1. s increases if $t > \tfrac{2}{3}$; s decreases if $t < \tfrac{2}{3}$.
　2. s increases if $t > -\tfrac{5}{4}$; s decreases if $t < -\tfrac{5}{4}$.
　3. s increases if $t < \tfrac{4}{5}$; s decreases if $t > \tfrac{4}{5}$.
　4. s increases if $t < 1$ or $t > 2$; s decreases if $1 < t < 2$.
　5. s increases if $t < -\tfrac{2}{3}$ or $t > 2$; s decreases if $-\tfrac{2}{3} < t < 2$.
　6. s increases if $t > 1$; s decreases if $t < 1$.
　7. Always increasing.
　8. Increasing if $t > \tfrac{2}{3}$; decreasing if $t < \tfrac{2}{3}$.
　9. Increasing if $t < \tfrac{2}{3}$; decreasing if $t > \tfrac{2}{3}$.
　10. Increasing if $t < 0$ or $t > 2$; decreasing if $0 < t < 2$.
　11. Increasing if $t < -\tfrac{2}{3}$ or $t > 0$; decreasing if $-\tfrac{2}{3} < t < 0$.
　12. Increasing if $t < -\tfrac{3}{2}$ or $t > \tfrac{1}{3}$, decreasing if $-\tfrac{3}{2} < t < \tfrac{1}{3}$.
　13. Increasing if $t > \tfrac{3}{2}$; decreasing if $t < \tfrac{3}{2}$.
　14. Increasing if $t > -\tfrac{3}{2}$; decreasing if $t < -\tfrac{3}{2}$.
　15. Increasing if $t > \tfrac{2}{3}$; decreasing if $t < \tfrac{2}{3}$.
　16. Increasing if $0 < t < 1$ or $t > 2$; decreasing if $t < 0$ or $1 < t < 2$.
　17. Increasing if $1 < t < 2$ or $t > 3$; decreasing if $t < 1$ or $2 < t < 3$.
　18. Increasing if $-2 < t < -\tfrac{1}{3}$ or $t > \tfrac{4}{3}$; decreasing if $t < -2$ or $-\tfrac{1}{3} < t < \tfrac{4}{3}$.

Page 29 (§ 12)

1. 2.12.	**4.** -0.47.	**7.** 0.33; 2.17.
2. 1.29.	**5.** 4.20.	**8.** -1.66; 1.12.
3. -2.21.	**6.** -1.88; 0.35; 1.53.	**9.** -1.22; 0.72.

Page 33 (§ 13)

1. $(\frac{5}{6}, -4\frac{1}{12})$.
2. $(-\frac{1}{2}, 3\frac{1}{4})$.
3. $(-2, 16), (2, -16)$.
4. $(0, 4), (1\frac{1}{3}, 5\frac{5}{27})$.
5. $(-1, 8), (1\frac{2}{3}, -1\frac{13}{27})$.

6. $(1\frac{2}{3}, 4\frac{5}{27}), (3, 3)$.
7. $(-2, 0), (\frac{2}{3}, 9\frac{13}{27})$.
8. $(3, -11)$.
9. $(-\frac{1}{2}, 1\frac{3}{8}), (0, 1), (2, -7)$.
10. $(1, 5)$.

Page 35 (§ 14)

1. $2x - y - 6 = 0$.
2. $5x + 2y + 4 = 0$.
3. $14x + y - 31 = 0$.
4. $x = 3$.

5. $y = 5$.
6. $x - \sqrt{3}y - 1 - 4\sqrt{3} = 0$.
7. $6x + 6y - 5 = 0$.
8. $8x - 12y + 17 = 0$.

Page 36 (§ 14)

9. $4x - 3y - 1 = 0$.
10. $5x + 4y - 27 = 0$.
11. $10x + 9y + 7 = 0$.
*12. $\tan^{-1}\frac{3}{11}$.
13. $\frac{\pi}{4}$.
14. $\tan^{-1}\frac{7}{9}$.

15. $\tan^{-1}7$
16. $\tan^{-1}2$.
17. $\tan^{-1}\frac{49}{16}$.
18. $\tan^{-1}\frac{7}{8}$; $\tan^{-1}\frac{7}{11}$; $\tan^{-1}(-7)$.
19. $(\frac{13}{17}, -\frac{1}{17})$.
20. $1\frac{2}{3}$.

Page 37 (§ 15)

1. $20x - y - 10 = 0$.
2. $9x - y + 20 = 0$; $9x - y - 12 = 0$.
3. $y = 0$; $16x + y - 32 = 0$; $4x - y + 8 = 0$.
4. $117x + 27y - 17 = 0$; $297x + 27y - 13 = 0$; $\tan^{-1}\frac{10}{73}$.
5. $27x + 27y - 58 = 0$; $x + y - 2 = 0$.
6. $(2, -1)$; $(-\frac{4}{3}, 7\frac{4}{27})$; $3x - y - 7 = 0$; $81x - 27y + 311 = 0$.

Page 38 (§ 15)

7. $15x - y + 70 = 0$; $15x - y - 38 = 0$.
8. $3x - 8y - 2 = 0$; $(-2, -1)$.

Page 39 (§ 16)

1. $(-\frac{1}{2}, 5), (\frac{1}{2}, 3)$.
2. $(-\frac{2}{3}, 5\frac{1}{27}), (\frac{4}{5}, -2\frac{12}{25})$.
3. $(-1.24, -7.4), (3.24, 37.4)$.

4. $(-2.4, 11.6), (0.4, 0.3)$.
5. $(-1.4, -0.4), (0.7, 4.3)$.
6. $(-2.1, 5.1), (0.8, -7.2)$.

Page 42 (§ 17)

1. $56\frac{1}{4}$ sq. in.
2. Side parallel to wall twice as long as side perpendicular to wall.

3. 10 ft.   4. 75.   5. $\dfrac{4\pi a^3 \sqrt{3}}{9}$.

* The symbol $\tan^{-1}\frac{3}{11}$ denotes the angle whose tangent is $\frac{3}{11}$ (cf. § 47).

6. Depth is one half side of base.

7. 2 portions 8 ft. long; 4 portions 2 ft. long.

8. Breadth $= \dfrac{2\,a\sqrt{3}}{3}$ in.; depth $= \dfrac{2\,\sqrt{6}}{3}$ in.

9. Altitude $= \dfrac{p\sqrt{2}}{4}$; base $= \dfrac{p}{4}$, where p is the perimeter.

10. 2000 cu. in.; 2547 cu. in.

11. Height of rectangle $=$ radius of semicircle; semicircle of radius $\dfrac{a}{\pi}$.

Page 43 (§ 17)

12. $2\sqrt{3}$ in.

Page 46 (§ 18)

7. 0.0001; 0.000001; 0.00000001.

8. 0.000015001; 0.000000150001.

9. 0.000003 sq. in.

10. 305.8 cu. in.

Page 47 (§ 19)

1. 96 sq. in.

2. $\dfrac{49\,\pi}{180}$ cu. in.; $\dfrac{7\,\pi}{15}$ sq. in.

3. $\dfrac{2\,\pi}{5}$ cu. in.; $\dfrac{3\,\pi}{25}$ cu. in.

4. 8.0036 cu. in.

5. 28.28 cu. in.

6. 606.0456.

7. 0.0004.

8. 5.99928.

Page 50 (§ 20)

1. 144 ft.

2. 48 ft.

3. 45 ft.

4. $82\frac{2}{3}$ ft.

5. 400 ft.

6. $y = x^2 + 3\,x + 3$.

7. $y = x^3 + \frac{1}{2}\,x^2 - 4\,x$.

8. $y = 55 + 6\,x - \frac{5}{2}\,x^2 - \frac{1}{3}\,x^3$.

9. $4\,y = x^2 - 17$.

10. $y = \frac{1}{3}\,x^3 - \frac{1}{2}\,x^2 + x + 92$.

Page 50 (General Exercises)

1. $\dfrac{5}{(1-x)^2}$.

2. $-\dfrac{2\,a}{(a+x)^2}$.

3. $-\dfrac{4\,x}{(x^2-1)^2}$.

4. $-\dfrac{4\,x}{(x^2-1)^2}$.

5. $\dfrac{1}{2\,\sqrt{x}}$.

6. $-\dfrac{1}{2\,x^{\frac{3}{2}}}$.

7. $\dfrac{x}{\sqrt{x^2+1}}$.

Page 51 (General Exercises)

11. $t < -2$, or $-\frac{2}{3} < t < 2$.

12. $t < -1$, or $1 < t < 5$.

13. $50\frac{22}{27}$ ft.

14. $1 < t < 5$; $10\frac{3}{4}$.

15. Up when $t < 9\frac{3}{8}$ sec.; down when $9\frac{3}{8}$ sec. $< t < 18\frac{3}{4}$ sec.

16. Increasing if $t < -\frac{1}{6}$; decreasing if $t > -\frac{1}{6}$.

17. Increasing if $t > \frac{1}{3}$; decreasing if $t < \frac{1}{3}$.

18. Increasing if $-5 < t < -\frac{2}{3}$ or $t > \frac{11}{3}$; decreasing if $t < -5$ or $-\frac{2}{3} < t < \frac{11}{3}$.

19. Increasing if $-4 < t < -1$ or $t > 2$; decreasing if $t < -4$ or $-1 < t < 2$.

Page 52 (General Exercises)

24. $A(x - x_1) + B(y - y_1) = 0.$

25. $B(x - x_1) - A(y - y_1) = 0.$

26. $(x_2 - x_1)(y - y_1) = (y_2 - y_1)(x - x_1).$

27. $(-3, 0), (1, 32).$

28. $(-\frac{1}{3}, 6\frac{2}{27}), (1\frac{1}{2}, -6\frac{1}{4}).$

29. $(-3, 81), (2, -44).$

33. $4x - y + 2 = 0;\ 4x - y - 2 = 0.$

34. $\tan^{-1}\frac{28}{159}.$

35. $(-0.2, 1.5), (2.9, 20).$

36. $18\frac{2}{7}.$

37. $3x + y = 0;\ 78x - 4y + 175 = 0;\ 9x - y - 7 = 0.$

Page 53 (General Exercises)

38. 16. **43.** $6\frac{2}{3}$ ft. long. **44.** Altitude of cone is $\frac{4}{3}$ radius of sphere.

45. Altitude $= \sqrt[4]{\dfrac{4k^2}{243}}$; side of base $= \sqrt[4]{\dfrac{4k^2}{27}}.$

46. 2 pieces 3 in. long; 3 pieces 1 in. long.

47. Side about which rectangle is revolved is 5 in. long; the other side is 10 in. long.

48. 2 ft.

49. $\dfrac{240}{8 + \pi}$ in.; $\dfrac{240 + 60\pi}{8 + \pi}$ in.

Page 54 (General Exercises)

51. Each side $= 5\sqrt{2}$ in.

52. 0.0003.

53. 0.00629.

57. 3%.

58. 18.17.

59. 1344 cu. in.

60. 403.83 k, where k is the proportionality factor.

Page 55 (General Exercises)

61. 0.09 cu. in.

62. 7.988 cu. in.

63. 0.6.

64. 0.66 ft. per sec.

65. 33.0144; 32.9856.

66. 24.0024 sq. in.

67. 600 ft.

68. 56 ft.

69. $y = x^2 + 3x - 13.$

70. $y = 16 + 8x - x^2 - x^3.$

71. $y = x^3 - x^2 - x + 1.$

72. $y = 16 + 12x - x^3.$

CHAPTER III

Page 58 (§ 21)

1. 14. **2.** 120. **3.** 92. **4.** $10\frac{2}{3}.$ **5.** $1\frac{1}{3}.$ **6.** 12; 96. **7.** $\frac{8}{27}.$ **8.** $21\frac{1}{3}.$

Page 64 (§ 22)

1. 12. **3.** $21\frac{1}{3}.$ **5.** $42\frac{2}{3}.$ **7.** $40\frac{191}{128}.$ **9.** $1\frac{1}{2}.$ **11.** 144.

2. $6\frac{7}{12}.$ **4.** 12. **6.** $11\frac{1}{4}.$ **8.** $3\frac{5}{8}.$ **10.** 36. **12.** $13\frac{1}{3}.$

Page 66 (§ 23)

1. 144 ft. **2.** 193 ft. **3.** $20\frac{5}{6}$ ft.

Page 67 (§ 23)

4. $-\frac{1}{2} < t < 2;\ 10\frac{5}{12}$ ft.

5. 1088 ft.

6. 4 ft.

7. 4500π ft.-lb.

8. $150,000\pi$ ft.-lb.

9. $12,000\pi$ ft.-lb.

Page 70 (§ 24)

1. $3\frac{51}{64}$ T. 3. 9 T. 5. 2.3 T. 7. $833\frac{1}{3}$ T. 9. $182\frac{7}{24}$ T.

2. $2\frac{17}{32}$ T. 4. $2\frac{1}{2}$ T. 6. $1\frac{53}{64}$ T.; $1\frac{11}{32}$ T. 8. $260\frac{5}{12}$ T.; $572\frac{11}{12}$ T. 10. $1041\frac{2}{3}$ T.

Page 71 (§ 24)

11. $1\frac{9}{32}$ T. 12. 1.6 ft. below top side.

Page 74 (§ 25)

1. $64\ \pi$ cu. ft. 2. $\dfrac{1944\sqrt{3}}{5}$.

Page 75 (§ 25)

3. $8.1\ \pi$. 6. 72 cu. in. 8. 12. 10. $16\ \pi$.

4. $\dfrac{128\ \pi}{105}$. 7. $\dfrac{128\ \pi}{15}$. 9. $\dfrac{128\ \pi}{5}$. 11. $\dfrac{32\ \pi}{15}$.

5. $16,920\ \pi$.

Page 76 (General Exercises)

5. $\dfrac{4\ a^2\sqrt{2}}{3}$. 8. $57\frac{1}{6}$. 11. $18\frac{2}{3}$. 14. $1\frac{1}{3}$ ft.

6. $10\frac{2}{3}$. 9. $20\frac{5}{6}$. 12. $4\frac{1}{3}$ ft. 15. $19\frac{2}{3}$ ft.

7. $21\frac{1}{12}$. 10. $57\frac{1}{6}$. 13. $32\frac{2}{3}$ ft. 16. $64\frac{2}{3}$ ft.

Page 77 (General Exercises)

17. 15 ft.

18. $358,593\frac{3}{4}\ \pi$ ft.-lb. 22. $\dfrac{9\ k}{8}$, where k is the proportionality factor.

19. $3583\frac{1}{3}\ \pi$ ft.-lb. 23. 2500 ft.-lb.

20. $27,333\frac{1}{3}\ \pi$ ft.-lb.

27. $\frac{2}{3}\ wa^3$, where w is the weight of a cubic unit of the liquid.

Page 78 (General Exercises)

28. 625 lb.

29. $3\ w\sqrt{3}$, where w is the weight of a cubic foot of water.

30. Twice as great.

31. $3\frac{3}{4}$ T.

32. $16\ w$, where w is the weight of a cubic unit of water.

39. $341\frac{1}{3}$ cu. in.

Page 79 (General Exercises)

40. $1000\sqrt{3}$ cu. in. 43. $\dfrac{162\ \pi}{35}$. 45. $36\sqrt{3}$. 48. 16.

41. $129\frac{3}{5}$. 46. $18\ \pi$. 49. $35.1\ \pi$; $18.9\ \pi$.

42. $8.1\ \pi$. 44. $627\frac{1}{5}\ \pi$. 47. 8.

CHAPTER IV

Page 86 (§ 27)

1. $x^2 + y^2 + 4\ x - 6\ y - 23 = 0$. 4. $5\ x - 3\ y - 8 = 0$.

2. $x^2 + y^2 + 6\ x - 8\ y = 0$. 5. $8\ x^2 + 9\ y^2 = 288$.

3. $6\ x - 4\ y + 19 = 0$.

Page 87 (§ 27)

6. $36 x^2 + 20 y^2 = 45.$
7. $y^2 - 8 x + 16 = 0.$
8. $y^2 = 16 x.$
9. $3 x^2 - y^2 + 6 x - 9 = 0.$
10. $x^2 + y^2 = 4.$

Page 88 (§ 28)

1. $(-2, 5)$; 4.
2. $(\tfrac{2}{3}, -\tfrac{1}{3})$; $\dfrac{2\sqrt{5}}{3}.$

Page 89 (§ 28)

3. $3 x - 2 y + 4 = 0.$
9. $\sqrt{7}.$
10. $x^2 + y^2 - 39 = 0.$

Page 92 (§ 30)

1. $(-1, 0).$
2. $(0, 2).$
3. $(\tfrac{3}{4}, 0).$
4. $(0, -1\tfrac{1}{4}).$
5. $4\tfrac{1}{2}$ ft.
6. $5 \sqrt{10}$ ft.
7. $25\tfrac{2}{5}$ ft.
8. $4 \pi \sqrt{6}$ in.
9. $y^2 + 10 x - 25 = 0.$
10. $x^2 - 4 x - 14 y + 11 = 0.$

Page 95 (§ 31)

1. $(\pm 5, 0)$; $(\pm 4, 0)$; $\tfrac{4}{5}.$
2. $(0, \pm 5)$; $(0, \pm \sqrt{21})$; $\dfrac{\sqrt{21}}{5}.$
3. $(\pm 1, 0)$; $\left(\pm\dfrac{\sqrt{2}}{2}, 0\right)$; $\dfrac{\sqrt{2}}{2}.$
4. $\left(\pm\dfrac{\sqrt{3}}{3}, 0\right)$; $\left(\pm\dfrac{\sqrt{30}}{15}, 0\right)$; $\dfrac{\sqrt{10}}{5}.$
5. $9 x^2 + 25 y^2 - 54 x - 144 = 0$
6. $9 x^2 + 5 y^2 - 20 y - 25 = 0.$
7. $13 x^2 + 49 y^2 = 637.$
8. $16 x^2 + 25 y^2 = 400.$
9. $3 x^2 + 4 y^2 = 108.$
10. $16 x^2 + 25 y^2 = 400.$

Page 99 (§ 32)

1. $(\pm 5, 0)$; $(\pm \sqrt{29}, 0)$; $2 x \pm 5 y = 0$; $\dfrac{\sqrt{29}}{5}.$
2. $(\pm 2, 0)$; $(\pm \sqrt{29}, 0)$; $5 x \pm 2 y = 0$; $\dfrac{\sqrt{29}}{2}.$
3. $(0, \pm \sqrt{3})$; $(0, \pm \sqrt{5})$; $\sqrt{3}\, x \pm \sqrt{2}\, y = 0$; $\dfrac{\sqrt{15}}{3}.$
4. $(\pm 4, 0)$; $(\pm 4 \sqrt{2}, 0)$; $x \pm y = 0$; $\sqrt{2}.$
5. $\left(\pm\dfrac{\sqrt{3}}{3}, 0\right)$; $\left(\pm\dfrac{\sqrt{30}}{6}, 0\right)$; $\sqrt{3}\, x \pm \sqrt{2}\, y = 0$; $\dfrac{\sqrt{10}}{2}.$
6. $(0, \pm 1)$; $\left(0, \pm\dfrac{\sqrt{5}}{2}\right)$; $2 x \pm y = 0$; $\dfrac{\sqrt{5}}{2}.$
7. $20 x^2 - 16 y^2 - 60 x + 25 = 0.$
8. $21 x^2 - 4 y^2 + 16 y - 100 = 0.$
9. $3 x^2 - y^2 = 12.$
10. $8 x^2 - y^2 = 32.$

Page 112 (§ 36)

1. $18 x^2 + 26 x.$
2. $10 x^4 + 21 x^2 + 3.$
3. $(x^2 - 1)(x + 2)^2(7 x^2 + 8 x - 3).$
4. $(x - 3)(4 x^2 - 3 x - 7).$

5. $\dfrac{16\,x}{(x^2+4)^2}$.

6. $-\dfrac{6(3\,x+1)(x+2)}{(2\,x-1)^4}$.

7. $\dfrac{3}{5}\left(\dfrac{1}{\sqrt[5]{x^2}}-\dfrac{1}{x\,\sqrt[5]{x^3}}\right)$.

8. $\dfrac{4(x-1)}{\sqrt[3]{3\,x^2-6\,x+1}}$.

9. $\dfrac{1}{(x+1)\sqrt{x^2-1}}$.

10. $\dfrac{2-x^2}{(x^3+2)^{\frac{4}{3}}}$.

11. $\dfrac{2\,x^2-2\,x-1}{\sqrt{x^2-2\,x}}$.

12. $\dfrac{12-18\,x}{(9\,x^2+4)^{\frac{3}{2}}}$.

13. $\dfrac{2\,x}{(1+x^3)^{\frac{5}{3}}}$.

14. $\dfrac{2\,x^4+2\,x^2-2\,x}{(x^2+2)^{\frac{1}{2}}(x^3-2)^{\frac{2}{3}}}$.

15. $\dfrac{2\,x^4-3\,x^2-1}{2(2\,x^3+x)^{\frac{3}{2}}}$.

16. $\dfrac{8\,x-3\,x^3}{\sqrt{4-x^2}}$.

17. $(6\,x^2+14\,x+1)(x^2+4\,x+1)^{\frac{3}{2}}$.

18. $-\dfrac{1}{(x^3+3\,x^2)^{\frac{2}{3}}}$.

19. $\dfrac{2}{(2-x)\sqrt{x^2-4}}$.

20. $\dfrac{6\,x^2}{(x^3-3)^{\frac{2}{3}}(x^3+3)^{\frac{4}{3}}}$.

21. $\dfrac{15\,x^2}{2\sqrt{x-1}}$.

22. $-\dfrac{5}{3\,x^2(x+4\,x^6)^{\frac{2}{3}}}$.

Page 114 (§ 37)

1. $\dfrac{y^2+1}{3\,y^2-2\,xy-1}$.

2. $\dfrac{\sqrt{y+x}-\sqrt{y-x}}{a}$.

3. $\dfrac{3\,x+y}{x+3\,y}$.

4. $\dfrac{y}{2\,y^2-2\,x-1}$.

5. $\dfrac{y}{x}$.

6. $-\dfrac{y+2}{x+3};\ \dfrac{2\,y+4}{(x+3)^2}$.

7. $\dfrac{1}{2\,y-1};\ -\dfrac{2}{(2\,y-1)^2}$.

8. $\dfrac{2\,x+y}{2\,y-x};\ 0$.

9. $-\dfrac{x^4}{y^4};\ -\dfrac{4\,a^5x^3}{y^9}$.

10. $-\dfrac{y^{\frac{1}{2}}}{x^{\frac{1}{2}}};\ \dfrac{a^{\frac{1}{2}}}{2\,x^{\frac{3}{2}}}$.

11. $-\dfrac{x-a}{y-b};\ -\dfrac{a^2+b^2}{(y-b)^3}$.

Page 116 (§ 38)

1. $3\,x+4\,y-19=0$.

2. $x+2\,y-2=0$.

3. $\tan^{-1}\tfrac{3}{4}$.

7. $(\tfrac{14}{25},-\tfrac{3}{4})$.

8. $\tan^{-1}\tfrac{12}{5}$.

9. $\dfrac{\pi}{2};\ \tan^{-1}\tfrac{18}{25}$.

10. $\tan^{-1}2$.

11. $\tan^{-1}\tfrac{3}{4};\ \tan^{-1}3$.

12. $\dfrac{\pi}{2}$.

13. $\tan^{-1}3$.

14. $\dfrac{\pi}{2};\ \tan^{-1}7$.

15. $\dfrac{\pi}{2}$.

Page 120 (§ 40)

1. $x^3=8\,y^2;\ t\sqrt{16+9\,t^2}$. **2.** $(y-2)^2=x;\ \sqrt{4\,t^2+1}$.

3. $5\,y=6\,x-2\,x^2;\ \sqrt{61-240\,t+400\,t^2};\ (1\tfrac{1}{2},\tfrac{9}{10})$.

4. $(y-2\,x)^2=625\,x;\ \sqrt{20\,t^2-200\,t+625};\ (25,-75)$.

5. $(y-2)^2=(x+3)^3;\ t\sqrt{4+9\,t^2};\ (-3,2)$.

6. $x^{\frac{1}{2}}+y^{\frac{1}{2}}=2;\ 8\sqrt{1-2\,t+2\,t^2};\ (1,1)$.

Page 121 (§ 40)

8. $\dfrac{v_0{}^2\sin 2\,\alpha}{g};\ v_0;\ \alpha$.

9. $\dfrac{\pi}{4}$.

10. $y=x\tan\alpha-\dfrac{gx^2}{2\,v_0{}^2\cos^2\alpha}$.

Page 124 (§ 41)

1. 0.2 cm. per sec.

2. 20.9 sq. in. per sec.

3. 0.26 in. per min.

4. 64 cu. ft. per sec.

5. $3\sqrt{2}$ ft. per sec.

6. 4.1 ft. per sec.

Page 125 (§ 41)

7. $\frac{1}{40}$ in. per min.

8. Circle; $\frac{15}{x}$ ft. per sec., $x =$ distance of point from wall.

9. 2.64 ft. per sec.   10. 6.6 ft. per sec.

11. $\frac{2\,x + 4\,y}{2\,x + y}$ ft. per sec., where x is distance of top of ladder and y is distance of foot of ladder from base of pyramid.

Page 127 (§ 42)

1. $\frac{16 - 4\sqrt{2}}{3}$ ft.   2. $12\frac{1}{4}$ ft.   3. $4\,x^3 = (3\,y + 10)^2$.   4. $x^2 + y^2 = 13$.

Page 128 (§ 42)

5. $xy - 2\,x + 1 = 0$.   7. $\frac{a^2}{6}$.   8. $\frac{1}{10}$.   9. $\frac{\pi a^3}{15}$.   10. $\frac{16\,\pi a^3}{35}$.

11. $259\frac{1}{8}\,w$, where w is weight of cubic unit of liquid.   12. $3\frac{9}{20}$ T.

Page 128 (General Exercises)

1. $\dfrac{x + \sqrt{x^2 - a^2}}{a\sqrt{x^2 - a^2}}$.

2. $\dfrac{a^2}{\sqrt{x^2 + a^2}(x + \sqrt{x^2 + a^2})^2}$.

3. $\dfrac{2\,x^4 - 3\,a^2x^2 + 2\,a^4}{(x^2 - a^2)^{\frac{3}{2}}}$.

4. $15\,x^3\sqrt{x^2 + a^2}$.

5. $\dfrac{a^2}{x^2\sqrt{a^2 - x^2}}$.

6. $\dfrac{x^3}{(a^2 - x^2)^{\frac{3}{2}}}$.

7. $\dfrac{a^2}{3\,y^2 - a^2}$; $-\dfrac{6\,a^4y}{(3\,y^2 - a^2)^3}$.

8. $-\dfrac{y^{\frac{1}{3}}}{x^{\frac{1}{3}}}$; $\dfrac{a^{\frac{2}{3}}}{3\,x^{\frac{4}{3}}y^{\frac{1}{3}}}$.

9. $-\dfrac{x^{n-1}}{y^{n-1}}$; $-\dfrac{(n-1)a^nx^{n-2}}{y^{2n-1}}$.

10. $-\dfrac{b^2x}{a^2y}$; $-\dfrac{b^4}{a^2y^3}$.

11. $\dfrac{ay - x^2}{y^2 - ax}$; $-\dfrac{2\,a^3xy}{(y^2 - ax)^3}$.

12. $\dfrac{1 - y^2}{2\,xy - 1}$; $\dfrac{2(y^2 - 1)(4\,x + y)}{(2\,xy - 1)^3}$.

Page 129 (General Exercises)

37. Circle.

Page 130 (General Exercises)

41. A straight line perpendicular to line of centers of circles.

43. $\dfrac{1}{\sqrt{A}}\sqrt{A(x_1{}^2 + y_1{}^2) + 2\,Gx_1 + 2\,Fy_1 + C}$.

44. $3\,x^2 + 2\,xy + 3\,y^2 - 12\,x - 12\,y = 0$.   49. $x_1^{-\frac{1}{3}}x + y_1^{-\frac{1}{3}}y = a^{\frac{2}{3}}$.

45. $3\,x^2 + 2\,xy + 3\,y^2 - 16\,x - 16\,y = 0$.   50. $x_1^{n-1}x + y_1^{n-1}y = a^n$.

46. $29\,x - 3\,y + 16\,a = 0$.

Page 131 (General Exercises)

56. $\tan^{-1} 2$.

57. $\tan^{-1} 1\frac{2}{5}$.

58. $\tan^{-1} \frac{4}{3}$.

59. $\frac{\pi}{2}$; $\tan^{-1} \frac{9}{13}$.

60. $\frac{\pi}{2}$.

61. $\tan^{-1} 1\frac{2}{5}$.

62. $\tan^{-1} 1\frac{1}{2}$.

63. $\tan^{-1} \frac{4}{3}$.

64. $y = 2\,x^2$; $2\sqrt{1 + 64\,t^2}$.

65. 2.1.

66. $x^2 - y^2 = 9$; 1.3.

67. $(y - 1)^2 = 4(x - 1)$; $\sqrt{\dfrac{t+1}{t}}$.

68. $(x - 3)^2 = 3(y - 2)$; 3.1.

Page 132 (General Exercises)

69. $1 < t < 3$; semicircle; $\dfrac{2}{\sqrt{-t^2 + 4\,t - 3}}$.

70. $x^{\frac{2}{3}} + y^{\frac{2}{3}} = 1$; $3\,t$.

71. $y = \dfrac{8}{x^2 + 4}$; $\dfrac{2\sqrt{(t^2 + 1)^4 + 4\,t^2}}{(t^2 + 1)^2}$.

72. $(x + 2)^2 = (y - 1)^3$; $\frac{1}{2}\sqrt{9\,t + 4}$.

73. $\dfrac{3\,s}{\sqrt{s^2 - 400}}$ ft. per sec., where s is the length of rope between the man and the boat.

74. 5.8 mi. per hr.; 28.8 mi.

75. 11.4 mi. per hr.

76. $9\,x^2 + 36\,y^2 = 4096$; $\dfrac{4}{3}\sqrt{\dfrac{256 - 3\,t^2}{64 - t^2}}$.

78. Increasing at rate of 2 in. per sec.

79. 0.06 ft. per min.

Page 133 (General Exercises)

80. 0.08 ft. per sec.

81. 0.08 ft. per min.

82. 0.01 in. per min.

83. $\frac{49}{51}$ sq. in. per min.

84. $\frac{1}{8}$ in. per sec.

85. $\dfrac{12800}{x^2}$ ft. per sec., where x is the distance the man has crossed.

86. Sides equal.

87. Base $= 4$ ft.; side $= 3$ ft.

88. Breadth $= 9$ in.; depth $= 9\sqrt{3}$ in.

89. Side of base $=$ twice the depth.

Page 134 (General Exercises)

90. Each dimension $= 3$ ft.

91. Inner dimensions: radius $= 2$ in.; altitude $= 4$ in.

92. Radius $= 3$ in.; height $= 6$ in.

93. Radius $= \sqrt[3]{30}$ ft.; length $= 2\sqrt[3]{30}$ ft.

94. Each 3 in.

95. $\frac{1}{2}$ in.

96. $\dfrac{1}{\sqrt{2}}$.

97. $\dfrac{a\sqrt{6}}{3}$.

98. When the passenger is landed at a point $1\frac{2}{3}$ mi. from point of shore directly opposite the vessel which is 4 mi. offshore.

Page 135 (General Exercises)

99. 8 mi. from point on bank nearest to A.

100. He should travel $4\frac{13}{16}$ mi. on land.

101. $a - \dfrac{bm}{\sqrt{n^2 - m^2}}$ mi. on land; $\dfrac{bn}{\sqrt{n^2 - m^2}}$ mi. in water.

102. $1\frac{13}{37}$ hr. later.

103. $\sqrt[3]{100}$ mi. per hr.

104. Speed in still water $= \dfrac{3\,a}{2}$ mi. per hr.

105. Base $= a\sqrt{3}$; altitude $= \dfrac{3\,b}{2}$.

106. 4.

Page 136 (General Exercises)

110. $y - 1 = ky(x - 1)$, where k is the factor of proportionality.

111. $x^2 - y^2 = c^2$.   **113.** 68 min.   **114.** 20 sec.   **115.** $\frac{1}{5}$.

116. $21\frac{1}{3}$.   **117.** $\dfrac{32\,\pi a^3}{105}$.

CHAPTER V

Page 146 (§ 46)

1. $8\cos 2x$.

2. $\sec^2 \dfrac{x}{3}$.

3. $3\sin 6x$.

4. $\tan 2x \sec^2 2x$.

5. $\cos^2 5x$.

6. $3\sin^3 3x \cos^2 3x$.

7. $3\sec^5 \dfrac{3x}{5} \tan \dfrac{3x}{5}$.

8. $-4\csc^2 4x \operatorname{ctn} 4x$.

9. $\frac{1}{4}\cos^3 \dfrac{x}{4}$.

10. $\tan^2 \dfrac{x}{3} \sec^4 \dfrac{x}{3}$.

11. $\dfrac{4x}{3}\cos \dfrac{2x}{3}$.

12. $4\csc 2x(\csc 2x - \operatorname{ctn} 2x)^2$.

13. $3\cos 6x$.

14. $\tan^4 \dfrac{x}{3}$.

15. $\sec 2x \tan 2x(1 + \sec 2x \tan 2x)$.

16. $6\sec 2x \tan^3 2x$.

17. $-\dfrac{3\tan 3x}{2\tan 2y}$.

18. $-\dfrac{y}{x}$.

19. $\dfrac{\sec^2(x-y) + \sec^2(x+y)}{\sec^2(x-y) - \sec^2(x+y)}$.

20. $\dfrac{y}{x}$.

Page 151 (§ 48)

1. $\dfrac{2}{\sqrt{1 - 4x^2}}$.

2. $\dfrac{2}{x\sqrt{9x^2 - 4}}$.

3. $\dfrac{1}{1 - 2x + 2x^2}$.

4. $-\dfrac{1}{(x+1)\sqrt{x^2 + 2x}}$.

5. $\dfrac{1}{x\sqrt{9x^2 - 1}}$.

6. $-\dfrac{1}{(2x+1)\sqrt{x^2 + x}}$.

7. $\dfrac{1}{\sqrt{4x - x^2}}$.

8. $\dfrac{2}{x^2 + 4x + 8}$.

9. $-\dfrac{2x}{(x^2+2)\sqrt{x^2+1}}$.

10. $-\dfrac{2}{x^2 + 4}$.

11. $\dfrac{4}{4 + x^2}$.

12. $\dfrac{1}{1 + x^2}$.

13. $\dfrac{54}{(x^2 + 9)^2}$.

14. $-\dfrac{2}{x\sqrt{x^2 - 4}}$.

15. $-\dfrac{1}{(1 + x)\sqrt{x}}$.

16. $\dfrac{2 - 3x}{\sqrt{9 - x^2}}$.

17. $\dfrac{2}{1 + 2x + 2x^2}$.

18. $4x\sqrt{1 - x^4}$.

19. $\dfrac{6 - x}{\sqrt{x(4 - x)^3}}$.

20. $-\dfrac{2}{(x-2)\sqrt{x^2 - 4x}}$.

Page 153 (§ 49)

1. $\mp 8\,\pi$ ft. per sec.; $\pm\,8\,\pi\,\sqrt{3}$ ft. per sec.

2. $\dfrac{15}{\pi}$.

3. 4 rad. per sec.

4. $\dfrac{4\,x - 4\,y}{x^2 + y^2}$ rad. per sec.

5. $\dfrac{t}{5}$ rad. per sec.

Page 156 (§ 50)

1. $s = 4\sin\dfrac{\pi t}{3}$.

2. $\dfrac{2\,\pi}{3}$; 10.

3. 20; 4.

6. $-4\,\sqrt{12\,s - s^2 - 32}$; $16(6 - s)$.

7. $\dfrac{\pi\,\sqrt{7}}{3}$ sec.

8. 5 ft.; $2\,\pi$ sec.

9. $\frac{5}{3}$.

10. $4\,\sqrt{2}$ ft.

11. $2\,\pi\,\sqrt{3}$ sec.

Page 158 (§ 51)

7. $\dfrac{b\sin\phi}{a - b\cos\phi}$; $\phi = \cos^{-1}\dfrac{b}{a}$.

Page 161 (§ 52)

1. $\dfrac{5\,a\,\sqrt{5}}{2}$.

2. $\dfrac{7\,\sqrt{7}}{4}$.

3. $\dfrac{2\,\sqrt{x(x + 3)^3}}{3}$.

4. $3(axy)^{\frac{1}{3}}$.

6. $\dfrac{17\,\sqrt{17}}{4}$.

7. $a\phi$.

8. $2\,a$.

9. $\dfrac{4\,\sqrt{2}}{\pi}$.

Page 162 (§ 53)

1. 2.

2. $2\,\pi\,a^2$.

3. $\dfrac{5\,\pi}{6}$.

4. $\sqrt{2} - 1$.

5. $\frac{1}{4}$.

6. $\frac{1}{16}(16 + 8\,\sqrt{2} - 3\,\pi\,\sqrt{2})$.

7. $\dfrac{\pi}{6}$.

8. $\dfrac{\pi(\pi + 4\,a)}{2}$.

9. $\dfrac{\pi(8 - \pi)}{2}$; $\dfrac{\pi(8 + \pi)}{2}$.

10. $\dfrac{\pi w}{4}$, where w = weight of cubic unit of water.

Page 163 (General Exercises)

1. $-2\sin 4\,x$.

2. $\dfrac{15}{2}\sec^6\dfrac{x}{2}$.

3. $9\cos^3 3\,x - 6\cos 3\,x$.

4. $8\cos^3 2\,x\sin 4\,x\cos 6\,x$.

5. $\operatorname{ctn}\dfrac{x}{2}\left(\csc\dfrac{x}{2} - \operatorname{ctn}\dfrac{x}{2}\right)$.

6. $4\,x^2\cos 2\,x$.

7. $a^4x^3\sin ax$.

8. $\dfrac{\cos 2\,x}{\cos 2\,y}$.

9. $\dfrac{y}{x}$.

10. $\dfrac{2}{(x + 2)\,\sqrt{2\,x}}$.

11. $-\dfrac{2}{x^2 + 1}$.

12. $\dfrac{2}{x\,\sqrt{9\,x^2 - 4}}$.

13. $\dfrac{2}{(x^2 - 1)\,\sqrt{x^2 - 2}}$.

14. $-\dfrac{1}{(x + 1)\,\sqrt{x^2 + 2\,x}}$.

15. $-\dfrac{2}{(x + 2)\,\sqrt{x^2 + 4\,x}}$.

16. $16\,x\sin^{-1}2\,x$.

17. $\dfrac{1 + x^4}{1 + x^6}$.

18. $\dfrac{x^2}{(4 - x^2)^{\frac{3}{2}}}$.

19. $\dfrac{y(1 - x^2 - y^2)}{x(1 + x^2 + y^2)}$.

20. $\dfrac{xy - y}{y^2 - x}$.

Page 164 (General Exercises)

35. $k \sqrt{a^2 \sin^2 kt + b^2 \cos^2 kt}$.

36. $2\frac{1}{2}$ ft.

37. $\sqrt{34}$; $\frac{3}{2}\left(\frac{\pi}{2} + \tan^{-1}\frac{5}{3}\right)$.

38. 3; 2.

39. 5π sec.

40. 40 ft.

41. $20 \sqrt{3}$ ft. per sec.

42. 60 ft.; 60 min.

43. $\dfrac{16 \sqrt{2}}{\pi^3}$.

44. $\dfrac{(\pi^2 + 1)^{\frac{3}{2}}}{2 \pi}$.

45. $2 a \sqrt{3}$.

Page 165 (General Exercises)

46. $\dfrac{(a^2 + b^2)^{\frac{3}{2}}}{2 ab \sqrt{2}}$.

47. $2(1 + \cos^2 \phi)^{\frac{3}{2}}$; $x^2 = 4(1 - y)$.

48. $\dfrac{13 \sqrt{13}}{3}$.

49. $\dfrac{a \sqrt{2}}{2}$.

51. $\dfrac{17 \pi}{2}$ mi. per min.

52. $\left(b \sin \theta + \dfrac{b^2 \sin \theta \cos \theta}{\sqrt{a^2 - b^2 \sin^2 \theta}}\right)$ times angular velocity of AB, where $\theta =$ angle CAB.

53. $\dfrac{(x - 2)^2}{9} + \dfrac{(y - 3)^2}{4} = 1$; $\sqrt{9 \sin^2 t + 4 \cos^2 t}$; when $t = (2 k + 1) \dfrac{\pi}{2}$.

54. $\dfrac{x^2}{4} - \dfrac{y^2}{16} = 1$; $6 \sec 3 t \sqrt{\tan^2 3 t + 4 \sec^2 3 t}$.

55. $6 \sin 2 \phi$. **56.** $ab\phi$. **57.** $xy = 4$; $12 \sqrt{2}$. **58.** $2 y^2 = (2 - x)^3$; $\sqrt{34}$.

Page 166 (General Exercises)

59. $x^2 = 2(2 - y)$; 6.

60. 0.

61. $\dfrac{\pi}{10} \cos \theta$ sq. ft. per sec.; increasing if $0 < \theta < \dfrac{\pi}{2}$; decreasing if $\dfrac{\pi}{2} < \theta < \pi$.

62. $\dfrac{\pi}{4}$. **63.** $\dfrac{\pi}{4}$. **64.** $5 \sqrt{15}$ ft. **66.** $\sqrt{2}$ ft.

67. At an angle $\tan^{-1} k$ with the ground.

Page 167 (General Exercises)

68. 16 in.

69. $5 \sqrt{5}$ ft.

70. $2 a \cos \dfrac{3 \pi}{8}$.

71. $13 \sqrt{13}$ ft.

72. $\tan^{-1} 2 \sqrt{2}$.

73. $\tan^{-1} \frac{4}{3}$.

74. 0; $\tan^{-1} 3 \sqrt{3}$.

75. $\tan^{-1} \frac{1}{2}$; $\tan^{-1} 4 \sqrt{2}$.

76. $\tan^{-1} \frac{2}{9}$; $\tan^{-1} \frac{6}{17}$.

77. $\tan^{-1} \dfrac{2(\sqrt{3} - 1)}{\sqrt{3} + 4}$.

78. $\tan^{-1} \dfrac{6 + \pi \sqrt{3}}{6 \sqrt{3} - \pi}$.

CHAPTER VI

Page 174 (§ 56)

1. $\dfrac{2}{x^2} e^{-\frac{2}{x}}$.

2. $\frac{1}{2}\left(e^{\frac{x}{a}} - e^{-\frac{x}{a}}\right)$.

3. $2 x \ln a \, a^{x^2 - 1}$.

4. $\dfrac{\ln a}{1 + x^2} a^{\tan^{-1} x}$.

5. $\dfrac{2 x + 6}{x^2 + 6 x - 1}$.

6. $\dfrac{2 x + 4}{2 x^2 + 8 x + 9}$.

7. $\dfrac{1}{x^2-16}$.

8. $\dfrac{1}{\sqrt{x^2+9}}$.

9. $\dfrac{5}{\sqrt{25\,x^2+1}}$.

10. $4\csc 2\,x$.

11. $\dfrac{3(e^{3x}-e^{-3x})}{e^{3x}+e^{-3x}}$.

12. $e^{-3x}(2\cos 2\,x-3\sin 2\,x)$.

13. $-\tan^{-1}x$.

14. $4\,x^2e^{2x}$.

15. $10\,e^{3x}\cos x$.

16. $\dfrac{2}{e^x+e^{-x}}$.

17. $2\sec^3 x$.

18. $\dfrac{1}{x\sqrt{x+1}}$.

19. $\dfrac{y-xy\,e^{x+y}}{x+xy\,e^{x+y}}$.

20. $\dfrac{1-y(x+y)}{x(x+y)-1}$.

Page 175 (§ 57)

1. $(3\ln 5)$ ft.

2. $x^2=8\,y$.

3. $x=3\,e^{y-2}$.

4. $\dfrac{1}{a}\,(e^{a^2}-1)$.

5. $4\ln 2$.

6. $a^2\!\left(e^{\frac{h}{a}}-e^{-\frac{h}{a}}\right)$.

7. $\frac{1}{2}(27-36\ln 2)$.

8. $\dfrac{\pi a^3}{4}\left(e^{\frac{2h}{a}}-e^{-\frac{2h}{a}}\right)+\pi a^2 h$.

9. $\pi(18+16\ln 2)$.

Page 177 (§ 58)

1. $y=6\,e^{\frac{x}{3}}$. **2.** $y=54.3\,e^{0.01\,x}$. **3.** $y=8\,e^{0.35\,x}$. **4.** \$448.

5. $P=10{,}000\,e^{0.031\,t}$, where P is the population at any time t.

6. $C=0.01\,e^{-0.037\,t}$, where C is the concentration at any time t.

7. 90 sec.

Page 181 (§ 59)

1. $y=0.62\,x-0.76$. **2.** $I=0.0017\,D$.

Page 182 (§ 59)

3. $y=0.30(2.7)^x$. **5.** $a=0.0000000048\,l^{3.06}$.

4. $c=0.010(0.84)^t$. **6.** $pv^{1.35}=10$.

Page 182 (General Exercises)

1. $\dfrac{1}{1+e^{2x}}$. **3.** $\dfrac{4}{\sqrt{16\,x^2+1}}$. **5.** $\dfrac{2\,e^{6x}}{1-e^{4x}}$. **8.** $a\tan^3 ax$.

2. $\dfrac{2\,x}{1-x^4}$. **4.** $\dfrac{3}{49\,x^2-9}$. **6.** $(\ln 2\,x)^2$. **9.** x^3e^{2x}.

7. $2\tan^{-1}2\,x$. **10.** $3\sec^{-1}3\,x$.

Page 183 (General Exercises)

25. $\sqrt{2}\,e^t$.

26. $\dfrac{(x^2+1)^{\frac{3}{2}}}{x}$; $\dfrac{3\sqrt{3}}{2}$.

27. $8\,a$.

28. $\dfrac{10\sqrt{10}}{3}$.

29. $\dfrac{(1+4\,e^2)^{\frac{3}{2}}}{8\,e}$.

31. $y=ax^n$.

32. $xy=c$.

33. $\frac{38}{15}-6\ln\frac{3}{2}$.

34. $\pi(42-40\ln\frac{5}{2})$.

35. 1.24.

Page 184 (General Exercises)

36. 16.5 hr.

37. 1090 sec.

38. $p=14.7\,e^{-0.00004\,h}$.

39. $p=0.018\,t+24$.

40. Load $=190-6.5$ length.

41. $s=25(0.40)^t$.

Page 185 (General Exercises)

42. $c=0.010(0.83)^t$. **43.** $t=0.1\sqrt{l}$. **44.** $I=0.023\sqrt{\theta}$. **45.** $y=0.40\,x^{1.54}$.

CHAPTER VII

Page 190 (§ 60)

14. Origin; $\left(\dfrac{3\sqrt{3}}{2}, \dfrac{\pi}{6}\right)$.

15. Origin; $\left(\pm a\sqrt[4]{\dfrac{3}{4}}, \dfrac{\pi}{3}\right)$.

16. Origin; $(2, 0)$.

17. Origin; $\left(\pm a, \dfrac{\pi}{2}\right)$; $\left(\pm\dfrac{a}{\sqrt[4]{2}}, \dfrac{\pi}{4}\right)$; $\left(\pm\dfrac{a}{\sqrt[4]{2}}, \dfrac{3\,\pi}{4}\right)$.

18. $r^2 \sin 2\,\theta + 4 = 0$.

19. $r = 2\,a(\cos\theta - \sin\theta)$.

20. $r + 2\,a\cos\theta = 0$.

21. $r^2 = a^2 \cos 2\,\theta$.

22. $y = a$.

23. $x^2 + y^2 - 2\,ay = 0$.

24. $x^4 + x^2 y^2 = a^2 y^2$.

25. $(x^2 + y^2)^3 = 4\,a^2 x^2 y^2$.

Page 192 (§ 61)

1. $r \sin\theta = a$.

2. $r \cos(\theta - \alpha) = a$.

3. $r = 2\,a \sin\theta$.

4. $r = \dfrac{k}{1 - \cos\theta}$; $r = \dfrac{k}{1 + \cos\theta}$.

Page 193 (§ 61)

5. $r = \dfrac{a}{2 + \cos\theta}$; $r = \dfrac{a}{2 - \cos\theta}$.

7. 75,000,000 mi., or 25,000,000 mi.

8. 1.2 million mi., or 4.8 million mi.

Page 196 (§ 62)

1. 0.

2. $\pi - \tan^{-1}\dfrac{4}{\sqrt{3}}$.

3. $\tan^{-1}\dfrac{1}{2}$; $\dfrac{\pi}{2}$.

4. 0; $\dfrac{\pi}{2}$.

5. $\dfrac{\pi}{6}$; $\tan^{-1}(-\frac{1}{2})$.

Page 197 (§ 63)

1. $2\,a^2$.

2. $\dfrac{\pi a^2}{4\,n}$.

3. $\dfrac{3\,\pi a^2}{2}$.

4. $\dfrac{59\,\pi}{2}$.

5. $11\,\pi$.

6. $\dfrac{3\,\pi a^2}{4}$.

7. $11\,\pi$.

8. $40\,\pi$.

9. $\pi + 16$.

10. $\dfrac{4\,\pi - 3\sqrt{3}}{3}$; $\dfrac{8\,\pi + 3\sqrt{3}}{3}$.

Page 198 (General Exercises)

15. $\left(\dfrac{4 + \sqrt{2}}{2}, \dfrac{\pi}{4}\right)$; $\left(\dfrac{4 - \sqrt{2}}{2}, \dfrac{5\,\pi}{4}\right)$.

16. Origin; $\left(\dfrac{a\sqrt{3}}{2}, \pm\dfrac{\pi}{6}\right)$.

17. Origin; $\left(\dfrac{a}{\sqrt{3}}, \sin^{-1}\dfrac{1}{\sqrt{3}}\right)$.

18. Origin; $\left(\pm\dfrac{\sqrt{6}}{2}, \dfrac{\pi}{6}\right)$; $\left(\pm\dfrac{\sqrt{6}}{2}, \dfrac{5\,\pi}{6}\right)$.

19. Origin; $\left(\dfrac{2\,a}{\sqrt{5}}, \tan^{-1}2\right)$.

20. Origin; $\left(\pm 2\,a, \dfrac{\pi}{4}\right)$.

21. $r = \dfrac{2\,a\sin^2\theta}{\cos\theta}$.

22. $r = a\,\mathrm{ctn}\,\theta$.

23. $(x^2 + y^2)^2 - 4\,a^2 xy = 0$.

24. $(x^2 + y^2 - ax)^2 = a^2(x^2 + y^2)$.

26. 0; $\dfrac{\pi}{2}$; $\tan^{-1}2$.

27. $\dfrac{\pi}{2}$; $\dfrac{\pi}{3}$.

Page 199 (General Exercises)

28. $\dfrac{\pi}{4}$.

29. 0; $\dfrac{\pi}{2}$; $\tan^{-1}3\sqrt{3}$.

30. $r = ce^{\frac{\theta}{k}}$, where k is the tangent of the angle at which the curve intersects a radius vector.

31. $r^2 = 2(\theta + 2)$.

33. $2\,a^2$.

35. $2\,a^2$.

32. $r(\theta - 1) = 1$.

34. $\dfrac{e^{\pi a} - 1}{4\,a}$.

36. $\dfrac{(8 - \pi)a^2}{4}$.

CHAPTER VIII

Page 205 (§ 65)

1. $1 + x + \dfrac{x^2}{2!} + \dfrac{x^3}{3!} + \cdots$.

4. $x + \dfrac{1}{2}\cdot\dfrac{x^3}{3} + \dfrac{1\cdot 3}{2\cdot 4}\cdot\dfrac{x^5}{5} + \dfrac{1\cdot 3\cdot 5}{2\cdot 4\cdot 6}\cdot\dfrac{x^7}{7} + \cdots$.

2. $1 - \dfrac{x^2}{2!} + \dfrac{x^4}{4!} - \dfrac{x^6}{6!} + \cdots$.

5. $x - \dfrac{x^3}{3} + \dfrac{x^5}{5} - \dfrac{x^7}{7} + \cdots$.

3. $x + \dfrac{x^3}{3} + \dfrac{2\,x^5}{15} + \dfrac{17\,x^7}{315} + \cdots$.

6. $\dfrac{1}{\sqrt{2}}\left(1 + x - \dfrac{x^2}{2!} - \dfrac{x^3}{3!} + \cdots\right)$.

7. $\ln 2 + \dfrac{x}{2} - \dfrac{1}{2}\cdot\dfrac{x^2}{2^2} + \dfrac{1}{3}\cdot\dfrac{x^3}{2^3} + \cdots$.

8. $1 - 2\cdot\dfrac{x^2}{2!} + 2^3\cdot\dfrac{x^4}{4!} - 2^5\cdot\dfrac{x^6}{6!} + \cdots$.

9. $4 + 2^3\cdot\dfrac{x^2}{2!} + 2^5\cdot\dfrac{x^4}{4!} + 2^7\cdot\dfrac{x^6}{6!} + \cdots$.

10. $x - \dfrac{x^2}{2} + \dfrac{x^3}{6} - \dfrac{x^4}{12} + \cdots$.

11. $1 + \dfrac{1}{2}\cdot x^2 - \dfrac{1\cdot 1}{2\cdot 4}\cdot x^4 + \dfrac{1\cdot 1\cdot 3}{2\cdot 4\cdot 6}\cdot x^6 + \cdots$.

Page 207 (§ 66)

1. $e^5\left[1 + (x - 5) + \dfrac{(x - 5)^2}{2!} + \dfrac{(x - 5)^3}{3!} + \cdots\right]$.

2. $\dfrac{1}{2} - \dfrac{(x - 1)}{2^2} + \dfrac{(x - 1)^2}{2^3} - \dfrac{(x - 1)^3}{2^4} + \cdots$.

3. $\dfrac{1}{2} + \dfrac{\sqrt{3}}{2}\left(x - \dfrac{\pi}{6}\right) - \dfrac{1}{2(2!)}\left(x - \dfrac{\pi}{6}\right)^2 - \dfrac{\sqrt{3}}{2(3!)}\left(x - \dfrac{\pi}{6}\right)^3 + \cdots$.

4. $\dfrac{1}{\sqrt{2}}\left[1 - \left(x - \dfrac{\pi}{4}\right) - \dfrac{1}{2!}\left(x - \dfrac{\pi}{4}\right)^2 + \dfrac{1}{3!}\left(x - \dfrac{\pi}{4}\right)^3 + \cdots\right]$.

5. $e^6\left[1 + 2(x - 3) + \dfrac{4(x - 3)^2}{2!} + \dfrac{8(x - 3)^3}{3!} + \cdots\right]$.

6. $\dfrac{\pi}{4} + \dfrac{x - 1}{2} - \dfrac{(x - 1)^2}{4} + \dfrac{(x - 1)^3}{12} + \cdots$.

7. $\sqrt{2}\left[1 + \dfrac{x - 1}{2} + \dfrac{(x - 1)^2}{8} - \dfrac{(x - 1)^3}{16} + \cdots\right]$.

8. $\sqrt{3} + 4\left(x - \dfrac{\pi}{3}\right) + 4\sqrt{3}\left(x - \dfrac{\pi}{3}\right)^2 + \dfrac{40}{3}\left(x - \dfrac{\pi}{3}\right)^3 + \cdots$.

9. $-\dfrac{1}{2}\ln 2 + \left(x - \dfrac{\pi}{4}\right) - \left(x - \dfrac{\pi}{4}\right)^2 + \dfrac{2}{3}\left(x - \dfrac{\pi}{4}\right)^3 + \cdots$.

Page 209 (§ 67)

1. 0.0523. **3.** 0.4695. **5.** 0.8746. **7.** 3.0042. **9.** 3.14.
2. 0.9781. **4.** 0.6947. **6.** 1.6487. **8.** 0.1823. **10.** 2.0801.

Page 210 (General Exercises)

1. $2\left(x + \dfrac{x^3}{3} + \dfrac{x^5}{5} + \dfrac{x^7}{7} + \cdots\right).$

4. $1 + x^2 + \dfrac{x^4}{2!} + \dfrac{x^6}{3!} + \cdots.$

2. $1 + \dfrac{x^2}{2!} + \dfrac{5\,x^4}{4!} + \dfrac{61\,x^6}{6!} + \cdots.$

5. $1 + x + \dfrac{x^2}{2} - \dfrac{x^4}{8} + \cdots.$

3. $x^2 - \dfrac{x^4}{3} + \dfrac{x^6}{5} - \dfrac{x^8}{7} + \cdots.$

6. $1 + x + \dfrac{x^2}{2} + \dfrac{x^3}{3} + \cdots.$

7. $1 - \dfrac{1}{2} \cdot x^2 + \dfrac{1 \cdot 3}{2 \cdot 4} \cdot x^4 - \dfrac{1 \cdot 3 \cdot 5}{2 \cdot 4 \cdot 6} \cdot x^6 + \cdots.$

8. $x - \dfrac{1}{2} \cdot \dfrac{x^3}{3} + \dfrac{1 \cdot 3}{2 \cdot 4} \cdot \dfrac{x^5}{5} - \dfrac{1 \cdot 3 \cdot 5}{2 \cdot 4 \cdot 6} \cdot \dfrac{x^7}{7} + \cdots.$

9. $x^2 - \dfrac{x^6}{3!} + \dfrac{x^{10}}{5!} - \dfrac{x^{14}}{7!}$

10. $1 + \dfrac{1}{2} \cdot x^4 + \dfrac{1 \cdot 3}{2 \cdot 4} \cdot x^8 + \dfrac{1 \cdot 3 \cdot 5}{2 \cdot 4 \cdot 6} \cdot x^{12} + \cdots.$

13. $1 + x - \dfrac{x^3}{3} - \dfrac{x^4}{6} + \cdots.$

14. 1.2214. **16.** 0.0875. **18.** 0.40547. **20.** 0.22314; 1.6094. **23.** 1.9680.
15. 0.5736. **17.** 0.3643. **19.** 0.69315; 1.0986. **21.** 0.8473; 1.946. **24.** 3.0366.

25. $x - \dfrac{x^3}{3(3!)} + \dfrac{x^5}{5(5!)} - \dfrac{x^7}{7(7!)} + \cdots.$

26. $x - \dfrac{x^3}{3} + \dfrac{x^5}{5(2!)} - \dfrac{x^7}{7(3!)} + \cdots.$

27. $x + \dfrac{1}{2} \cdot \dfrac{x^4}{4} + \dfrac{1 \cdot 3}{2 \cdot 4} \cdot \dfrac{x^7}{7} + \dfrac{1 \cdot 3 \cdot 5}{2 \cdot 4 \cdot 6} \cdot \dfrac{x^{10}}{10} + \cdots.$

CHAPTER IX

Page 214 (§ 68)

1. $5\,x^4 + 3\,x^2y^2 + y^4$;
$2\,x^3y + 4\,xy^3 - 5\,y^4.$

2. $\dfrac{y^3 + x^2y}{(y^2 - x^2)^2}$, $-\dfrac{x^3 + xy^2}{(y^2 - x^2)^2}.$

3. $\dfrac{1}{1 + x^2}$; $\dfrac{1}{1 + y^2}.$

4. $\dfrac{y}{\sqrt{1 - x^2y^2}}$; $\dfrac{x}{\sqrt{1 - x^2y^2}}.$

5. $\dfrac{x^2 - y^2}{x(x^2 + y^2)}$; $\dfrac{y^2 - x^2}{y(x^2 + y^2)}.$

6. $\dfrac{y^2}{(x - y)^2} \sin \dfrac{xy}{x - y}$;

$-\dfrac{x^2}{(x - y)^2} \sin \dfrac{xy}{x - y}.$

7. $e^{\frac{x}{y}} \left[\dfrac{x^2 \sin \dfrac{y}{x} - y^2 \cos \dfrac{y}{x}}{x^2 y}\right]$;

$e^{\frac{x}{y}} \left[\dfrac{y^2 \cos \dfrac{y}{x} - x^2 \sin \dfrac{y}{x}}{xy^2}\right].$

8. $\dfrac{1}{\sqrt{x^2 + y^2}}$; $\dfrac{y}{(x + \sqrt{x^2 + y^2})\sqrt{x^2 + y^2}}.$

Page 215 (§ 69)

    1. $\dfrac{x^2 - y^2}{x^2 + y^2}$.   2. $2\,e^x \sin(y - x)$.   3. $-\dfrac{2}{(y + 2\,x)^2}$.

Page 219 (§ 70)

    1. 0.000410299. 2. $1.277;\ 1.279$. 3. $-\dfrac{16\,\pi}{15}$ cu. ft. 4. $\tfrac{9}{50}$ sq. ft. 5. 3%.

Page 220 (§ 70)

    6. 0.007.   7. 1735.   8. $\tfrac{1}{104}$.

Page 227 (§ 72)

    1. $-z$.   2. 2.   3. $\dfrac{\pi}{2}\,e^{\frac{\pi}{2}}$.

Page 228 (§ 72)

    4. 0.53 sq. in.   7. 0.

    6. -0.006.   8. In direction making angle $135°$ with OX.

    10. In direction making angle $(2\,k + 1)\pi + ay$ with OX.

Page 230 (§ 73)

    5. $\dfrac{1}{\alpha^2}\,(\cos \alpha x + \alpha x \sin \alpha x - 1)$.   7. $\dfrac{1}{2}\left(\dfrac{x}{\alpha^2} \cdot \dfrac{1}{x^2 + \alpha^2} + \dfrac{1}{\alpha^3}\tan^{-1}\dfrac{x}{\alpha}\right)$.

    6. $\dfrac{1}{\alpha^2}\,(\sin \alpha x - \alpha x \cos \alpha x)$.   8. $\dfrac{x}{\alpha^2\,\sqrt{\alpha^2 - x^2}}$.

Page 231 (§ 73)

    9. $\dfrac{(\alpha + 1)x^{\alpha+1}\ln x + (1 - x^{\alpha+1})}{(\alpha + 1)^2}$.   10. $\dfrac{e^{\alpha x}(\alpha x - 1) + 1}{\alpha^2}$.

Page 231 (General Exercises)

    1. $\dfrac{x + y}{xy}$.   2. 0.   13. 0.0325 in.   14. $\tfrac{7}{320}$.

Page 232 (General Exercises)

    15. $\tfrac{1}{150}$ in.   18. 6360 ft.

    16. $\dfrac{9}{8\sqrt{19}}$ ft.   19. 0.2887 sq. ft.

                    20. $17.92\,k$, where k is the factor of proportionality.

    17. 1.25 in.

Page 233 (General Exercises)

    21. $\dfrac{\sqrt{6}}{3}$. 22. 2.9 sq. in. per sec. 24. $\dfrac{1}{\sqrt{(x - 1)^2 + (y - 1)^2}}$; 0. 25. $\dfrac{\sqrt{2}}{5\,a}$; 0.

        23. $-\tfrac{24}{125}$.

    26. In direction making angle $\tan^{-1}\tfrac{3}{4}$ with OX; $5\,k$.

    27. $-\tfrac{1}{2}(\cos \phi + \sqrt{3}\sin \phi)$; 1.

    28. $\dfrac{1}{\alpha^3}\,[(2 - \alpha^2 x^2)\cos \alpha x + 2\,\alpha x \sin \alpha x - 2]$.

29. $\dfrac{1}{\alpha^3}[(\alpha^2 x^2 - 2)\sin \alpha x + 2\,\alpha x \cos \alpha x]$.

30. $\dfrac{1}{\alpha^4}\,[e^{\alpha x}(\alpha^3 x^3 - 3\,\alpha^2 x^2 + 6\,\alpha x - 6) + 6]$.

31. $\dfrac{x^{\alpha+1}(\ln x)^2}{\alpha + 1} - \dfrac{2\,x^{\alpha+1}\ln x}{(\alpha + 1)^2} + \dfrac{2(x^{\alpha+1} - 1)}{(\alpha + 1)^3}$.

CHAPTER X

Page 238 (§ 75)

1. $2\,x^4 + 3\,x^2 + \dfrac{1}{x^3}$.

2. $3(x - 2)x^{\frac{2}{3}}$.

3. $\dfrac{6\,x^4 + 28}{7\sqrt{x}}$.

4. $\dfrac{x^2}{2} + 2\ln x - \dfrac{1}{2\,x^2}$.

5. $\dfrac{x^3}{3} + \dfrac{x^2}{2} + x + \ln(x - 1)$.

6. $\frac{1}{12}(x^3 + 3)^4$.

7. $\frac{1}{10}(x^4 - 8)^{\frac{5}{2}}$.

8. $\frac{1}{2}(x^3 + 3)^{\frac{2}{3}}$.

9. $\frac{1}{2}\ln(e^{2x} - e^{-2x})$.

10. $\frac{1}{3}\ln(3\,x + \cos 3\,x)$.

11. $\dfrac{1}{a(\cos ax - e^{ax})}$.

12. $-\dfrac{1}{\sqrt{2\,x - \cos 2\,x}}$.

13. $\frac{1}{6}\ln(2\,x^3 - 3\,x^2 + 1)$.

14. $\dfrac{1}{a}\ln(1 + \tan ax)$.

15. $\frac{1}{9}\sin^3 3\,x$.

16. $\frac{1}{4}\sin^2(2\,x + 3)$.

17. $\frac{1}{60}(3\sin^4 5\,x - 2\sin^6 5\,x)$.

18. $\frac{1}{6}(3\tan 2\,x + \tan^3 2\,x)$.

19. $-\frac{1}{9}\csc^3(3\,x + 2)$.

20. $-\frac{1}{45}[15\cos(3\,x - 1) - 10\cos^3(3\,x - 1) + 3\cos^5(3\,x - 1)]$.

Page 242 (§ 76)

1. $\frac{1}{4}\sin^{-1}\dfrac{4\,x}{3}$.

2. $\dfrac{1}{\sqrt{5}}\sin^{-1}\dfrac{x\sqrt{10}}{4}$.

3. $\dfrac{1}{\sqrt{5}}\tan^{-1}\dfrac{x}{\sqrt{5}}$.

4. $\dfrac{1}{\sqrt{21}}\tan^{-1}\dfrac{x\sqrt{21}}{3}$.

5. $\ln(x + \sqrt{x^2 + 3})$.

6. $\frac{1}{2}\ln(2\,x + \sqrt{4\,x^2 - 9})$.

7. $\frac{1}{16}\ln\dfrac{x - 2}{x + 2}$.

8. $\dfrac{1}{2\sqrt{15}}\ln\dfrac{3\,x - \sqrt{15}}{3\,x + \sqrt{15}}$.

9. $\dfrac{1}{\sqrt{3}}\sin^{-1}\dfrac{3\,x - 2}{2}$.

10. $\sin^{-1}\dfrac{x - 3}{\sqrt{11}}$.

11. $\dfrac{1}{6}\ln\dfrac{x}{x + 6}$.

12. $\dfrac{1}{\sqrt{29}}\ln\dfrac{10\,x + 3 - \sqrt{29}}{10\,x + 3 + \sqrt{29}}$.

13. $\tan^{-1}(x + 4)$.

14. $\dfrac{2}{\sqrt{31}}\tan^{-1}\dfrac{4\,x - 3}{\sqrt{31}}$.

15. $\dfrac{1}{\sqrt{3}}\sin^{-1}\dfrac{3\,x + 2}{\sqrt{10}}$.

16. $\ln(x + 2 + \sqrt{x^2 + 4\,x})$.

17. $\dfrac{1}{\sqrt{2}}\ln(4\,x + 1 + 2\sqrt{4\,x^2 + 2\,x + 2})$.

18. $\frac{1}{2}\ln(x^2 - 4) + \dfrac{3}{4}\ln\dfrac{x - 2}{x + 2}$.

19. $\dfrac{3}{8}\ln(4\,x^2 + 9) + \dfrac{7}{6}\tan^{-1}\dfrac{2\,x}{3}$.

20. $-\sqrt{9 - x^2} - 2\sin^{-1}\dfrac{x}{3}$.

21. $\dfrac{2}{3}\sqrt{3\,x^2 + 4} + \sqrt{3}\ln(3\,x + \sqrt{9\,x^2 + 12})$.

Page 244 (§ 77)

1. $-\frac{1}{4}\cos(4x+3)$.

2. $\frac{1}{3}\sin(3x-2)$.

3. $-\frac{3}{2}\ln\cos\frac{2x}{3}$.

4. $\frac{1}{4}\ln\sin(4x-2)$.

5. $\frac{1}{2}\ln[\sec(2x+4)+\tan(2x+4)]$.

6. $\frac{1}{3}\ln[\csc(3x-2)-\operatorname{ctn}(3x-2)]$.

7. $-\frac{1}{3}\sec(2-3x)$.

8. $\frac{1}{3}\operatorname{ctn}(1-3x)$.

Page 245 (§ 77)

9. $3\tan\frac{x}{3}$.

10. $\frac{1}{5}\csc(2-5x)$.

11. $\frac{1}{8}\left(4x-5\sin\frac{4x}{5}\right)$.

12. $\frac{1}{2}[\tan(2x+3)-2x]$.

13. $-\frac{2\sqrt{2}}{3}\cos\frac{3x}{2}$.

14. $\frac{1}{3}(3x+\cos 3x)$.

15. $\sin 2x-\frac{1}{2}\ln(\sec 2x+\tan 2x)$.

16. $\frac{x}{2}+\sin\frac{x}{2}$.

17. $\frac{1}{32}\left(4x-3\sin\frac{4x}{3}\right)$.

18. $3\sqrt{2}\sin\frac{x}{3}$.

19. $-\frac{1}{10}(\cos 5x+5\cos x)$.

20. $\frac{1}{2\sqrt{2}}\ln(\csc 2x-\operatorname{ctn} 2x)$.

Page 246 (§ 78)

1. $\frac{1}{5}e^{5x+3}$.

2. $\frac{1}{2}e^{x^2}$.

3. $\frac{1}{6}(e^{6x}-e^{-6x})+2x$.

4. $\ln(e^x+e^{-x})$.

5. $\ln(e^x+e^{-x})$.

6. $x-2\ln(1+e^x)$.

7. $-e^{\cos x}$.

8. $e^{\tan^{-1}x}$.

9. $e^x+\frac{x^{e+1}}{e+1}$.

10. $\frac{10^x}{\ln 10}+\frac{x^{11}}{11}$.

11. $\frac{e^{a+bx}c^{a+bx}}{b(1+\ln c)}$.

12. $-e^{\frac{1}{x}}$.

Page 249 (§ 79)

1. $\frac{1}{\sqrt{3}}\ln\frac{\sqrt{x+3}-\sqrt{3}}{\sqrt{x+3}+\sqrt{3}}$.

2. $\frac{1}{33}(3x^2-x+1)(5x+1)^{\frac{1}{5}}$.

3. $\frac{4}{3}(x+10)\sqrt{2x+5}+5\sqrt{5}\ln\frac{\sqrt{2x+5}-\sqrt{5}}{\sqrt{2x+5}+\sqrt{5}}$.

4. $\frac{x}{3\sqrt{3-x^2}}$.

5. $\frac{(2x^2+25)\sqrt{x^2-25}}{1875x^3}$.

6. $\frac{x^2+8}{\sqrt{x^2+4}}$.

7. $\frac{1}{4}\tan^{-1}\frac{x}{2}-\frac{x}{2x^2+8}$.

8. $-\frac{x}{4\sqrt{x^2-4}}$.

9. $\frac{x}{\sqrt{9-x^2}}-\sin^{-1}\frac{x}{3}$.

10. $\frac{x^3}{27(4x^2+9)^{\frac{3}{2}}}$.

11. $\frac{(5x^3-24)(x^3+8)^{\frac{5}{3}}}{40}$.

12. $\frac{(4x^2-9)^{\frac{5}{2}}}{45x^5}$.

13. $-\frac{\sqrt{4x^2+9}}{9x}$.

14. $\frac{15x^3-2x^5}{135(3-x^2)^{\frac{5}{2}}}$.

15. $\frac{2}{3}\left(\sqrt{x^3+4}+\ln\frac{\sqrt{x^3+4}-2}{\sqrt{x^3+4}+2}\right)$.

Page 252 (§ 80)

1. $\left(\dfrac{2x-1}{4}\right)e^{2x}$.

2. $\frac{1}{27}(9x^2 - 6x + 2)e^{3x}$.

3. $x \cos^{-1} x - \sqrt{1 - x^2}$.

4. $x \tan^{-1} x - \frac{1}{2}\ln(1 + x^2)$.

5. $\sin x - x \cos x$.

6. $\dfrac{1}{4}(1 - 2x^2)\cos 2x + \dfrac{x}{2}\sin 2x$.

7. $\dfrac{x^3}{9}(3 \ln x - 1)$.

8. $\frac{1}{4}x^2 + \frac{1}{12}x \sin 6x + \frac{1}{72}\cos 6x$.

9. $\frac{1}{4}(x^4 - 1)\tan^{-1} x - \frac{1}{12}(x^3 - 3x)$.

10. $\frac{1}{8}(4x^2 \sec^{-1} 2x - \sqrt{4x^2 - 1})$.

11. $(x^2 - 2)\sin x + 2x \cos x$.

12. $\cos x(1 - \ln \cos x)$.

Page 254 (§ 81)

1. $\frac{1}{6}\ln x^2(2x + 3)$.

2. $\dfrac{1}{3}\ln \dfrac{(2x+1)^{27}}{(3x+2)^{23}}$.

3. $x + \dfrac{1}{6}\ln \dfrac{(2x-1)^9}{(3x+1)^8}$.

4. $\dfrac{3x^2}{2} + \dfrac{1}{3}\ln(x+1)(2x-1)^2$.

5. $\ln \dfrac{x^2 - 2x}{x + 2}$.

6. $\ln \dfrac{x^2 - 1}{(x + 2)^2}$.

7. $2x + \ln \dfrac{2x^2 + x}{x - 1}$.

8. $2x + \frac{1}{9}\ln x^{18}(9x^2 - 4)$.

9. $\dfrac{1}{2}\ln x^4(x^2 - x + 2)^3 + \dfrac{5}{\sqrt{7}}\tan^{-1}\dfrac{2x-1}{\sqrt{7}}$.

10. $\dfrac{1}{8}\ln(2x-1)(4x^2 + 2x + 1)^2 + \dfrac{\sqrt{3}}{4}\tan^{-1}\dfrac{4x+1}{\sqrt{3}}$.

Page 257 (§ 82)

1. $\frac{7}{12}$.

2. $\frac{2}{9}$.

3. $\dfrac{2\sqrt{2} - 1}{6}$.

4. $\dfrac{\pi}{2}$.

5. $\dfrac{\pi}{3}$.

6. $\dfrac{\pi}{6}$.

7. $\ln 3$.

8. $\frac{1}{3}(e - 1)$.

9. $\frac{1}{3}(e^2 - 1)$.

10. $\frac{1}{9}\ln 2$.

11. $\frac{11}{18}$.

12. $\dfrac{\sqrt{3} - \sqrt{2}}{18}$.

13. $\frac{9}{32}$.

14. $\frac{1}{24}(9\sqrt{3} - 10\sqrt{2})$.

15. $\frac{1}{27}(6 - 2\sqrt{3})$.

16. $\frac{1}{10}$.

17. 3π.

18. $23\frac{11}{15}$.

19. $13\frac{47}{189}$.

20. $1 - \ln 2$.

21. $\frac{1}{4}$.

22. $2(\ln 2)^2 - 2\ln 2 + \frac{3}{4}$

Page 258 (General Exercises)

1. $\dfrac{x^4}{4} - \dfrac{x^2}{2} + \dfrac{1}{2}\ln(x^2 + 1)$.

2. $2\ln(x^2 + 3) + \sqrt{3}\tan^{-1}\dfrac{x}{\sqrt{3}}$.

3. $\dfrac{2}{\sqrt{7}}\tan^{-1}\dfrac{4x-1}{\sqrt{7}}$.

4. $\dfrac{1}{4}\ln \dfrac{3x-1}{x+1}$.

5. $\ln(x^2 + x + 3) + \dfrac{2}{\sqrt{11}}\tan^{-1}\dfrac{2x+1}{\sqrt{11}}$.

6. $\ln(2x^2 + 3x + 5) + \dfrac{4}{\sqrt{31}}\tan^{-1}\dfrac{4x+3}{\sqrt{31}}$.

7. $\frac{1}{4} \ln(6\,x^2 + 6\,x - 5) + \frac{5}{4\sqrt{39}} \ln \frac{6\,x + 3 - \sqrt{39}}{6\,x + 3 + \sqrt{39}}$.

8. $\frac{3}{4} \ln(2\,x^2 - x + 1) + \frac{11}{2\sqrt{7}} \tan^{-1} \frac{4\,x - 1}{\sqrt{7}}$.

9. $\sin^{-1} \frac{x - 3}{3}$.

10. $\frac{1}{\sqrt{2}} \ln\left(2\,x + 2 + \sqrt{4\,x^2 + 8\,x - 10}\right)$.

11. $\frac{1}{\sqrt{2}} \sin^{-1} \frac{2\,x + 1}{\sqrt{3}}$.

12. $\frac{1}{\sqrt{3}} \ln\left(3\,x - 1 + \sqrt{9\,x^2 - 6\,x - 3}\right)$.

13. $\sqrt{3\,x^2 + 2\,x + 1} - 2\sqrt{3} \ln\left(3\,x + 1 + \sqrt{9\,x^2 + 6\,x + 3}\right)$.

14. $\frac{29}{5\sqrt{5}} \sin^{-1} \frac{5\,x + 2}{3} - \frac{3}{5} \sqrt{1 - 4\,x - 5\,x^2}$.

15. $\frac{16}{3\sqrt{3}} \sin^{-1} \frac{3\,x - 1}{\sqrt{7}} - \frac{1}{3} \sqrt{2 + 2\,x - 3\,x^2}$.

16. $\frac{3}{16} \ln(8\,x^2 + 24\,x + 15) - \frac{5\sqrt{6}}{48} \ln \frac{4\,x + 6 - \sqrt{6}}{4\,x + 6 + \sqrt{6}}$.

17. $3 \sin \frac{x}{3} - \sin^3 \frac{x}{3}$.

18. $-2\left(3 \operatorname{ctn} \frac{x}{6} + \operatorname{ctn}^3 \frac{x}{6}\right)$.

19. $\frac{1}{30}[3 \cos^5(2\,x + 3) - 5 \cos^3(2\,x + 3)]$.

20. $\frac{1}{15}[3 \sec^5(x + 3) - 5 \sec^3(x + 3)]$.

21. $\frac{\sqrt{2}}{4} \ln \frac{\sqrt{2} \cos x + 1}{\sqrt{2} \cos x - 1}$.

22. $2\left(\tan \frac{x}{2} - \operatorname{ctn} \frac{x}{2}\right) - 4\,x$.

23. $-\frac{1}{3} \operatorname{ctn} 3\,x - x$.

24. $\sin 2\,x$.

25. $\frac{1}{4}(\sin 4\,x + \cos 4\,x)$.

26. $\ln(\csc x - \operatorname{ctn} x)$.

Page 259 (General Exercises)

27. $\frac{1}{4} \tan 2\,x$.

28. $\frac{4}{3}(3 \cos x - 2 \cos^3 x)$.

29. $-\frac{1}{2}(\cos 2\,x + \sin 2\,x)$.

30. $2 \ln(x - 2) + \frac{1}{x - 2}$.

31. $\frac{1}{35}(5\,x^2 - 6\,x + 6)(2\,x + 3)^{\frac{3}{2}}$.

32. $-\frac{\sqrt{9 - x^2}}{9\,x}$.

33. $-\frac{3}{64} \tan^{-1} \frac{x}{2} - \frac{3\,x^2 + 8}{32\,x(x^2 + 4)}$.

34. $\frac{4}{45}(3\,x + 8)(3\,x - 2)^{\frac{1}{4}}$.

35. $\frac{1}{10}(2\,x^3 - 3)(1 + x^3)^{\frac{2}{3}}$.

36. $-\frac{\sqrt{2 - x^2}}{x} - \sin^{-1} \frac{x}{\sqrt{2}}$.

37. $-\frac{(4\,x^2 + 1)^{\frac{5}{2}}}{5\,x^5}$.

38. $\frac{2}{9}(x^3 - 2)\sqrt{1 + x^3}$.

39. $\frac{4\,x^3 - 15\,x}{3(5 - x^2)^{\frac{3}{2}}} + \sin^{-1} \frac{x}{\sqrt{5}}$.

40. $-\frac{x^5}{5(4\,x^2 - 1)^{\frac{5}{2}}}$.

41. $\frac{1}{6}(x^4 - 8) \sqrt{x^4 + 4}$.

42. $\frac{1}{27} \ln\left(3\,x + \sqrt{9\,x^2 + 4}\right) - \frac{x}{9\sqrt{9\,x^2 + 4}}$.

43. $(3x - 9)e^{\frac{x}{3}}$.

44. $\dfrac{x^3}{9}(3\ln 3x - 1)$.

45. $\dfrac{x^3}{3}\tan^{-1} x - \dfrac{x^2}{6} + \dfrac{1}{6}\ln(x^2 + 1)$.

46. $\ln\dfrac{(2x + 3)^2}{x - 2}$.

47. $\dfrac{x^2}{2} + 2x + \dfrac{1}{2}\ln(3x^2 - 4x)$.

48. $\ln(x - 2)^4\left(\dfrac{2x + 1}{2x - 1}\right)^{\frac{3}{4}}$.

49. $\ln(x + 1)^3\left(\dfrac{x - 3}{x + 3}\right)^{\frac{2}{3}}$.

50. $2x + \ln x^2\sqrt{\dfrac{x - 3}{(x + 3)^3}}$.

51. $\ln\dfrac{x}{x^2 + x + 1} - \dfrac{2}{\sqrt{3}}\tan^{-1}\dfrac{2x + 1}{\sqrt{3}}$.

52. $4(\ln 3 - 1)$.

53. $\ln 2$.

54. $3\frac{1}{9}$.

55. $\dfrac{\pi}{8}$.

56. $\frac{1}{12}\ln\frac{7}{3}$.

57. $\frac{1}{2}\ln(2 + \sqrt{5})$.

58. $\frac{1}{8}(9\sqrt{3} - 11)$.

59. $\dfrac{1}{\sqrt{2}}$.

60. $\dfrac{\pi}{4}$.

61. $\frac{2}{3}$.

62. $\frac{1}{3}(4\sqrt{2} - 5)$.

63. $\dfrac{15\pi + 44}{192}$.

64. $\dfrac{1}{3\sqrt{2}}\ln 3$.

65. $22\frac{5}{112}$.

66. $\frac{2465}{5184}$.

67. $\dfrac{\sqrt{3}}{12}$.

68. $\dfrac{\pi}{4}$.

69. $\frac{1}{175}(35 - 2\sqrt{35})$.

70. $\frac{1}{6}(9\sqrt{2} - 7\sqrt{3})$.

71. $\frac{1}{3}(3\sqrt{3} - \pi)$.

72. $\ln\frac{3}{2}$.

73. $\frac{1}{3}$.

74. $\pi - 2$.

75. $\frac{1}{24}(5\pi - 6\sqrt{3})$.

CHAPTER XI

Page 270 (§ 86)

1. $\dfrac{12\sqrt{3}}{5}$.

2. $\frac{1}{3}$.

3. $3\pi a^2$.

4. $30 - 16\ln 4$.

5. 18.

6. $\dfrac{2a^2}{3}(3\pi - 2)$.

7. $\dfrac{3\pi a^2}{2}$.

8. $\frac{8}{3}(2\pi + 3\sqrt{3})$.

9. 18π.

10. $\frac{1}{4}(120 + 9\pi)$.

11. $\dfrac{a^2}{3}(3\sqrt{3} - \pi)$.

12. $\pi + 3\sqrt{3}$.

13. $\dfrac{\pi a^3}{15}$.

14. $64\pi^2$.

15. $\dfrac{4096\pi\sqrt{3}}{135}$.

16. $48\pi[\sqrt{3} - \ln(2 + \sqrt{3})]$.

17. 32.

Page 271 (§ 86)

18. $\dfrac{324\sqrt{3}}{5}$.

19. $1.40\,\mathrm{T}$.

20. $\dfrac{w}{3}(8\pi + 9\sqrt{3})$.

21. $\frac{2}{15}\,\mathrm{T.}\,;\,0.024\,\mathrm{T}$.

Page 273 (§ 87)

1. $\dfrac{\pi a}{4}$, where a is radius of semicircle.

2. $\dfrac{2a}{\pi}$, where a is radius of semicircle.

3. $\dfrac{2a}{\pi}$.

4. 17.

5. $\dfrac{\pi a^2}{3}$.

6. $\dfrac{\pi}{6}$.

7. 100 r.p.m.

8. 2.

9. $\dfrac{2ka}{\pi}$.

10. 6.93 lb. per sq. in.

Page 276 (§ 88)

1. $\frac{2}{27}(13\sqrt{13}-8)$.

2. $\pi\sqrt{2}$.

3. $\frac{1}{27}(229\sqrt{229}-8)$ ft.

4. $\sqrt{2}(1-e^{-\pi})$.

5. $\dfrac{15\,\pi a}{8}$.

6. $8\,a$.

7. $\dfrac{a}{2}\left(e^{\frac{h}{a}}-e^{-\frac{h}{a}}\right)$.

8. $\ln\left(\dfrac{e^2+1}{e}\right)$.

9. $4\sqrt{3}$.

Page 278 (§ 89)

1. $2\,\pi ah$.

2. $4\,\pi^2 ab$.

3. $\dfrac{12\,\pi a^2}{5}$.

4. $\dfrac{\pi a^2}{2}\left(e^{\frac{2h}{a}}-e^{-\frac{2h}{a}}\right)+2\,\pi ah$.

5. $\dfrac{\pi a^2}{2}\left(e^{\frac{2h}{a}}-e^{-\frac{2h}{a}}\right)-2\,\pi a^2\left(e^{\frac{h}{a}}-e^{-\frac{h}{a}}\right)+2\,\pi ah$.

6. $\dfrac{\pi k^2}{64}\,[36\sqrt{5}-\ln(9+4\sqrt{5})]$.

7. $\dfrac{64\,\pi a^2}{3}$.

8. $\dfrac{32\,\pi a^2}{3}$.

9. $4\,\pi a^2(2-\sqrt{2})$.

10. $4\,\pi a^2\sqrt{2}$.

Page 280 (§ 90)

1. 104.

2. $\dfrac{m}{a}$.

3. $1066\frac{2}{3}$ ft.-lb.

4. $\dfrac{\pi ka}{12}$.

5. $2{,}700{,}000$ ft.-lb.

6. 1178 ft.-lb.

7. $2\,kca^2$, where k is the proportionality factor.

8. $\dfrac{\pi k}{4}\,(a^2+b^2)$.

9. $\dfrac{waR}{R+a}$ mi.-lb., where R is the radius of the earth in miles.

Page 281 (§ 90)

10. 1.17 ft.-lb.; 0.97 ft.-lb.

Page 284 (§ 91)

3. $\left(0,\ \dfrac{a(e^4+4\,e^2-1)}{4\,e(e^2-1)}\right)$.

4. $\left(\pi a,\ \dfrac{4\,a}{3}\right)$.

5. On axis, distant $\frac{3}{8}$ of radius from base.

6. On axis of segment, distant $\dfrac{3[2\,a^2(h_2{}^2-h_1{}^2)-(h_2{}^4-h_1{}^4)]}{4[3\,a^2(h_2-h_1)-(h_2{}^3-h_1{}^3)]}$ from center of sphere.

7. On axis, $\dfrac{a}{3}$ from base.

8. On axis, $\dfrac{5\,b}{32}$ from base.

9. On axis of solid, distant $\frac{9}{8}$ from base.

Page 289 (§ 92)

1. $\frac{1}{12}\,Ma^2$.

2. $\frac{1}{2}\,Ma^2$.

3. $\frac{1}{6}\,Ma^2$.

4. $\frac{1}{4}\,Ma^2$; $\frac{1}{4}\,Mb^2$.

5. $M\,\dfrac{h^2(b+3\,a)}{6(b+a)}$.

6. $\frac{8}{35}\,Ma^2$.

7. $\frac{1}{12}\,M(a^2+b^2)$.

8. $\frac{1}{2}\,M(r_2{}^2+r_1{}^2)$.

9. $\frac{1}{6}\,M(a^2+b^2)$.

Page 290 (§ 92)

10. $\frac{1}{2}\,Mr^2$.

11. $\frac{2}{5}\,Ma^2$.

12. $\frac{62}{9}\,M$.

Page 292 (§ 93)

1. $\dfrac{kM}{c(c+l)}$.

2. $\dfrac{2\,kM}{c\sqrt{l^2+4\,c^2}}$.

3. $\dfrac{kcM}{(c^2+a^2)^{\frac{3}{2}}}$.

4. $\dfrac{2\,kcM}{a^2}\left(\dfrac{1}{c}-\dfrac{1}{\sqrt{c^2+a^2}}\right)$.

5. $\dfrac{2\,kM}{a^2l}\left[l+\sqrt{c^2+a^2}-\sqrt{(c+l)^2+a^2}\right]$.

6. $\dfrac{kM}{a^2}(\sqrt{2}-1)$.

Page 293 (§ 93)

7. $\dfrac{3\,ka(2\,b-a)M}{2\,b[b^3-(b^2-a^2)^{\frac{3}{2}}]}$.

8. $\dfrac{8\,kM}{81}$.

Page 293 (General Exercises)

1. $10\sin^{-1}\tfrac{4}{5}$.

2. $12\sin^{-1}\sqrt{\dfrac{2}{3}-\dfrac{4\sqrt{2}}{5}}$.

3. $\dfrac{8\,a^2}{15}$.

4. $20\tfrac{4}{15}$.

5. $2\,\pi ab$.

6. $4\,a^2$.

7. $\dfrac{3\,\pi ab}{4}$.

8. $\dfrac{3\,\pi a^2}{8}$.

9. $\dfrac{a^2}{n}$.

10. $21\tfrac{1}{3}$.

11. $\dfrac{a^2}{8}(\pi-2)$.

12. $\dfrac{1}{4\,a}(e^{4\pi a}-1)(e^{\pi a}-1)$.

13. $\dfrac{a^2}{12}(2\,\pi+3\sqrt{3})$.

14. 16.

Page 294 (General Exercises)

15. $\dfrac{a^2}{16}(8\,\pi+9\sqrt{3})$.

16. $\dfrac{a^2\sqrt{3}}{4}$.

17. $\tfrac{1}{2}\,\pi h^2\sqrt{k_1k_2}$, where k_1 and k_2 are values for k in the equation $y^2=kx$.

18. $\dfrac{68\,\pi}{15}$.

19. $\dfrac{2\,\pi a^3\sqrt{2}}{3}$.

20. $\dfrac{2\,\pi a^3}{5}$.

21. $\dfrac{64\,a^3}{105}$.

22. $\dfrac{64\,\pi\sqrt{2}}{5}$.

23. $\dfrac{32\,\pi}{15}$.

24. $\pi a^3\tan\theta$.

25. 438 lb.

Page 295 (General Exercises)

26. 7.49 lb.

27. 1440 lb.

28. $\tfrac{125}{6}(8\,\pi+9\sqrt{3})w$.

30. $a(2\,\pi-4)$.

31. $\dfrac{32\,\pi}{3}$.

32. $\dfrac{\pi a^3}{6}$.

33. $\dfrac{4\,ab}{3}$.

35. $\tfrac{2}{3}$.

Page 296 (General Exercises)

36. 957 lb. per sq. ft.

37. $6\,a$.

38. $8\,\pi^2 a$.

39. $\dfrac{2\,a}{3}(\pi+12-6\sqrt{3})$.

40. $\dfrac{4\sqrt{3}}{3}$.

41. $4\left(\dfrac{b^3-a^3}{b^2-a^2}\right)$.

42. $16\,a$.

44. $\dfrac{3\,\pi a}{2}$.

45. $2\,\pi b^2+\dfrac{2\,\pi ab}{e}\sin^{-1}e$, where e is eccentricity of ellipse.

46. $2\,\pi a^2+\dfrac{2\,\pi ab^2}{\sqrt{a^2-b^2}}\ln\dfrac{a+\sqrt{a^2-b^2}}{b}$.

47. $\dfrac{12\,\pi a^2}{5}$. **48.** $\dfrac{18\,\pi a^2}{5}$. **49.** $\dfrac{32\,\pi a^2}{5}$. **50.** $\dfrac{9\,k}{8\,a^{\frac{2}{3}}}$.

Page 297 (General Exercises)

51. $\dfrac{3\,ka^2}{2}$.

52. $\dfrac{3\,k}{8\,a^2}$.

53. $586\frac{2}{3}$ ft.-lb.

54. $54{,}000\,\pi$ ft.-lb.

55. $\dfrac{w}{2\,R}\,(2\,aR - a^2)$, where R is radius of earth.

56. $2\,\pi C$.

57. $\left(0, \dfrac{2\,a}{5}\right)$.

58. $(\frac{253}{95}, 0)$.

59. $\left(\dfrac{7\,a}{5}, \dfrac{a\sqrt{3}}{4}\right)$.

60. On axis of solid, distant $\dfrac{k}{6}$ from base.

Page 298 (General Exercises)

61. On axis of solid, distant $\dfrac{9\,b}{16}$ from smaller base.

62. $\frac{1}{3}\,Ma^2$.

63. $\frac{17}{2}\,M$.

64. $\frac{1}{2}\,M(r_2{}^2 + r_1{}^2)$.

65. $\frac{157}{6}\,M$.

66. $\dfrac{3\,M}{10}\left(\dfrac{r_2{}^5 - r_1{}^5}{r_2{}^3 - r_1{}^3}\right)$.

67. $\frac{40}{9}\,M$.

68. $\frac{1093}{140}\,M$.

69. $\dfrac{2\,k\rho}{c}$.

70. $\dfrac{2\,kM}{lc}\sin\dfrac{\alpha}{2}$.

71. $\dfrac{2\,kM^2}{cl^2}\left(\sqrt{c^2 + l^2} - c\right)$.

72. $\frac{1}{45}\,kM$.

Page 299 (General Exercises)

73. $\frac{3}{16}\,kM(2 + \sqrt{2})$.

75. $\dfrac{3\,kM(1 - \cos\alpha)}{2(a_1{}^2 + a_1a_2 + a_2{}^2)}$.

CHAPTER XII

Page 302 (§ 94)

1. $\frac{1}{2}\ln 3 - \frac{2}{9}$.

2. $\frac{1}{2}$.

3. $\frac{3}{64} - \frac{1}{2}\ln 2$.

4. 1.

5. $\frac{1}{2}(\pi - 2)$.

6. $\dfrac{\pi}{4}\ln 4$.

7. $\sqrt{2} - 1$.

8. $4(2\sqrt{2} - \pi)$.

9. $\dfrac{\pi}{12}$.

10. $a(\pi - 2)$.

11. $\dfrac{a^2}{6}$.

12. $\dfrac{\pi a^3}{16}$.

Page 311 (§ 96)

1. On axis of segment, $\dfrac{3\,a}{5}$ from vertex.

2. On axis of quadrant, $\dfrac{4\,a\sqrt{2}}{3\,\pi}$ from center of circle, a being radius of circle.

3. Intersection of medians.

4. $\left(\dfrac{\pi}{2}, \dfrac{\pi}{8}\right)$.

5. $(5\frac{2}{5}, 5\frac{2}{5})$.

6. On axis, $\dfrac{4\,a^2 + 3\,\pi ab + 6\,b^2}{3\,\pi a + 12\,b}$ from base.

7. $\left(\pi a, \dfrac{5\,a}{6}\right)$.

Page 312 (§ 96)

9. $\left(\dfrac{5\,a}{6}, 0\right)$.

10. $(\frac{17}{9}, 0)$.

11. $\left(\dfrac{3\,a(8\,\pi - 11\sqrt{3})}{16(3\sqrt{3} - \pi)}, 0\right)$.

Page 313 (§ 97)

2. On line of centers, $\dfrac{(r_1 + r_2)r_2{}^2}{r_1{}^2 + r_2{}^2}$ from center of circle of radius r_1.

3. On axis of shell, $\dfrac{3(r_2{}^4 - r_1{}^4)}{8(r_2{}^3 - r_1{}^3)}$ from common base of the bounding hemispheres.

4. Middle point of axis.

Page 314 (§ 97)

5. On axis, $\dfrac{h_2{}^4 - h_1{}^4}{4(h_2{}^3 - h_1{}^3)}$ from base.

6. On axis of cone, $\frac{2}{3}$ of distance from vertex to base.

7. $(5\frac{1}{12}, 5\frac{1}{12})$, if outer edges of square are taken as OX and OY.

8. On axis, 4.9 from corner of square.

9. On axis, 3.98 in. from center of cylinder in direction of larger ball.

10. On axis, 3.4 ft. from base of pedestal.

Page 316 (§ 98)

3. $\frac{1}{2}$ base $\times$ altitude.

4. $\dfrac{8\,\pi a^2 b}{15}$, where a is altitude and b is base of segment.

5. $\dfrac{4\,\pi a^2 b}{5}$, where a is altitude and b is base of segment.

6. $2\,\pi a^2 b$; $8\,\pi ab$.

Page 317 (§ 98)

7. $\dfrac{\pi ab}{3}\,(b + 3\,c)$; $\pi\left[2\,ca + 2\,bc + b^2 + (2\,c + b)\sqrt{a^2 + b^2}\,\right]$.

8. 7.07 T.

9. $\pi abcw$, where w is the weight of a cubic unit of the liquid.

10. $\dfrac{2\,ab^2w}{3}$, where w is the weight of a cubic unit of the liquid.

11. $\dfrac{2\,ab(5\,c + 3\,a)w}{15}$, where a is the altitude and b the base of the segment and w is the weight of a cubic unit of the liquid.

12. Increase of $cw \times$ area, where w is the weight of a cubic foot of water.

13. On axis, $\dfrac{4\,a}{3\,\pi}$ from base, a being radius of semicircle.

14. On axis, $\dfrac{2\,a}{\pi}$ from center of semicircumference, a being the radius.

Page 319 (§ 99)

1. $22\frac{1}{2}$.　　2. $\frac{1}{5}(5120\,\pi - 8192)$.　　3. $\frac{8}{5}(18 - 5\,\pi)$.　　4. $\dfrac{\pi a^4}{4}$.　　5. $\dfrac{35\,\pi a^4}{16}$.

6. $\dfrac{35\,\pi a^4}{16}$.　　7. $\dfrac{a^4}{24}\,(152\,\pi + 135\sqrt{3})$.　　8. $\frac{1}{6}(1792 + 297\,\pi)$.

Page 320 (§ 99)

9. $\dfrac{a^4}{24}\,(33\sqrt{3} - 16\,\pi)$.　　　　10. $\frac{27}{8}(20\,\pi + 21\sqrt{3})$.

Page 322 (§ 100)

1. $\frac{5}{4} Ma^2$, a being radius of circle.
2. 1875.6.
3. 3751.3.

4. 6395.3.
5. $\frac{5}{16} Ma^2$.
6. $\frac{11}{12} Ma^2$.
7. 4536.

8. 3483.
9. $\frac{1}{2} M(r_2{}^2 + 3 r_1{}^2)$.
10. $\frac{1}{2} M(r_1{}^2 + 3 r_2{}^2)$.

Page 336 (§ 103)

1. 8π.
3. $\frac{2}{15}$.
4. π.
5. $\dfrac{3 \pi a^3}{4}$.

Page 337 (§ 103)

6. $\dfrac{\pi}{32}$.
7. $\dfrac{2 a^3}{9} (3 \pi - 4)$.
8. $\dfrac{7 \pi a^3}{6}$.
9. $\dfrac{8 \pi a^3}{7}$.
10. $\dfrac{a^3}{48} (56 - 3 \pi)$.

Page 338 (§ 104)

1. $\left(\dfrac{a}{4}, \dfrac{b}{4}, \dfrac{c}{4}\right)$.

2. $\left(\dfrac{3 a}{8}, \dfrac{9 \pi a}{64}, \dfrac{9 \pi a}{64}\right)$.

3. $\left(\dfrac{16 a}{15 \pi}, \dfrac{16 b}{15 \pi}, \dfrac{2 c}{3}\right)$.

4. $\left(\dfrac{3 a}{8}, \dfrac{3 b}{8}, \dfrac{3 c}{8}\right)$.

5. On axis of ring, 2 ft. from center of shell.

6. $\left(\dfrac{26 a}{25 \pi}, \dfrac{26 a}{25 \pi}, \dfrac{9 a}{10}\right)$.

7. $\left(\dfrac{3(\pi - 2)}{8 \pi(2 - \sqrt{2})}, \dfrac{3(\pi - 2)}{8 \pi(2 - \sqrt{2})}, \dfrac{6 + 3\sqrt{2}}{16}\right)$.

8. $\left(0, 0, \dfrac{3 a^2(2 b^2 - a^2)}{8\left[b^3 - (b^2 - a^2)^{\frac{3}{2}}\right]}\right)$.

Page 340 (§ 105)

1. $\frac{70}{99} M$.
2. $\frac{1}{6} M(a^2 + b^2)$.

3. $\frac{1}{4} M(a^2 + b^2)$.
4. $\frac{1}{5} M(a^2 + b^2)$.

5. $\dfrac{2 a^2(15 \pi - 26)}{25(3 \pi - 4)} M$

Page 341 (§ 105)

6. $\frac{3}{8} Ma^2$.
7. $\frac{5}{6} Ma^2$.
8. $\frac{1}{6} M(b^2 + c^2)$.
9. $\frac{1}{20} M(3 a^2 + 2 h^2)$.
10. $\frac{3}{20} M(a^2 + 4 h^2)$.
11. $\frac{1}{12} M(3 a^2 + 4 h^2)$.
12. $\frac{13}{4} Ma^2$.

Page 341 (General Exercises)

1. $\left(\frac{8}{5}, \frac{8}{7}\right)$.

2. $\left(\dfrac{\sqrt{3}}{4}, \dfrac{64}{15}\right)$.

3. $\left(\dfrac{8 + 40 \ln 2}{15}, \dfrac{73}{252}\right)$.

4. $\left(\dfrac{256 a}{315 \pi}, \dfrac{256 a}{315 \pi}\right)$.

5. $\left(\dfrac{4 a}{3 \pi}, \dfrac{4(a + b)}{3 \pi}\right)$.

6. $\left(0, \dfrac{264}{10 + 15 \pi}\right)$.

7. $\left(\dfrac{1088 \sqrt{2}}{560 + 35 \pi}, 0\right)$.

Page 342 (General Exercises)

8. $\left(\dfrac{10 \pi + 16}{\pi + 12}, 0\right)$.

9. $\left(-\dfrac{2 a(88 + 15 \pi)}{15(16 + 9 \pi)}, 0\right)$.

10. On axis of loop, $\dfrac{128 a\sqrt{2}}{105 \pi}$ from 0.

11. On axis of segment, $\dfrac{4(a^2 - b^2)^{\frac{3}{2}}}{3\left[\pi a^2 - 2 a^2 \sin^{-1} \dfrac{b}{a} - 2 b \sqrt{a^2 - b^2}\right]}$ from center of circle.

12. On axis, $\dfrac{2\,a}{3(\pi + 2\sqrt{3})}$ from base of triangle and away from semicircle.

13. On axis, $\dfrac{4\,a^2 + 2\,ab\sqrt{3} + b^2}{2(4\,a + b\sqrt{3})}$ from base.

14. On axis, $\dfrac{116}{32 - 3\,\pi}$ from center of circle.

15. On axis, $\dfrac{4(r_2{}^3 - r_1{}^3)}{3\,\pi(r_2{}^2 - r_1{}^2)}$ from center of circumferences.

16. On axis of T-square, 8 in. from bottom.

17. On axis, $\dfrac{2\sqrt{3}}{5}$ in. from center of original hexagon.

18. On line through centers of square and circle, $\dfrac{3}{16\,\pi - 1}$ from center of circle in direction away from center of square.

19. On axis, $\dfrac{c^2 d}{ab - c^2}$ from center of ellipse.

20. On axis, $5\frac{3}{7}$ in. from corner of original square.

Page 343 (General Exercises)

21. $\frac{10}{7}\,M$.

22. $\frac{9}{22}(264\,\pi - 225\sqrt{3})$.

23. $\frac{1}{4}\,M\pi a^2$.

24. $\frac{35}{6}\,M$.

25. $\frac{1}{8}\,M\pi a^2$.

26. $\frac{1}{48}(681\,\pi + 1792)$.

27. $\frac{5}{8}\,Ma^2$.

28. $\frac{1}{4}\,M(r_1{}^2 + 5\,r_2{}^2)$.

29. $\frac{125}{12}\,M$.

30. $\frac{425}{12}\,M$.

31. $\frac{50}{3}\,M$.

32. $\frac{125}{12}\,M$.

33. $\frac{1}{3}(1024 - 12\,\pi)$.

34. $\frac{1}{3}(1024 - 12\,\pi)$.

35. $\frac{2}{3}(1024 - 12\,\pi)$.

36. $\dfrac{a^4}{24}(15\,\pi - 32)$.

Page 344 (General Exercises)

44. $\dfrac{4\,\pi a^3}{35}$.

45. $4\,\pi\sqrt{2}$.

46. $\dfrac{9\,\pi}{4}$.

47. $\dfrac{32\,a^3}{9}$.

48. $\dfrac{3\,\pi a^4}{32\,b}$.

49. $\dfrac{a^3}{9}(3\,\pi + 20 - 16\sqrt{2})$.

50. $\dfrac{15\,\pi a^3}{64}$.

51. $\dfrac{16\,a^3\sqrt{2}}{105}$.

52. $\left(\dfrac{3\,a(15\,\pi - 16)}{10(9\,\pi - 8)},\ 0,\ \dfrac{a(315\,\pi - 512)}{32(9\,\pi - 8)}\right)$.

53. $(0,\ 0,\ 3\frac{5}{21})$.

Page 345 (General Exercises)

54. $\frac{7}{3}\,M$.

55. $\frac{8}{25}\,Ma^2$.

56. $7\,\pi$.

57. $\frac{185}{63}\,M$.

58. $\dfrac{2(r_2{}^5 - r_1{}^5)}{5(r_2{}^3 - r_1{}^3)}\,M$.

59. $\frac{1}{4}\,M(4\,b^2 + 3\,a^2)$.

60. $\frac{1}{12}\,M(3\,b^2 + 4\,h^2)$.

61. $\left(\dfrac{6\,a}{5},\ 0,\ \dfrac{27\,\pi a}{128}\right)$.

62. $\frac{48}{25}\,Ma^2$.

63. $\dfrac{32\,a^3}{9}$.

64. $\left(\dfrac{32\,a\sqrt{2}}{35},\ 0,\ \dfrac{27\,\pi a}{64}\right)$.

65. $\frac{48}{25}\,Ma^2$.

66. $\dfrac{a^3}{420}(105\,\pi + 64\sqrt{2})$.

67. $a^5\left(\dfrac{256\sqrt{2}}{3465} + \dfrac{3\,\pi}{32}\right)$.

68. $3\,\pi a^3$.

69. $\frac{11}{6}\,Ma^2$.

70. $\dfrac{4\,\pi}{15}\left[(2\,r_2{}^2 + 3\,a^2)(r_2{}^2 - a^2)^{\frac{3}{2}} - (2\,r_1{}^2 + 3\,a^2)(r_1{}^2 - a^2)^{\frac{3}{2}}\right]$.

INDEX

Lateral surface of a cone $= \pi r s$